Mathematics and Psychology

PERSPECTIVES IN PSYCHOLOGY

William Kessen

George Mandler

General Editors

George A. Miller

Mathematics and Psychology

Mathematics and Psychology

George A. Miller, Harvard University

New York • London • Sydney   John Wiley & Sons, Inc.

Library of Congress Card Number: 64–13220
Printed in the United States of America

Foreword

Perspectives in Psychology is a series of original books written
for psychologists and students who are concerned with the history of ideas in psychology.

It is our intention to present fresh and thoughtful assessments
of the current psychological scene in the context of relevant historical changes. Many authors of the *Perspectives* books will examine a selected slice of the history of psychology by way of
selected and annotated readings. This is not to say that *Perspectives* is a uniform or systematic encyclopedia of the history
of psychology. Psychologists, by disposition and training, are
reluctant to work their ideas into a standard weave—homespun
or exotic—and *Perspectives* represents well the happy diversity
of the discipline.

Some books in the series are scholarly disquisitions on the
historical antecedents of a current problem in psychological analysis; some books move—after a brief glance at historical antecedents—directly toward a discussion of contemporary psychology and its future; some books deal with the past largely as a
platform for polemical exposition. And, occasionally, *Perspectives*
will present an original work in psychology that escapes the historical definition altogether.

Perspectives in Psychology, by using the avenues of docu-
mented history and informed discussions of current as well as
classical issues, will emphasize that psychology has a history as
well as a past and that it advances as it grows.

WILLIAM KESSEN
GEORGE MANDLER

Preface

This volume, the first in the *Perspectives in Psychology* series, is concerned with applied mathematics, not applied psychology. Since its title leaves the question open, I should say immediately that the book is concerned solely with the use of mathematics by psychologists in psychological theory and measurement; the alternate possibility, that it might be concerned with the self-conscious application of psychological principles to the problems, creative and pedagogic, of the mathematician, is not developed or even seriously considered. There is a long history of our attempts to apply mathematics to the problems of psychology, a history extending back at least to Daniel Bernoulli's famous paper in 1738 and perhaps, if one cares to make the argument, even back to Aristotle himself. It is this story that concerns us here.

The book is predicated on the hypothesis that there is something intrinsically coherent in the various uses that psychologists have made of logical and mathematical reasoning, something sufficiently regular and homogeneous to justify isolating them and their history from the main body of psychological thought. I should confess that the first time I heard this hypothesis presented it struck me as absurd. Applied mathematics is a tool; there is nothing interesting or coherent in the class of all objects constructed with a particular tool. But as I tried to explain why the idea seemed so absurd, my arguments became progressively weaker, and the longer I debated the matter, the more historical trends I discovered, the more interesting interrelations I remembered, until eventually I was caught by my own uncertainty. The present volume is, in a sense, the result of my own curiosity to discover whether such a volume, historical but short, mathematical but intelligible to the general reader, was possible. Needless to say, I am presently convinced that it is possible, that the story of psychology's long and not always happy affair with mathematics can be told coherently, and that the lessons to be learned from it are as amusing as they are instructive. The reader, of course, is entitled to his own opinions, but I hope he will form them after he examines the following pages, rather than before.

It is disconcerting to discover that something you thought did not exist has a long history. To find that it even has a handbook is the final persuader. R. D. Luce, R. R. Bush, and E. Galanter have now edited a large and impressive *Handbook of Mathematical Psychology* (New York: Wiley, 1963). Since I was privileged to contribute to it, I naturally knew something of the editors' plans for summarizing the present state of this burgeoning enterprise, and so could select my materials for the present volume in such a way as to complement theirs, rather than to compete with it. Not only did they and their several distinguished contributors finally convince me that mathematical psychology exists (and so is entitled to a history), but they even encouraged me to presume that my volume might add a useful perspective to theirs.

I say "my volume" with inexcusable conceit, of course, for this is not really mine, but is the compound work of the numerous authors whose articles and books I have selected. The possessive pronoun should be understood to express a feeling, not of ownership, but of responsibility. My principal hope is that I have not obscured or distorted their contributions by embedding them in so much of my own commentary. I wish to express my appreciation to all those authors and publishers who granted permission to reprint the selections included here.

Finally, I would like to take this opportunity to express my special gratitude to R. Duncan Luce for his valuable criticisms of an early version of this book. Although his advice did much to improve the final product, he should not, of course, be held responsible for any errors of fact or judgment that may remain. I would also like to express my appreciation to Esther Mahr, who faithfully typed and frequently edited the connective material that I have inserted between the successive selections.

GEORGE A. MILLER

Oxford, England
January 1964

Contents

Mathematics and Psychology

Varieties of Mathematical Psychology

Mathematical psychology is more an attitude than a topic. It was never self-consciously "born" or "founded" as an independent branch of general psychology. Rather, it has been born and founded repeatedly in dozens of places with scores of sponsors, each pioneering in a new direction, each independently hopeful that mathematical devices might help to dispel some of the confusion surrounding his own particular problem. There was in the beginning no basic mathematical law of mental life that was later to be elaborated and applied to diverse branches of the subject, as Newton's laws of motion were elaborated and applied in classical physics. Instead, there were many beginnings, mostly unrelated and differing widely in spirit and purpose. To pretend that there has been historical continuity in this development is probably the kind of thing Voltaire had in mind when he said that history is the bag of tricks we play on the dead.

When one surveys the mixed collection of aspirations and accomplishments that answer to the name of mathematical psychology, it is not easy to find a narrative thread to tie it all together. It is clear that the use of mathematics—especially statistics—has been increasing in psychology. It is also clear that some mathematical formulations have been more seminal than others. It is even clear that the mathematical maturity and competence of psychologists has improved over the years. But it is not at all clear that any one kind of mathematics or any particular formal theory dominates or inspires all the others.

The simplest thread to tie it all together would be chronological, of course. But when the following selections are arranged in order by their dates, there is seldom any relation apparent between successive items. At the very outset, therefore, we must recognize that it is not a single history we have to tell, but several. The problem is how best to organize the separate narratives.

We could, of course, arrange things mathematically. We might put all the selections requiring the calculus together in one section, all the probability papers in another, all the matrix algebra somewhere else, and so on. Perhaps such an organization would please a mathematical audience, but for psychologists it does too much violence to the substantive issues involved.

Sometimes it is possible to use a biographical approach to this kind of problem, to conceal the unintelligible heterogeneity of history behind the acceptable heterogeneity of individual personalities. We could list the famous and familiar names—Herbart, Fechner, Helmholtz, Galton, Pearson, Spearman, Thurstone, Hull—and illustrate the use each of them made of mathematics. This is probably the safest kind of organization and, when done properly, it can have considerable human interest for the reader. But focusing on the men instead of their work is rather risky while the men involved are still able to be embarrassed or outraged by what is said about them. And since most of mathematical psychology has developed in the past thirty years, many of its creators are still very much alive and working. Some of the most interesting work would be omitted if we insisted that every author had to be a time-honored genius.

The correct way to do it, of course, would be in terms of substantive issues. Some wonderful legends have grown up around various psychological problems, and they are worth repeating for every new generation of readers.* There is the legend of *psychophysics*, beginning with E. H. Weber's fraction and G. T. Fechner's integral and coming down to S. S. Stevens's power function and to the statistical theories of detection that are cur-

---

* E. G. Boring, *A history of experimental psychology*, 2nd ed. New York: Appleton-Century-Crofts, 1950.

rently exciting interest. There is the story of *reaction time,* beginning with the astronomer's "personal equation," going through the "mental chronometry" of F. C. Donders and W. Wundt on down to W. J. McGill's stochastic latency mechanisms today. There is the story of *learning,* beginning with H. Ebbinghaus' empirical equation to describe the amount forgotten as a function of time, through C. L. Hull's ambitious effort to create a general theory of behavior in mathematical language, down to the contemporary interest in the stochastic theories of learning of W. K. Estes and R. R. Bush and F. Mosteller. There is the story of *choice,* beginning with D. Bernoulli, which was nourished and developed by theoretical economists, and which broke onto the psychological scene only recently when psychologists recognized that many of their experimental situations required the subject to make a choice among well-defined alternatives. There is a long and beautiful story about *individual differences,* beginning with F. Galton and K. Pearson and flowering into our modern statistical theories of mental tests and factor analysis. There is the story of *attitudes,* beginning perhaps with K. Bühler and almost immediately exploding into the modern industry of public-opinion measurement with all the elegant theories that L. L. Thurstone, S. S. Stevens, P. F. Lazarsfeld, L. Guttman, C. H. Coombs, and others have devised to rationalize psychological scales of measurement. There is the story of *language,* a process so complex that until recently it seemed that only statistical summaries could ever touch it, but one that is currently being attacked successfully by N. Chomsky and others with the weapons of formal logic. Even shorter is the story of *tracking,* which grew out of engineering efforts to incorporate men into servo systems during World War II, and which is closely tied to the cybernetic hypothesis that the basic unit of neural activity is the feedback loop. The story of *small groups* is also brief in its mathematical version, but sociometric matrices and linear-graph theory are now exciting much interest. Shortest of all, perhaps, is the story of *thinking,* in which formal theories embodied in computer programs were only beginning to be tested as the 1960's began.

These are some of the substantive areas in which significant psychological ideas have been formulated in the language of mathematics. Each of them deserves at least a chapter or two of its own. Unfortunately, however, there are more legends than we have space to tell. We will try to recount as much of this history as we can, but the most we can hope to do is to sample a passage here and there from some of these various topics.

None of these schemes for organizing our material is wholly adequate, yet each of them has attractive features. The problem is to do them all: to cover as wide a chronological period as possible, to illustrate as many different varieties of mathematics as possible, to select writings from (or at least to mention) as many famous names as possible, to sample as many different areas of psychology as possible, and to do it all within a reasonable number of pages.

The plan that was finally adopted was an attempt at such a compromise. It seemed to come more from the selections themselves than from any a priori intent of the editor. Once the selections were actually assembled it was almost inevitable that they would, in spite of their conspicuous diversity, fall into categories, and would arrange themselves in a progression that had a certain amount of sense to it. Each category contained articles that seemed to have a homogeneous scientific style—articles whose authors might not agree, but who could at least argue intelligibly with each other about their conception of what psychology should accomplish and how mathematics should contribute to it.

There were four of these categories, corresponding to four relatively distinct uses of mathematics in psychology. For convenience, we shall call them *discursive, normative, functional,* and *structural.* Perhaps a more discerning reviewer could have drawn even finer distinctions, but these four, at least, seemed essential if we were to avoid making a complete hash of the subject.

The *discursive* mode uses mathematical notation as a convenient extension of natural language. Ordinary language is frequently inefficient or even inadequate to express the full complexity of an author's ideas. In that situation a formal symbol can often summarize, if only metaphorically, what would take many long and tedious qualifying phrases. Or it can serve as a mnemonic device to remind the reader of an idea or constellation of ideas developed in detail elsewhere. This discursive, ideographic use of mathematics is extremely widespread among psychological writers, but, since it seldom undergoes any cumulative development, its history is almost impossible to trace. We shall, however, consider some examples of this style, if only to distinguish it from other, more ambitious efforts to exploit the resources of mathematics.

Bona fide applications of mathematical reasoning are of two types, normative and descriptive. *Normative* applications use mathematics to discover or to demonstrate the most efficient way to attain certain goals. This type of mathematical argument has been much more popular among economists than among psychologists; at one time there was a great deal of economic theory phrased in terms of a psychological myth about a "rational man" who always calculated his optimal gain and who always wanted to maximize his own pleasure. By and large, however, psychologists have been more concerned with what people *do* do, rather than with what they *should* do. Nevertheless, in recent years some psychologists have become increasingly interested in the psychology of choice, and various aspects of the economist's techniques for representing factors involved in decision making have come to look increasingly ingenious and attractive.

Descriptive uses of mathematics can be further divided into either functional or structural descriptions. A *functional* description is what most people expect to hear when they listen to a mathematical psychologist. We have grown accustomed to physicists who state laws of nature in terms of functional equations, so when we are told that a psychologist is using the same tools, we naturally expect him to use them in the same way. There are, of course, numerous examples in psychology that do follow this familiar pattern—so many, in fact, that it is necessary to insist that mathematical psychology need not all be of this one type. It is not fair to judge the merits of all the different uses of mathematics by standards appropriate to only one of them. Reasonable evaluation of the various mathematical enterprises in psychology should respect their differences in spirit and intent, without trying to force them all into any single pattern.

In grouping the various selections into chapters, the functional applications proved so large a category that it was necessary to subdivide them even further into two parts, one dealing with determinate functions, the other with statistical functions.

By *structural* description is meant the use of mathematical notation to represent the reduction in degrees of freedom that must occur in any structured domain. In a mechanical device the spatial relations of the parts in the whole may be obvious from inspection. When the same idea is transposed to our psychological machinery, however, the structure is seldom obvious or available to perception. Nevertheless, many psychologists have insisted that structure is there—in perception, in memory, in language, in social groups—and have tried to use mathematics to characterize it.

In the following pages we will try to exemplify each of these four mathematical modes in psychology. The reader should not be misled, however, to search for any deeper significance in the tidy-looking dichotomies on which our classification rests than follows from their convenience in organizing our narrative. We have adopted them, not for their ultimate truth, but because by grouping the various studies in this way we hope to bring a little more order into our topic than might otherwise be apparent.

Even within these four categories, moreover, we must not pretend that there are simple, dominant themes; even here we are still faced with history proceeding in parallel, rather than in series. It would be misleading to suggest otherwise. Mathematical psychology, like psychology generally, covers a vast domain of problems, and over this domain the mathematical theories that have been proposed range from the absurd to the sublime. We shall sample all parts of this spectrum in the selections that follow.

In closing these introductory remarks a final word should be said about the limited scope of this book. It is limited first with respect to difficulty; a deliberate (and almost successful) attempt has been made to select passages that do not require for their appreciation any very advanced knowledge of mathematics. And, second, it is limited with respect to subject matter; little mention will be made here of the extensive use of *statistical analysis* in psychology generally. Nor will we do much more than mention the closely related topic of *psychological scales* and the various theories and methods of psychological measurements. This is not because these are small or unimportant topics. Quite the contrary, they are so important and bulk so large in the history of mathematical psychology that it is impossible for us to ignore them completely. But precisely because they are so important in their own right they deserve separate and fuller treatment than we can give them here.

As we shall see, quite enough remains to keep us profitably occupied without them.

2

Discursive Applications

The use of mathematical notation to enrich the vocabulary and grammar of ordinary language is at least as old as Aristotle. In Aristotle's writings we can find such passages as, "Let A, the objectively white, be related to B, the objectively black, as the idea C is related to the idea D. Now if the ideas CD attach to a certain thing, they will be related to each other just as AB are related to each other."*

This kind of symbolism is so common today that we scarcely recognize it as a mathematical device at all. It was, however, one of Aristotle's great innovations, the introduction of *variables* into psychological theory. Instead of restating the same argument for every concrete term, it is stated once and for all with the variables A, B, C, and so on. The significance of this innovation was greater, no doubt, in the context of the syllogism than in the context of psychology, because it was an essential step forward in the development of formal logic, and only a discursive convenience for the development of his psychological theories. Nevertheless, the deeper significance of this symbolic device should not be overlooked.†

* Quoted from B. Rand, *The classical psychologists*. Boston: Houghton Mifflin, 1912, p. 76.
† See J. Lukasiewicz, *Aristotle's syllogistic*. New York: Oxford University Press, 1951, pp. 7–10.

During the latter half of the seventeenth century Gottfried Wilhelm Leibniz also recognized the scientific importance of linguistic innovations. But Leibniz was far more daring. He dreamed of developing a whole, new universal language—he called it *characteristica universalis*—in which all concepts could be precisely expressed and whose grammar would be a form of combinatorial calculus—he called it *calculus ratiocinator*—based on the laws of reasoning, so that all arguments could be developed as mechanically and efficiently as mathematical ones.* Leibniz, of course, did not create such a universal language. Logic has realized some parts of his dream, and for that reason Leibniz is frequently honored as the father of modern logic. Leibniz himself, however, was too ambitious. To enrich natural language is one thing; to replace it entirely is something else.

Most discursive uses of mathematical ideas fall somewhere between Aristotle's (which is probably the irreducible minimum that we should recognize as mathematical) and Leibniz's (which is too grandiose—probably the unattainable maximum that we could only imagine). Between these extremes there are many different illustrations of discursive mathematics.

To begin with a curious example, we can go back some two hundred years to the middle of the eighteenth century when the British physician, psychologist, and philosopher David Hartley summarized his religious ideas in the formula $W = F^2/L$, in which W is love of the World, F is Fear of God, and L is Love of God. As we grow older, Hartley said, L increases toward infinity, so that W approaches zero.† At the time that he wrote, faith in the power of mathematics to capture and express all the essential truths of nature was unsurpassed, so perhaps he actually thought his equation might develop into something more than a discursive device. But history passed it by; not all uses of mathematics are equally valuable.

---

* E. T. Bell, *Men of mathematics*. New York: Simon and Schuster, 1937, Chap. 7.

† Quoted by M. Kline, *Mathematics in western culture,* New York: Oxford University Press, 1953, p. 338.

William James was playing this same game in 1890 when he wrote that

$$\text{Self-esteem} = \frac{\text{Success}}{\text{Pretensions}}$$

"Such a fraction," James remarked, "may be increased as well by diminishing the denominator as by increasing the numerator,"[*] but he gave no hint as to how the three quantities should be measured. James was making an argument, not proposing an experiment. This particular instance was probably never intended to be other than discursive.

Another example of discursive mathematics occurs whenever differential psychologists argue that heredity and environment stand in a multiplicative rather than an additive relation for determining personal characteristics; if either goes to zero, their product must be zero.[†] (A very similar metaphor is sometimes used to discuss the relations between need and skill, or drive and habit, as determiners of behavior.) This way of putting the problem is often quite helpful for beginning students, even though they recognize it as a gross oversimplification. Somehow, the mathematical analogy helps them to understand what the psychologists are arguing about. But, obviously, it can never provide the basis for a truly adequate mathematical theory of development.

Still another example turns up frequently in the work of Gestalt psychologists, who are fond of saying, "The whole is greater than the sum of its parts." As is so often the case when mathematical ideas are borrowed discursively, it is not perfectly obvious what they have in mind, but it would seem to be a general condemnation of any psychological theory that incorporates the linearity condition, $f(x) + f(y) = f(x + y)$.

Some psychologists like to summarize lists in functional notation. E. C. Tolman, for example, once wrote that

$$B = f(S, P, H, T, A)$$

[*] W. James, *The principles of psychology*. New York: Holt, 1890, Vol. I, pp. 310–311.
[†] See, for example, A. Anastasi, *Differential psychology*, 3rd ed. New York: Macmillan, 1958, p. 72.

which was his shorthand way of saying that behavior B is some function f of stimulation S, physiological drive P, heredity H, previous training T, and age A.* This use of mathematical symbolism (which has been curiously popular with many psychologists) remains discursive as long as f is unspecified and no methods or units are indicated for measuring the several variables.

These examples should suffice to suggest what is meant by the discursive use of mathematics in psychology. By their very nature, applications of this type are mathematically trivial. They exploit some already well-known mathematical concept—variable, function, ratio, integral, and so on—without the slightest intention of extending or developing it, but only for its linguistic convenience in expressing a particular idea or set of ideas.

To say that discursive applications are mathematically trivial, however, does not mean that they are psychologically unimportant. Their value as theoretical contributions to psychology should not be measured by the elegance and originality of their mathematics. Some discursive uses of mathematics have had important consequences for the way psychologists think about their problems. And even the poorest efforts in this direction can still add something to the *Zeitgeist;* they indicate an author's willingness to see his argument translated into formal terms, and stand as an invitation to a better mathematician to find a more precise formulation. Out of such signs and indications come a general ethos that encourages mathematical adventures and a general optimism that psychology is gradually becoming ripe for some kind of formal calculus.

Another common characteristic of discursive applications is that they usually neglect measurement. They imply rather vaguely that the love of God, self-esteem, heredity, behavior, and so on, could easily be represented by simple, scalar quantities, but they make no suggestions for the appropriate methods or units to use in measuring them. As a result, discursive applica-

---

* E. C. Tolman, *Collected papers in psychology*. Berkeley: University of California Press, 1951, p. 117. For an ambitious use of this device in sociology, see S. C. Dodd, *Dimensions of society*, New York: Macmillan, 1942.

tions often seem as empty empirically as they are trivial mathematically.

Again, however, we must be cautious about dismissing these ideas too quickly. There is much psychological wisdom that is not numerical in character, and psychologists would all be in a difficult position if we judged them solely in terms of the number of significant figures in their measurements.

Moreover, we are in some danger here of confusing mathematics and arithmetic. There are vast domains of modern mathematics in which specific numbers almost never appear. It is perfectly possible, with full mathematical rigor, to discuss magnitudes without assigning numbers to them. Good examples abound in mathematical economics; the economists who first tried to dress their ideas in mathematical garb were quite clear on this point. As early as 1838 Augustin Cournot, who was the first person to formulate economic problems in the language of differential equations, said that one of the most important functions of mathematical analysis is to determine the relations among quantities whose numerical values, even whose algebraic forms, were completely indeterminant. In 1871 W. S. Jevons argued eloquently that mathematical theories of utility could not wait for precise psychological measurements of pleasure and pain. F. Y. Edgeworth repeated the point again in 1881 in a little book entitled *Mathematical Psychics:* "Where there are data which, though not *numerical* are *quantitative*—for example, that a quantity is *greater* or *less* than another, *increases* or *decreases,* is *positive* or *negative,* a *maximum* or *minimum,* there mathematical reasoning is possible and may be indispensable."* Edgeworth reinforces the argument with examples from mathematical physics, examples that begin with "loose quantitative relations" rather than numerical data and that proceed by mathematical reasoning to derive consequences of great generality and importance. If physicists can do it, he argues, so can social scientists. Mathematical science need not be exact science.

In short, if mathematical psychology (or any other mathematical discipline) must be limited to the analysis of numerical data, it will be forced to neglect some of the most attractive

* F. Y. Edgeworth, *Mathematical psychics.* London: Kegan Paul, 1881, p. 2.

features that mathematics has to offer. The fact that discursive uses of mathematics ignore the measurement problem, therefore, is not in itself a sufficient reason for dismissing them as worthless or unimportant.

Many, perhaps most, discursive uses of mathematics in psychology are quite brief, as were all the examples just cited. But brevity is not a necessary feature, and some authors develop linguistic innovations at great length. Moreover, some mathematical theories are unevenly developed and use discursive patches to hold together diverse models of a more explicit nature; exactly where the discursive component stops and something more ambitious begins is often difficult to detect.

Our first excerpt is from one of the earliest attempts to create a mathematical psychology. It is deliberately discursive in nature, because its author, Johann Friedrich Herbart, did not believe that anything more was possible in psychology. The book from which this sample is taken was first published in 1816—which means that mathematical psychology (in this discursive vein, at least) antedates scientific psychology by at least half a century.

But first a word about the author and his place in the history of psychology.* Today Herbart is remembered principally as the "father of scientific pedagogy." His educational theories, however, were based on psychology, and it was that dependency that motivated his psychological essays. Most of what has proved memorable in Herbart's psychology derives directly from Leibniz. Leibniz spoke of ideas that rose spontaneously into consciousness as being apperceived, to contrast them with ideas arising from perception; Herbart borrowed the term, emphasized the importance of past experience in determining the contents of consciousness, and made the development of a large "apperceptive mass" the cornerstone of his pedagogical theory. Leibniz spoke of fluctuations in the level of consciousness of an idea; Herbart elaborated these fluctuations in great detail, added the concept of a "threshold of consciousness," and proposed a mathematical language for talking about them. In this Herbart

* E. G. Boring, *A history of experimental psychology*, 2nd ed. New York: Appleton-Century-Crofts, 1950, pp. 250–261.

performed an important service to psychology. His mathematical treatment of the threshold influenced G. T. Fechner's psychophysics; his discussion of concepts inhibiting and repressing one another prepared the ground for Sigmund Freud's elaborate theories of unconscious dynamics. But, whereas Leibniz's psychology treated ideas as completely independent, unitary "monads," acting together through some preestablished harmony, Herbart imagined the fluctuations of consciousness to be the result of violent rivalries and interactions among ideas; in this respect Herbart's theory was the very antithesis of Leibniz's.

To our modern eyes, however, the most curious feature of Herbart's argument was that psychology could be mathematical, but not experimental or physiological. The following passage illustrates his discursive use of mathematical reasoning on a sustained basis, without appeal to any criteria other than his own intuition and the reader's common sense.

*   *   *

Johann Friedrich Herbart

Concepts as Forces

1* Concepts become forces when they resist one another. This resistance occurs when two or more opposed concepts encounter one another.

J. F. Herbart, *A textbook of psychology,* transl. by M. K. Smith. New York: Appleton, 1891, pp. 9–19. Original German edition: *Lehrbuch der Psychologie,* Königsberg und Leipzig, 1816; the present translation from the second revised edition, 1834.

* In this, and in all subsequent selections, section headings, tables, figures, equations, and footnotes have been renumbered for clarity and consistency in the present context.

At first let us take this proposition as simply as possible. In this connection, therefore, we shall not think of complex nor of compound concepts of any kind whatever; nor of such as indicate an object with several characteristics, neither of anything in time nor space, but of entirely simple concepts or sensations—e. g., red, blue, sour, sweet, etc. It is not our purpose to consider the general notions of the above-mentioned sensations, but to consider such representations as may result from an instantaneous act of sense-perception.

Again, the question concerning the origin of the sensations mentioned does not belong here, much less has the discussion to do with the consideration of anything else that might have previously existed or occurred in the soul.

The proposition as it stands is that opposed concepts resist one another. Concepts that are not opposed—e. g., a tone and a color—may exist, in which case it will be assumed that such concepts offer no resistance to one another. (Exceptions to this latter proposition may occur, of which more hereafter.)

Resistance is an expression of force. To the resisting concept, however, its action is quite accidental; it adjusts itself to the attack which is mutual among concepts, and which is determined by the degree of opposition existing between them. This opposition may be regarded as that by which they are affected collectively. In themselves, however, concepts are not forces.

2 Now, what is the result of the resistance mentioned?

Do concepts partially or wholly destroy one another, or, notwithstanding the resistance, do they remain unchanged?

Destroyed concepts are the same as none at all. However, if, notwithstanding the mutual attack, concepts remain unchanged, then one could not be removed or suppressed by another (as we see every moment that they are). Finally, if all that is conceived of each concept were changed by the contest, then this would signify nothing more than, at the beginning, quite another concept had been present in consciousness.

The presentation (concept), then, must yield without being destroyed—i.e., the real concept is changed into an effort to present itself.

Here it is in effect stated that, as soon as the hindrance yields, the concept by its own effort will again make its appearance in consciousness. In this lies the possibility (although not for all cases the only ground) of reproduction.

3 When a concept becomes not entirely, but only in part, transformed into an effort, we must guard against considering this part as a severed portion of the whole concept. It has certainly a definite magnitude (upon the knowledge of which much depends), but this magnitude indicates only a degree of the obscuration of the whole concept. If the question be in regard to several parts of one and the same concept, these parts must not be regarded as different, severed portions, but the smaller divisions may be regarded as being contained in the larger. The same is true of the remainders after the collisions—i. e., of those parts of a concept which remain unobscured, for those parts are also degrees of the real concept.

4 When a sufficiency of opposition exists between concepts, the latter are in equilibrium. They come only gradually to this point. The continuous change of their degree of obscuration may be called their movement.

The statics and mechanics of the mind have to do with the calculation of the equilibrium and movement of the concepts.

5 All investigations into the statics of the mind begin with two different quantitative factors, viz., the sum (or the aggregate amount) of the resistances and the ratio of their limitation. The former is the quantity which rises from their encounter, to be divided between the opposing concepts. If one knows how to state it, and knows also the ratio in which the different concepts yield in the encounter, then, by a simple calculation in proportion, the statical point of each concept—i.e., the degree of its obscuration. in equilibrium—may be found.

6 The sum as well as the ratio of the mutual limitation depends upon the strength of each individual concept which is affected in inverse ratio to its strength, and upon the degree of opposition between the two concepts. For their influence upon each other stands in direct ratio to the strength of each.

The principle determining the sum of the mutual limitation is, that it shall be considered as small as possible, because all concepts strive against suppression, and certainly submit to no more of it than is absolutely necessary.

7 By actual calculation, the remarkable result is obtained that, in the case of the two concepts, the one never entirely obscures the other, but, in the case of three or more, one is very easily obscured, and can be made as ineffective—notwithstanding its continuous struggle—as if it were not present at all. Indeed, this obscuration may happen to a large number of concepts as well as to one, and may be effected through the agency of two, and even through the combined influence of concepts less strong than those which are suppressed.

Here the expression "threshold of consciousness" must be explained, as we shall have occasion to use it. A concept is in consciousness in so far as it is not suppressed, but is an actual representation. When it rises out of a condition of complete suppression, it enters into consciousness. Here, then, it is on the threshold of consciousness. It is very important to determine by calculation the degree of strength which a concept must attain in order to be able to stand beside two or more stronger ones exactly on the threshold of consciousness, so that, at the slightest yielding of the hindrance, it would begin to rise into consciousness.[1]

8 Among the many, and, for the most part, very complicated laws underlying the movement of concepts, the following is the simplest:

While the arrested portion (*Hemmungssumme*) of the concept sinks, the sinking part is at every moment proportional to the part unsuppressed.

---

[1] The expression "A concept is in consciousness" must be distinguished from that, "I am conscious of my concept." To the latter belongs inner perception; to the former not. In psychology, we need a word that will indicate the totality of all simultaneous actual presentations. No word except consciousness can be found for this purpose.

Here we are obliged to be content with a circumlocution—and this all the more, because the inner perception which is usually attributed to consciousness has no fixed limit where it begins or ceases, and, moreover, the act of perceiving is not itself perceived; so that, since we are not conscious of it in ourselves, we must exclude it from consciousness, although it is an active knowing, and in no way a restricted or suppressed concept.

By this it is possible to calculate the whole course of the sinking even to the statical point.[2]

9 When to several concepts already near equilibrium a new one comes, a movement arises which causes them to sink for a short time beneath their statical point, after which they quickly and entirely of themselves rise again—something as a liquid, when an object is thrown into it, first sinks and then rises. In this connection several remarkable circumstances occur:

10 First, upon an occasion of this kind, one of the older concepts may be removed entirely out of consciousness even by a new concept that is much weaker than itself. In this case, however, the striving of the suppressed concept is not to be considered wholly ineffective, as shown above (see **7**); it works with all its force against the concepts in consciousness. Although its object is not conceived, it produces a certain condition of consciousness. The way in which these concepts are removed out of consciousness and yet are effective therein may be indicated by the expression, "They are on the mechanical threshold." The threshold mentioned above (**7**) is called for the sake of distinction the statical threshold.[3]

[2] Mathematically, the above law may be expressed: $\sigma = S\left(1 - e^{-t}\right)$ in which $S =$ the aggregate amount suppressed, $t =$ the time elapsed during the encounter, $\sigma =$ the suppressed portion of all the concepts in the time indicated by t.

As the latter quantity is apportioned among the individual concepts, it is found that those which fall directly beneath the statical threshold (**7**) are very quickly driven thence, while the rest do not reach exactly their statical point in any given finite time. On account of this latter circumstance, the concepts in the mind of a man of most equable temperament are, while he is awake, always in a state of gentle motion. This is also the primary reason why the inner perception never meets an object which holds it quite motionless.

[3] If the concepts on the statical threshold acted in the same way on the mechanical threshold we should find ourselves in a state of the most intolerable uneasiness, or rather the body would be subjected to a condition of tension that must in a few moments prove fatal, even as under present conditions sudden fright will sometimes cause death; for all the concepts which, as we are accustomed to say, the memory preserves, and which we well know can upon the slightest occasion be reproduced, are in a state of incessant striving to rise, although the condition of consciousness is not at all affected by them.

11 Second, the time during which one or more concepts linger upon the mechanical threshold can be extended if a series of new, although weaker, concepts come in succession to them.

Every employment to which we are unaccustomed puts us in this condition. The earlier concepts are pressed back of the later ones. The former, however, because they are the stronger, remain tense, affect the physical organism more and more, and finally make it necessary that the employment cease, when the old concepts immediately rise, and we experience what is called a feeling of relief which depends in part upon the physical organism, although the first cause is purely psychological.

12 Third, when several concepts are driven in succession to the mechanical threshold, several sudden successive changes in the laws of reciprocal movements arise.

In this way is to be explained the fact that the course of our thoughts is so often inconsequent, abrupt, and apparently irregular. This appearance deceives in the same way as the wandering of the planets. The conformity to law in the human mind resembles exactly that in the firmament.[4]

13 The easily conceivable metaphysical reason why opposed concepts resist one another is the unity of the soul, of which they are the self-preservations. This reason explains without difficulty the combination of our concepts (which combination is known to exist). If, on account of their opposition, they did not suppress one another, all concepts would compose but one act of one soul; and, indeed, in so far as they are not divided into a manifold by any kind of arrests whatever, they really constitute but one act. Concepts that are on the threshold of consciousness can not enter into combination with others, as they are completely transformed into effort directed against other definite concepts, and are thereby, as it were, isolated. In consciousness, however, concepts com-

[4] As a counterpart to the concepts which sink simultaneously are to be observed those which rise simultaneously, especially when they rise free—i.e., when a restricting environment or a general pressure suddenly disappears. With the rising the amount of suppression increases. Hence, in the case of three, one may be, as it were, bent back, and under certain conditions may sink quite to the threshold. Their elevation is greater than the depression to which, sinking together, they would have pressed one another, because in sinking the sum of their mutual limitation depends upon the total strength, which in the gradual rising is not the case.

bine in two ways: First, concepts which are not opposed or contrasted with one another (as a tone and a color) so far as they meet unhindered, form a complex; second, contrasted concepts (e. g., red and yellow), in so far as they are affected neither by accidental foreign concepts nor by unavoidable opposition, become blended (fused).

Complexes may be complete; blendings (fusions) from their nature must always be (more or less) incomplete.[5]

14 That which is complicated or blended out of several concepts furnishes an aggregate of force, and for this reason works according to quite other statical and mechanical laws than those according to which the individual concepts would have acted. Also the thresholds of consciousness change according to the complex or blending (fusion), so that on account of a combination a concept of the very weakest kind may be able to remain and exert an influence in consciousness.[6]

15 *Problem:* After an encounter between two concepts, P and Π, the remainders, r and ρ, are blended (or incompletely united). The problem is to indicate what help one of the two concepts, in case it should be still more suppressed, would receive from the other.

[5] Of such complexes as are partially or almost complete, we have remarkable instances in the concepts of things with several characteristics and of words used as signs of thoughts. In the mother-tongue the latter, words and thoughts, are so closely connected that it would appear that we think by means of words. (Concerning both examples more hereafter.) Among the blendings are especially remarkable, partly those which include in themselves an æsthetic relation (which, taken psychologically, is created at the same time with the blending), partly those which involve succession, in which serial forms have their origin.

[6] The computation for complexes and blendings depends upon the same principles as that for simple concepts; it is, however, much more intricate, especially for the reason that in the case of incomplete combinations the forces as well as their arrests are only partially interwoven with one another (and do not fully enter as factors into the product).

Combinations of concepts consist not only of two or three members, but they often contain many members in very unequal degrees of complication, or blending, in which case no calculation can estimate the multiplicity. Nevertheless, from the latter, the simplest cases may be chosen and the more intricate ones estimated according to them. For every science the simplest laws are the most important.

Solution: Let P be the helping concept; it helps with a force equal to r, but Π can only appropriate this force in the ratio of $\rho:\Pi$. Hence through P, Π receives the help $\frac{r\rho}{\Pi}$ and in the same way P receives from Π the help $\frac{r\rho}{P}$.

The proof lies immediately in the analysis of the ideas. It is plain that the two remainders, r and ρ, taken together, determine the degree of union between the two concepts. One of them is the helping force; the other, compared with the concept to which it belongs, is to be considered as a fraction of the whole; and, of the totality of help which could be rendered by the first remainder, it yields that portion which here attains efficient activity.

16 The following principles may be observed here:

a. Beyond the point of union no help extends its influence.

If the concept Π has more clearness in consciousness than the remainder ρ indicates, then by the striving of the concept P, which might come to the help of the former, already more than enough has been done; hence for the present it exerts no more influence.

b. The farther the one of the concepts is below the point of union, so much the more effectively does the other help.[7]

[7] This gives the following differential equation:
$$\frac{r\rho}{\Pi}\frac{\rho-\omega}{\rho}dt = d\omega,$$
whence by integration $\omega = \rho\left(1 - e^{-\frac{rt}{\Pi}}\right)$.

This equation contains the germ of manifold investigations which penetrate the whole of psychology. It is indeed so simple that it can not really occur in the human soul, but all investigations into applied mathematics begin with such simple presuppositions as only exist in abstraction —e.g., the mathematical lever, or the laws of bodies falling in a vacuum. Here merely the influence of the help is considered, which, if everything depended upon it alone, would bring into consciousness during the time t a quantity ω from Π. Besides, if we take into consideration the single circumstance that Π meets with an unavoidable arrest from other concepts, then the calculation becomes so complicated that it can be only approximately solved by an integration of the following form:
$$d^3\omega = ad^2\omega dt + bd\omega dt^2 + c\omega dt^3.$$

It is self-evident that it much more nearly expresses the facts which are to be observed experimentally.

Herbart's mathematical ideas were further developed in a subsequent work, *Psychology as a Science Founded for the First Time on Experience, Metaphysics, and Mathematics* (1824), but this sample is enough to indicate how the trick is performed. Although some of his ideas were influential, nobody seems to have found any good use for his equations. Until they do, therefore, we must consider Herbart's work our prime example of the discursive mode.

Before we conclude that such discussions are all safely buried in the archives of psychology, however, perhaps we should examine a more recent specimen. Here we begin to tread on delicate ground, of course, for no matter how vigorously we proclaim that the merit of a psychological theory or hypothesis should not be judged in terms of its mathematical elegance, the author who finds his use of mathematics classified as "merely discursive" is certain to resent it. And since the author of the following selection still has many colleagues and students actively developing his theoretical ideas, some bitter complaints can be expected. Nevertheless, Kurt Lewin's use of topological concepts to express his psychological hypotheses fits remarkably well into this category. Indeed, readers who approach him in any other spirit are likely to bounce off in anger and dismay.

In 1954 a small group of American psychologists tried to evaluate various psychological theories that had been proposed to explain results obtained from experimental studies of the learning process. Lewin's topological formulation of Gestalt psychology was one they included on their list. They approached it in good faith as if it were what it seemed to be—a mathematical theory, rather than an enrichment of English syntax—and they came away baffled and disappointed. ". . . Lewin has not operated under the restraints accepted by most other theorists," they protested.

Where most learning theorists consider successful predictions of behavior to be the principal test of good theory, Lewin's system requires only an "adequate," according to the theorist, description and symbolic representation of a situation. . . . By carrying over into psychology some of the verbal phraseology of physical field theories without the mathematics, Lewin has given us a facsimile of a field theory which resembles the real article in much the same way that a masterpiece of taxidermy resembles a live animal.*

Because Lewin's mathematics were only discursive, these reviewers reacted to him as if he had cheated them.

It is quite true that Lewin did not regard his mathematics as something to be "tested" by experiments. Instead, it was a convenient language for expressing his highly spatial, Gestalt conception of psychological and social processes. We do not "test" the languages we speak; we accept them and use them as best we can to express what we want to say. Anyone who discards Lewin's theories because his mathematics are discursive must be puzzled to understand how he could have had such a powerful and stimulating effect on students and colleagues. What is there in his egg-shaped diagrams of the life space that aroused so much excitement and led to so much novel and worthwhile research? Unless one is prepared to admit the value of discursive theories, this success of Lewin's school must remain a confusing mystery.

The discursive use of mathematical symbols can do more than dignify the commonplace; it can lend a certain brevity and terseness to the account, and, more important, it can frequently reveal analogies that would go undetected without this linguistic transformation. Regarded in this context, the rich harvest that Lewin and his colleagues reaped from their mathematical formulations is perhaps easier to comprehend.

The following passage is an excerpt from a book published in 1936.

* W. K. Estes et al., *Modern learning theory: A critical analysis of five examples*. New York: Appleton-Century-Crofts, 1954, pp. 341–342. Copyright, 1954, Appleton-Century-Crofts, Inc. Reprinted by permission of the publisher.

Kurt Lewin

Topology of the Psychological Environment

We shall start our discussion of topological problems in psychology by considering the psychological environment. In order to simplify the presentation we shall occasionally use concepts such as that of force which will not be defined until we discuss vector psychology.

One should choose coordinating definitions in such a way that they hold without exception and are univocal. As far as possible we shall try to use reversible coordinations.

The Psychological Region

Definition: To each part of the life space a region is to be coordinated.

Thus we have to represent as a region (1) everything in which an object of the life space, for instance a person, has its place; in which it moves; through which it carries out locomotions; (2) everything in which one can distinguish several positions or parts at the same time, or which is part of a more inclusive whole.

This definition implies that the person itself has to be represented as a region in the life space, further that the life space as a whole is a region.

The reverse of the definition of a psychological region also holds: everything that is shown as a region in representing a situation must be a part of the life space.

In determining whether we are dealing with one or with several psychological regions one can build on either of two facts:

K. Lewin, *Principles of topological psychology*, transl. by F. Heider and G. M. Heider. New York: McGraw-Hill, 1936, pp. 93–103. Reprinted by permission of the publisher.

(1) one can characterize a region by its qualitative properties and can find out its relations of position by determining which regions are contained in others (have the relation to each other of part and whole, $X < Y$), how they overlap ($X \cdot Y \neq 0$ or = 0), which regions have common boundaries (b), and which do not ($b_X \cdot b_Y \neq 0$ or = 0). (2) One can build on psychological processes which connect different points (part regions) in the life space, for instance on locomotions. The locomotions cross or do not cross certain boundaries or other regions. This characteristic makes it possible, on the basis of the coordination of locomotion and path (about which see below), to make topological statements about the regions to which the points (part regions) belong.

The following are examples of qualitative characterizations of regions: ground which is easy or difficult to walk on; region of a forest; a region within which one may be seen from a certain point; a region of a certain color; the sphere of influence of a person; a social group; an occupation; a region in which certain actions are permitted. To determine the position of such regions, for instance the sphere of influence of a person, one can ascertain whether it overlaps the spheres of influence of other persons or groups and if so which; with which spheres of influence it has or has not points of contact (common boundaries).

In determining the position of regions one can use any bodily, quasi-social, or quasi-conceptual locomotion. We have already given sufficient examples of these locomotions. Locomotion makes it possible to make statements about the position not only of the region of departure and of destination but also of those regions which the locomotion crosses.

In psychological investigations one will have to use qualitative properties as well as locomotions in determining psychological regions and their positions. Sometimes the one, sometimes the other gives better results. On the whole the more reliable method of determining the topological characteristics of regions seems to be that of referring to locomotions.

The determination of a region, for instance by certain qualitative characteristics, does not in itself imply whether or not this region is a connected one. For instance, the region which corresponds to the property of a person or the region which corresponds to a certain social group has to be represented sometimes as a connected, sometimes as a non-connected region according to the actual distribution of the property or the members of the group. Also in this point therefore the psychological concept of region agrees with that of mathematics.

Psychological Locomotion

Definition: A path is to be coordinated mathematically to each psychological locomotion.[1]

The question arises whether this coordinating definition can be reversed. Such a reversal would take the following form: To each path in the life space corresponds a locomotion. However, there are cases in which one can connect mathematically points in two different regions of the life space, but when the corresponding locomotion can actually not be carried out. For instance, in our example the prisoner cannot carry out bodily locomotion from the region within the prison to the region outside. Nevertheless, in this case other objects in the life space of the prisoner can carry out such a locomotion and he himself can move in his thoughts from one region to the other. But it is at least conceivable that there can be regions in the life space into which even a conceptual locomotion cannot be carried out.

In spite of this difficulty it is possible to reverse the definition. We have already mentioned that it is sometimes easy, sometimes difficult to carry out a locomotion. A locomotion which cannot be carried out can therefore be thought of as an extreme case of difficult locomotion. Thus the concept of an impossible locomo-

---

[1] As stated above, one understands by path a part of a Jordan curve, *i.e.*, a curve which does not intersect itself. On the other hand psychological locomotion can, at least in a certain sense, pass the same place twice. In these cases locomotion would have to be presented by a curve which intersects itself. However, we shall generally speak of paths, since this is very unlikely to lead to error in the practical application of our concepts. (Besides, mathematics itself sometimes uses the concept of path in this more general sense.) It should be emphasized once more that in the following discussion we mean by locomotion not only quasi-physical but also quasi-social or quasi-conceptual locomotion.

tion is entirely legitimate and even unavoidable. In other words one has to distinguish between the applicability of the concept of locomotion and its factual possibility. For our purposes we can state the definition in its reverse form as follows: To each path in the psychological life space corresponds a locomotion which can or cannot be carried out.[2]

On the basis of these coordinating definitions of the psychological region and the psychological locomotion one can represent mathematically the topological relationships of an unlimited number of different situations. It is the task of the single psychological investigations to carry out these constructions. Here we only want to demonstrate by means of simple examples the general method of making such constructions.

We have explained that the different social positions differ significantly in space of free movement that is available to the person. A change in a person's social position can often be represented as a locomotion from one region to another. In general the fact that a person (P) is in a particular region (R)[3] at a given moment $(P < R)$ is of decisive importance for his behavior. We shall explain that more exactly by means of a few examples.

An investigation has been made of the effect of social pressure on the behavior of children during meals. It shows that one of the most important means by which the adult induces the child to eat an undesired food is to bring him into the "eating situation." If a particular kind of food is not desired, the otherwise unified action of eating usually breaks up into a series of separate steps such as: putting the hand on the table (h); taking the spoon (sp); putting the food on the spoon (f); bringing the spoon halfway to the mouth (hw); bringing it to the mouth (m); taking the food into the mouth (i); chewing (ch); swallowing (sw). These steps correspond topologically to a series of regions (cf. Figure 1a). The procedure of the adult is sometimes to bring the child (C) step by step through these regions closer to the region of the

---

[2] Analogous definitions are common in mathematics. Thus one usually defines function as follows: a is called a function of b if the value of a varies, or does not vary, with the value of b.

[3] The region R may be defined in such a way as to include the objects located in it.

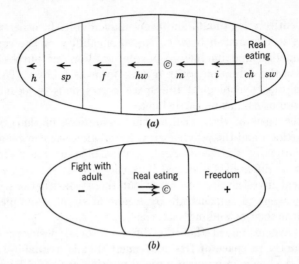

Figure 1.   Situation of child facing disliked food: (a) before entering the region of real eating; (b) after entering the region of real eating. The following symbols are used:

← force: the direction of the arrow represents the direction of the force; its length, the strength of the force; its point the point of application of the force.

←-- locomotion: the point of the arrow designates the place of termination of the locomotion; the other end of the dotted line designates the point of departure.

+ positive valence.
— negative valence.

"real eating" (chewing and swallowing). In doing so he usually meets with increasing resistance in accordance with the fact that with approach to the undesired action the repulsive forces (represented as arrows in Figure 1) increase. However, as soon as the food is once in the mouth it is often not spit out, even when the adult has fed the child against its will. Instead the child goes on to chewing and swallowing the food.

One can show in detail that this change of behavior is brought about essentially by the fact that as the child enters the region of "real eating" his position and the direction of the field forces are entirely changed. When the child is in one of the preceding regions, for instance, when he holds the spoon halfway to his mouth, then a region of greater unpleasantness into which the adult tries to push him, still lies ahead. The adult therefore may have to exert great pressure to induce the child to make a locomotion into the disagreeable region. When the child is once within this region of real eating then the region which lies ahead of him is a more pleasant one of relative freedom (Figure 1b). The child therefore often prefers a locomotion in this direction to spitting out, which is a locomotion in the direction of a disagreeable fight with the adult.

I cannot discuss further the various and often very complicated details of this situation. But I would like to point out that a similar technique is often used to force an adult to do something against his will, for instance in a political struggle. A social group may fight bitterly against the attempt to change its position. If however one succeeds in bringing about a *fait accompli* the group will accept its new position without resistance. This is one reason why the *fait accompli* is so dreaded in politics.

Another example: A two-year-old child does not want to stop playing and go in to wash his hands. The mother who knows that the child especially likes to wet the wash cloth in the basin for himself asks, "Do you want to wet the cloth or should I do it?" The child wants to do it and so he lets himself be washed without further trouble. The question has sufficed to transfer the child from the play situation to the washing situation and it begins to behave according to the requirements of the new region.

Again, Werfel, in his book *The Forty Days of Musa Dagh*, describes how a group of Armenian peasants decide to defend themselves on a mountain against their common enemies. But they cannot come to an agreement about how to settle the property rights in their mountain camp. The priest finds a way to delay the discussion of the question. Later when they are once on the mountain the question of property adjusts itself according to the situation in a way which had been strongly rejected while they were still outside of the situation.

The importance of the act of decision for behavior lies mainly in the fact that by it the person changes his position.

These examples may suffice to make it clear how important it is whether one stands within or outside of a situation; expressed in mathematical terms whether one stands within $(P < R)$ or outside of a certain region $(P \cdot R = 0)$.

Why the region in which a person stands is so important for his behavior becomes intelligible when one realizes how great the change is which is brought about by a transition from one region into another, even within an otherwise unchanged life space. As a rule all relations of neighborhood are changed by such a transition: Regions which were before adjacent to the region of the person are no longer so and vice versa. Different locomotions are now possible and impossible. Even when the same regions are still attainable the course of the path which one must follow to reach them has changed because of the new point of departure. This usually means a change in direction and distance of other regions of the life space and thereby a change in the direction and magnitude of the forces which affect the person. But above all, it is important that the region itself in which he is located has a different character.

In short, the dynamic condition of a person depends in almost every respect directly on his position in a certain region. Methodologically therefore in almost every psychological problem one should give first place to the question of the region in which a person is at a certain moment, or what change of position is just occurring.

* * *

Lewin maintains this style throughout the remainder of his book and continues it in several other theoretical monographs, but we have sampled enough for our present purposes. With these examples in mind, the discovery of further instances of the discursive application of mathematics to psychology can be left as an exercise for the reader.

It should now be obvious why the discursive mode has little coherent tradition of its own, but instead seems to break out spontaneously at widely separated times and places. These are simply not bona fide mathematical theories. Yet, even though they hold no mathematical interest, they often contain hints and anticipations that later psychologists can pick up and develop rigorously. Thus, Herbart's work *suggested*, although he did not create, the kind of functional mathematics that eventually developed in the study of psychophysics; Lewin's work *suggested*, but did not create, a kind of structural mathematics that is currently developing in the study of social groups. Between the suggestion and the actual accomplishment, however, the gap is larger than many people have been willing to admit.

We have not included here a discursive suggestion anticipating normative mathematics, although we could have. That topic, which has shown some continuity in its historical development, is postponed to the next chapter.

3

Normative Applications

Not all advances in psychological theory are made by professional psychologists. Philosophers, biologists, physicians, anthropologists, linguists—many varieties of scholars contribute their wisdom to enrich our psychological conception of man. In this chapter it is principally the logicians and mathematical economists who will engage our attention.

For many years psychologists regarded the work of their economic colleagues as a good example of bad psychology. Economists seemed too much concerned with the rational and ethical problems of what people *ought* to do. Psychologists, fancying themselves natural scientists, not logicians or moral philosophers, insisted on searching instead for the laws that govern what people *actually* do. The vast gap between what they actually do and what they ought to do is overwhelmingly clear to everyone, so it seemed that the normative approach of the economist had to be rejected a priori in psychology.

Beginning around 1950, however, the psychological aspects of economic theory began to grow increasingly interesting to many psychologists. It is tempting to speculate on the sources of this growth. In part, no doubt, it was simply one aspect of a growing interest in mathematical models generally. Or perhaps psychologists were becoming more concerned to include normal as well as average behavior in their theories. Or perhaps they had become sensitized to the importance of the decision process in all phases of behavioral science. Or perhaps they were influenced by new developments in mathematical statistics that reorganized much of our thinking about the nature and purpose of probable inferences. Or perhaps a new generation of psychologists had grown to maturity without being frightened by the traditional taboo against normative theories.

One consequence of this new interest is that we are now forced to go outside our customary disciplinary boundaries in order to trace its historical development. None of the selections in this chapter was written by a professional psychologist. Nevertheless, they have in recent years attracted an increasing number of psychological readers, so it seems appropriate to include them.

What is implied by the concept of normative theory, or a normative application of mathematical reasoning? Traditionally, the distinction between normative and descriptive theories has been most explicit in the study of deductive logic, so let us consider it first in that context.

Today it is widely accepted that logic tells us how we ought to think, not how we do. This attitude is, however, relatively new. For example, until fairly late in the nineteenth century it was generally assumed that the laws of logic *are* the laws of thought. They were generally said to consist of the Law of Identity, $(A = A)$; the Law of the Excluded Middle (either A or not-A must be true); and the Law of Contradiction (A and not-A cannot both be true). As modern logic and modern psychology began to take shape, however, both logicians and psychologists grew uneasy about this identification of logic and thought. To psychologists, on the one hand, it was becoming increasingly obvious that these could not be natural laws, since people violated them constantly. To logicians, on the other hand, it was becoming increasingly burdensome and irrelevant to consider all the heterogeneous types of logical fallacies that people will often accept. In this situation a tacit bargain was easily struck: the psychologist would determine empirically how people actually think, and the logician would determine formally how they ought to think if they want to be self-consistent. The logician does not try to specify *what* people ought to think—he is not normative in that sense—but he does try to specify *how* they ought to think if they hope to reach valid conclusions. Whether or not they can or will follow his recommendations is their concern, not his. (Of course, logic can be used descriptively, as when it is applied to switching networks or neural nets; its normative character emerges only if we use it to describe human reasoning.) Once freed from the burdens of psychologism, logic entered upon one of the most fruitful and exciting periods of its long history. Psychology, however, left to explain all the reasonings that made no sense, could make little headway with the illogical residue; the psychology of reasoning has blundered along blindly ever since, getting nowhere in particular. Nevertheless, this pattern—logicians taking a normative approach to correct thinking, and psychologists picking up whatever was left over—has persisted at least into the second half of the twentieth century.

Instead of the laws of thought, the economist confronts us with some deceptively simple postulates about preferences, but otherwise the situation is much the same. The economist does not try to prescribe *what* people ought to want—he is not normative in that sense—but he does try to prescribe *how* they should go about getting what they want. For example, consider the assumption that for any two conceivable acts a person always knows (can identify consistently) which he would prefer to do. If we interpret this postulate as an empirical description, it is all too easy to find examples that contradict it. At this point we could, and most psychologists traditionally did, dismiss the whole argument as obviously false and undeserving of further study. Or we could, and some modern psychologists have become increasingly willing to, regard the postulate, not as a natural law, but as a normative, logic-like rule that people try to invoke to the limit of their ability, whenever they want to act consistently in an economically defined situation.

It is possible that in recent years a subtle shift has begun in the way some psychologists conceive their science, a shift away from an exclusive commitment to the discovery and verification of natural laws and toward the formulation of normative rules, away from the traditional goals of physics and biology and toward those of logic and economics. Too often what seemed at first to be a universal law of nature turned out on closer study to be merely a social convention. This shift has been quite apparent among psychologists who try to formulate psychological problems in mathematical terms; most of their major advances since 1947 have resulted from better ways of characterizing individual choice behavior. And choice, if it is to retain its traditional meaning, can scarcely be reduced to the automatic operation of immutable laws of nature. The newer strategy is to specify some of the logical, ethical, procedural rules that are available in our society and that we can try to use to guide our own choices in the direction of greater self-consistency.*

A basic concept in the history of economic theory is *utility*, which we can interpret here to mean the subjective correlate of objective wealth, much as auditory pitch is the subjective correlate of the acoustic frequency of vibration, or visual brightness is the subjective correlate of the physical intensity of illumination, and so on. In all such cases the two quantities—subjective and objective—covary closely but not perfectly, so we face an empirical problem of determining exactly what law governs their covariation.

The simplest assumption one might make about utility would be that it is a rectilinear function of the amount of money involved: each unit increase in wealth produces a unit increase in satisfaction. The first suspicion that this psychological assumption is too simple—that units of money might not also be units of utility—seems to have occurred sometime during the first half of the eighteenth century. Like many of the early formulations of probability theory, this one also was set in the context of risk and gambling. The precise history is a little obscure, but we do know that Daniel Bernoulli in 1738 was among the first to state these suspicions formally in a manner that attracted wide popular attention. The following is an English translation of Bernoulli's famous paper.

* R. D. Luce, *Individual choice behavior*. New York: Wiley, 1959, p. 1.

Daniel Bernoulli

Exposition of a New Theory on the Measurement of Risk*

1   Ever since mathematicians first began to study the measurement of risk there has been general agreement on the following
proposition: *Expected values are computed by multiplying each
possible gain by the number of ways in which it can occur, and
then dividing the sum of these products by the total number of
possible cases where, in this theory, the consideration of cases
which are all of the same probability is insisted upon.* If this rule
be accepted, what remains to be done within the framework of
this theory amounts to the enumeration of all alternatives, their
breakdown into equiprobable cases and, finally, their insertion
into corresponding classifications.
2   Proper examination of the numerous demonstrations of this
proposition that have come forth indicates that they all rest upon
one hypothesis: *since there is no reason to assume that of two
persons encountering identical risks,[1] either should expect to have
his desires more closely fulfilled, the risks anticipated by each
must be deemed equal in value.* No characteristic of the persons
themselves ought to be taken into consideration; only those matters should be weighed carefully that pertain to the terms of the
risk. The relevant finding might then be made by the highest

D. Bernoulli, Exposition of a new theory on the measurement of risk, transl. by L.
Sommer. *Econometrica*, 1954, **22**, 23–36. Reprinted by permission of The Econo-
metric Society.

* Translated from Latin into English by Dr. Louise Sommer, The American University, Washington, D.C., from "Specimen Theoriae Novae de
Mensura Sortis," *Commentarii Academiae Scientiarum Imperialis Petro-
politanae*, Tomus V [*Papers of the Imperial Academy of Sciences in
Petersburg*, Vol. V], 1738, pp. 175–192. Professor Karl Menger, Illinois Institute of Technology, has written footnotes 3, 8, 9, and 14.

[1] That is, risky propositions (gambles). [Translator.]

judges established by public authority. But really there is here no
need for judgment but of deliberation, i.e., rules would be set up
whereby anyone could estimate his prospects from any risky
undertaking in light of one's specific financial circumstances.

3   To make this clear it is perhaps advisable to consider the following example: Somehow a very poor fellow obtains a lottery
ticket that will yield with equal probability either nothing or
twenty thousand ducats. Will this man evaluate his chance of
winning at ten thousand ducats? Would he not be ill-advised to
sell this lottery ticket for nine thousand ducats? To me it seems
that the answer is in the negative. On the other hand I am in-
clined to believe that a rich man would be ill-advised to refuse to
buy the lottery ticket for nine thousand ducats. If I am not
wrong then it seems clear that all men cannot use the same rule
to evaluate the gamble. The rule established in §1 must, therefore, be discarded. But anyone who considers the problem with
perspicacity and interest will ascertain that the concept of *value*
which we have used in this rule may be defined in a way which
renders the entire procedure universally acceptable without reservation. To do this the determination of the *value* of an item must
not be based on its *price*, but rather on the *utility* it yields. The
price of the item is dependent only on the thing itself and is equal
for everyone; the utility, however, is dependent on the particular
circumstances of the person making the estimate. Thus there is
no doubt that a gain of one thousand ducats is more significant
to a pauper than to a rich man though both gain the same
amount.

4   The discussion has now been developed to a point where anyone may proceed with the investigation by the mere paraphrasing
of one and the same principle. However, since the hypothesis is
entirely new, it may nevertheless require some elucidation. I
have, therefore, decided to explain by example what I have explored. Meanwhile, let us use this as a fundamental rule: *If the
utility of each possible profit expectation is multiplied by the
number of ways in which it can occur, and we then divide the
sum of these products by the total number of possible cases, a
mean utility*[2] *[moral expectation] will be obtained, and the profit*

[2] Free translation of Bernoulli's "emolumentum medium," literally: "mean
utility." [Translator.]

which corresponds to this utility will equal the value of risk in question.

5 Thus it becomes evident that no valid measurement of the value of a risk can be obtained without consideration being given to its *utility*, that is to say, the utility of whatever gain accrues to the individual or, conversely, how much profit is required to yield a given utility. However it hardly seems plausible to make any precise generalizations since the utility of an item may change with circumstances. Thus, though a poor man generally obtains more utility than does a rich man from an equal gain, it is nevertheless conceivable, for example, that a rich prisoner who possesses two thousand ducats but needs two thousand ducats more to repurchase his freedom, will place a higher value on a gain of two thousand ducats than does another man who has less money than he. Though innumerable examples of this kind may be constructed, they represent exceedingly rare exceptions. We shall, therefore, do better to consider what usually happens, and in order to perceive the problem more correctly we shall assume that there is an imperceptibly small growth in the individual's wealth which proceeds continuously by infinitesimal increments. Now it is highly probable that *any increase in wealth, no matter how insignificant, will always result in an increase in utility which is inversely proportionate to the quantity of goods already possessed.* To explain this hypothesis it is necessary to define what is meant by the *quantity of goods.* By this expression I mean to connote food, clothing, all things which add to the convenience of life, and even to luxury—anything that can contribute to the adequate satisfaction of any sort of want. There is then nobody who can be said to possess nothing at all in this sense unless he starves to death. For the great majority the most valuable portion of their possessions so defined will consist in their productive capacity, this term being taken to include even the beggar's talent: a man who is able to acquire ten ducats yearly by begging will scarcely be willing to accept a sum of fifty ducats on condition that he henceforth refrain from begging or otherwise trying to earn money. For he would have to live on this amount, and after he had spent it his existence must also come to an end. I doubt whether even those who do not possess a farthing and are burdened with financial obligations would be willing to free themselves of their debts or even to accept a still greater gift on such a condition. But if the beggar were to refuse such a contract unless immediately paid no less than one hundred ducats and the man pressed by creditors similarly demanded one thousand ducats, we might say that the former is possessed of wealth worth one hundred, and the latter of one thousand ducats, though in common parlance the former owns nothing and the latter less than nothing.

6 Having stated this definition, I return to the statement made in the previous paragraph which maintained that, in the absence of the unusual, the *utility resulting from any small increase in wealth will be inversely proportionate to the quantity of goods previously possessed.* Considering the nature of man, it seems to me that the foregoing hypothesis is apt to be valid for many people to whom this sort of comparison can be applied. Only a few do not spend their entire yearly incomes. But, if among these, one has a fortune worth a hundred thousand ducats and another a fortune worth the same number of semi-ducats and if the former receives from it a yearly income of five thousand ducats while the latter obtains the same number of semi-ducats it is quite clear that to the former a ducat has exactly the same significance as a semi-ducat to the latter, and that, therefore, the gain of one ducat will have to the former no higher value than the gain of a semi-ducat to the latter. Accordingly, if each makes a gain of one ducat the latter receives twice as much utility from it, having been enriched by two semi-ducats. This argument applies to many other cases which, therefore, need not be discussed separately. The proposition is all the more valid for the majority of men who possess no fortune apart from their working capacity which is their only source of livelihood. True, there are men to whom one ducat means more than many ducats do to others who are less rich but more generous than they. But since we shall now concern ourselves only with one individual (in different states of affluence) distinctions of this sort do not concern us. The man who is emotionally less affected by a gain will support a loss with greater patience. Since, however, in special cases things can conceivably occur otherwise, I shall first deal with the most

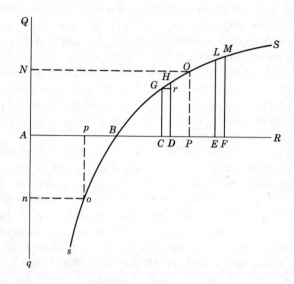

general case and then develop our special hypothesis in order thereby to satisfy everyone.

7 Therefore, let *AB* represent the quantity of goods initially possessed. Then after extending *AB*, a curve *BGLS* must be constructed, whose ordinates *CG*, *DH*, *EL*, *FM*, etc., designate *utilities* corresponding to the abscissas *BC*, *BD*, *BE*, *BF*, etc., designating gains in wealth. Further, let *m*, *n*, *p*, *q*, etc., be the numbers which indicate the number of ways in which gains in wealth *BC*, *BD*, *BE*, *BF*, etc., can occur. Then (in accord with §4) the *moral* expectation of the risky proposition referred to is given by:

$$PO = \frac{m \cdot CG + n \cdot DH + p \cdot EL + q \cdot FM + \cdots}{m + n + p + q + \cdots}$$

Now, if we erect *AQ* perpendicular to *AR*, and on it measure off *AN* = *PO*, the straight line *NO* − *AB* represents the gain which may properly be expected, or the value of the risky proposition in question. If we wish, further, to know how large a stake the individual should be willing to venture on this risky proposition, our curve must be extended in the opposite direction in such a way that the abscissa *Bp* now represents a loss and the ordinate *po* represents the corresponding decline in utility. Since in a fair game the disutility to be suffered by losing must be equal to the utility to be derived by winning, we must assume that $An = AN$, or $po = PO$. Thus Bp will indicate the stake more than which persons who consider their own pecuniary status should not venture.

Corollary I

8 Until now scientists have usually rested their hypothesis on the assumption that all gains must be evaluated exclusively in terms of themselves, i.e., on the basis of their intrinsic qualities, and that these gains will always produce a *utility* directly proportionate to the gain. On this hypothesis the curve BS becomes a straight line. Now if we again have:

$$PO = \frac{m \cdot CG + n \cdot DH + p \cdot EL + q \cdot FM + \cdots}{m + n + p + q + \cdots},$$

and if, on both sides, the respective factors are introduced it follows that:

$$BP = \frac{m \cdot BC + n \cdot BD + p \cdot BE + q \cdot BF + \cdots}{m + n + p + q + \cdots},$$

which is in conformity with the usually accepted rule.

Corollary II

9 If AB were infinitely great, even in proportion to BF, the greatest possible gain, the arc BM may be considered very like an infinitesimally small straight line. Again in this case the usual rule (for the evaluation of risky propositions) is applicable, and may continue to be considered approximately valid in games of insignificant moment.

10 Having dealt with the problem in the most general way we turn now to the aforementioned particular hypothesis, which, indeed, deserves prior attention to all others. First of all the nature of curve sBS must be investigated under the conditions postulated in §7. Since on our hypothesis we must consider infinitesimally small gains, we shall take gains BC and BD to be nearly equal, so that their difference CD becomes infinitesimally small. If we draw Gr parallel to BR, then rH will represent the infinitesimally small gain in *utility* to a man whose fortune is AC and who obtains the small gain, CD. This *utility*, however, should be related not only to the tiny gain CD, to which it is, other things being equal, proportionate, but also to AC, the fortune previously owned to which it is inversely proportionate. We therefore set: $AC = x$, $CD = dx$, $CG = y$, $rH = dy$ and $AB = \alpha$; and if b designates some constant we obtain $dy = \dfrac{bdx}{x}$ or $y = b \log \dfrac{x}{\alpha}$. The curve sBS is therefore a logarithmic curve, the subtangent[3] of which is everywhere b and whose asymptote is Qq.

11   If we now compare this result with what has been said in paragraph 7, it will appear that: $PO = b \log AP/AB$, $CG = b \log AC/AB$, $DH = b \log AD/AB$ and so on; but since we have

$$PO = \frac{m \cdot CG. + n \cdot DH + p \cdot EL + q \cdot FM + \cdots}{m + n + p + q + \cdots}$$

it follows that

$$b \log \frac{AP}{AB} =$$

$$\frac{\left(mb \log \dfrac{AC}{AB} + nb \log \dfrac{AD}{AB} + pb \log \dfrac{AE}{AB} + qb \log \dfrac{AF}{AB} + \cdots \right)}{(m + n + p + q + \cdots)} :$$

and therefore

$$AP = (AC^m \cdot AD^n \cdot AE^p \cdot AF^q \cdots)^{1/m+n+p+q+\cdots}$$

[3] The tangent to the curve $y = b \log \dfrac{x}{\alpha}$ at the point $\left(x_0, \log \dfrac{x_0}{\alpha} \right)$ is the line $y - b \log \dfrac{x_0}{\alpha} = \dfrac{b}{x_0}(x - x_0)$. This tangent intersects the Y-axis ($x = 0$) at the point with the ordinate $b \log \dfrac{x_0}{\alpha} - b$. The point of contact of the tangent with the curve has the ordinate $b \log \dfrac{x_0}{\alpha}$. So also does the projection of this point on the Y-axis. The segment between the two points on the Y-axis that have been mentioned has the length b. That segment is the projection of the segment on the tangent between its intersection with the Y-axis and the point of contact. The length of this projection (which is b) is what Bernoulli here calls the "subtangent." Today, by the subtangent of the curve $y = f(x)$ at the point $(x_0, f(x_0))$ is meant the length of the segment on the X-axis (and not the Y-axis) between its intersection with the tangent and the projection of the point of contact. This length is $f(x_0)/f'(x_0)$. In the case of the logarithmic curve it equals $x_0 \log \dfrac{x_0}{\alpha}$. —Karl Menger.

and if we subtract AB from this, the remaining magnitude, BP, will represent the value of the risky proposition in question.

12 Thus the preceding paragraph suggests the following rule: *Any gain must be added to the fortune previously possessed, then this sum must be raised to the power given by the number of possible ways in which the gain may be obtained; these terms should then be multiplied together. Then of this product a root must be extracted the degree of which is given by the number of all possible cases, and finally the value of the initial possessions must be subtracted therefrom; what then remains indicates the value of the risky proposition in question.* This principle is essential for the measurement of the value of risky propositions in various cases. I would elaborate it into a complete theory as has been done with the traditional analysis, were it not that, despite its usefulness and originality, previous obligations do not permit me to undertake this task. I shall therefore, at this time, mention only the more significant points among those which have at first glance occurred to me.

13 First, it appears that in many games, even those that are absolutely fair, both of the players may expect to suffer a loss; indeed this is Nature's admonition to avoid the dice altogether. . . . This follows from the concavity of curve sBS to BR. For in making the stake, Bp, equal to the expected gain, BP, it is clear that the disutility po which results from a loss will always exceed the expected gain in utility, PO. Although this result will be quite clear to the mathematician, I shall nevertheless explain it by example, so that it will be clear to everyone. Let us assume that of two players, both possessing one hundred ducats, each puts half this sum as a stake in a game that offers the same probabilities to both players. Under this assumption each will then have fifty ducats plus the expectation of winning yet one hundred ducats more. However, the sum of the values of these two items amounts, by the rule of §12, to only $(50^1 \cdot 150^1)^{\frac{1}{2}}$ or $\sqrt{50 \cdot 150}$, i.e., less than eighty-seven ducats, so that, though the game be played under perfectly equal conditions for both, either will suffer an expected loss of more than thirteen ducats. We must strongly emphasize this truth, although it be self evident: the imprudence of a gambler will be the greater the larger the part of his fortune which he exposes to a game of chance. For this purpose we shall modify the previous example by assuming that one of the gamblers, before putting up his fifty ducat stake possessed two hundred ducats. This gambler suffers an expected loss of $200 - \sqrt{150 \cdot 250}$, which is not much greater than six ducats.

14   Since, therefore, everyone who bets any part of his fortune, however small, on a mathematically fair game of chance acts irrationally, it may be of interest to inquire how great an advantage the gambler must enjoy over his opponent in order to avoid any expected loss. Let us again consider a game which is as simple as possible, defined by two equiprobable outcomes one of which is favorable and the other unfavorable. Let us take a to be the gain to be won in case of a favorable outcome, and x to be the stake which is lost in the unfavorable case. If the initial quantity of goods possessed is α we have $AB = \alpha$; $BP = a$; $PO = b \log \dfrac{\alpha + a}{\alpha}$ (see §10), and since (by §7) $po = PO$ it follows by the nature of a logarithmic curve that $Bp = \dfrac{\alpha a}{\alpha + a}$. Since however Bp represents the stake x, we have $x = \dfrac{\alpha a}{\alpha + a}$ a magnitude which is always smaller than a, the expected gain. It also follows from this that a man who risks his entire fortune acts like a simpleton, however great may be the possible gain. No one will have difficulty in being persuaded of this if he has carefully examined our definitions given above. Moreover, this result sheds light on a statement which is universally accepted in practice: it may be reasonable for some individuals to invest in a doubtful enterprise and yet be unreasonable for others to do so.

15   The procedure customarily employed by merchants in the insurance of commodities transported by sea seems to merit special attention. This may again be explained by an example. Suppose Caius,[4] a Petersburg merchant, has purchased commodities in Amsterdam which he could sell for ten thousand rubles if he had

[4] Caius is a Roman name, used here in the sense of our "Mr. Jones." Caius is the older form; in the later Roman period it was spelled "Gaius." [Translator.]

them in Petersburg. He therefore orders them to be shipped there by sea, but is in doubt whether or not to insure them. He is well aware of the fact that at this time of year of one hundred ships which sail from Amsterdam to Petersburg, five are usually lost. However, there is no insurance available below the price of eight hundred rubles a cargo, an amount which he considers outrageously high. The question is, therefore, how much wealth must Caius possess apart from the goods under consideration in order that it be sensible for him to abstain from insuring them? If x represents his fortune, then this together with the value of the expectation of of the safe arrival of his goods is given by $\sqrt[100]{(x + 10000)^{95}x^5} = \sqrt[20]{(x + 10000)^{19}x}$ in case he abstains. With insurance he will have a certain fortune of $x + 9200$. Equating these two magnitudes we get: $(x + 10000)^{19}x = (x + 9200)^{20}$ or, approximately, $x = 5043$. If, therefore, Caius, apart from the expectation of receiving his commodities, possesses an amount greater than 5043 rubles he will be right in not buying insurance. If, on the contrary, his wealth is less than this amount he should insure his cargo. And if the question be asked "What minimum fortune should be possessed by the man who offers to provide this insurance in order for him to be rational in doing so?" We must answer thus: let y be his fortune, then

$$\sqrt[20]{(y + 800)^{19} \cdot (y - 9200)} = y$$

or approximately, $y = 14243$, a figure which is obtained from the foregoing without additional calculation. A man less wealthy than this would be foolish to provide the surety, but it makes sense for a wealthier man to do so. From this it is clear that the introduction of this sort of insurance has been so useful since it offers advantages to all persons concerned. Similarly, had Caius been able to obtain the insurance for six hundred rubles he would have been unwise to refuse it if he possessed less than 20478 rubles, but he would have acted much too cautiously had he insured his commodities at this rate when his fortune was greater than this amount. On the other hand a man would act unadvisedly if he were to offer to sponsor this insurance for six hundred rubles when he himself possesses less than 29878 rubles. However, he would be well advised to do so if he possessed more than that amount. But no one, however rich, would be managing his affairs properly if he individually undertook the insurance for less than five hundred rubles.

16 Another rule which may prove useful can be derived from our theory. This is the rule that it is advisable to divide goods which are exposed to some danger into several portions rather than to risk them all together. Again I shall explain this more precisely by an example. Sempronius owns goods at home worth a total of 4000 ducats and in addition possesses 8000 ducats worth of commodities in foreign countries from where they can only be transported by sea. However, our daily experience teaches us that of ten ships one perishes. Under these conditions I maintain that if Sempronius trusted all his 8000 ducats of goods to one ship his expectation of the commodities is worth 6751 ducats. That is

$$\sqrt[10]{12000^9 \cdot 4000^1} - 4000.$$

If, however, he were to trust equal portions of these commodities to two ships the value of his expectation would be

$$\sqrt[100]{12000^{81} \cdot 8000^{18} \cdot 4000} - 4000, \text{ i.e., } 7033 \text{ ducats.}$$

In this way the value of Sempronius' prospects of success will grow more favorable the smaller the proportion committed to each ship. However, his expectation will never rise in value above 7200 ducats. This counsel will be equally serviceable for those who invest their fortunes in foreign bills of exchange and other hazardous enterprises.

17 I am forced to omit many novel remarks though these would clearly not be unserviceable. And, though a person who is fairly judicious by natural instinct might have realized and spontaneously applied much of what I have here explained, hardly anyone believed it possible to define these problems with the precision we have employed in our examples. Since all our propositions harmonize perfectly with experience it would be wrong to neglect them as abstractions resting upon precarious hypotheses. This is further confirmed by the following example which inspired these thoughts, and whose history is as follows: My most honorable cousin the celebrated Nicolas Bernoulli, Professor utriusque juris[5] at the University of Basle, once submitted five problems to the highly distinguished[6] mathematician Montmort.[7] These problems are reproduced in the work *L'analyse sur les jeux de hazard de M. de Montmort*, p. 402. The last of these problems runs as follows:

Peter tosses a coin and continues to do so until it should land "heads" when it comes to the ground. He agrees to give Paul one ducat if he gets "heads" on the very first throw, two ducats if he gets it on the second, four if on the third, eight if on the fourth, and so on, so that with each additional throw the number of ducats he must pay is doubled. Suppose we seek to determine the value of Paul's expectation. My aforementioned cousin discussed this problem in a letter to me asking for my opinion. Although the standard calculation shows[8] that the value of Paul's expectation is infinitely great, it has, he said, to be admitted that any fairly reasonable man would sell his chance, with great pleasure, for twenty ducats. The accepted method of calculation does, indeed, value Paul's prospects at infinity though no one would be willing to purchase it at a moderately high price. If, however, we apply our new rule to this problem we may see the solution and thus unravel the knot. The solution of the problem by our principles is as follows.

[5] Faculties of law of continental European universities bestow up to the present time the title of a Doctor utriusque juris, which means Doctor of both systems of laws, the Roman and the canon law. [Translator.]

[6] Cl., i.e., Vir Clarissimus, a title of respect. [Translator.]

[7] Montmort, Pierre Rémond, de (1678–1719). The work referred to here is the then famous "Essai d'analyse sur les jeux de hazard," Paris, 1708. Appended to the second edition, published in 1713, is Montmort's correspondence with Jean and Nicolas Bernoulli referring to the problems of chance and probabilities. [Translator.]

[8] The probability of heads turning up on the 1st throw is $\frac{1}{2}$. Since in this case Paul receives one ducat, this probability contributes $\frac{1}{2} \cdot 1 = \frac{1}{2}$ ducats to his expectation. The probability of heads turning up on the 2nd throw is $\frac{1}{4}$. Since in this case Paul receives 2 ducats, this possibility contributes $\frac{1}{4} \cdot 2 = \frac{1}{2}$ to his expectation. Similarly, for every integer n, the possibility of heads turning up on the n-th throw contributes $\frac{1}{2}^n \cdot 2^{n-1} = \frac{1}{2}$ ducats to his expectation. Paul's total expectation is therefore $\frac{1}{2} + \frac{1}{2} + \ldots + \frac{1}{2} + \ldots$, and that is infinite —Karl Menger.

18 The number of cases to be considered here is infinite: in one half of the cases the game will end at the first throw, in one quarter of the cases it will conclude at the second, in an eighth part of the cases with the third, in a sixteenth part with the fourth, and so on.[9] If we designate the number of cases through infinity by N it is clear that there are $\frac{1}{2}N$ cases in which Paul gains one ducat, $\frac{1}{4}N$ cases in which he gains two ducats, $\frac{1}{8}N$ in which he gains four, $\frac{1}{16}N$ in which he gains eight, and so on, ad infinitum. Let us represent Paul's fortune by α; the proposition in question will then be worth

$$\sqrt[N]{(\alpha+1)^{N/2}\cdot(\alpha+2)^{N/4}\cdot(\alpha+4)^{N/8}\cdot(\alpha+8)^{N/16}\cdots}-\alpha$$
$$=\sqrt{(\alpha+1)}\cdot\sqrt[4]{(\alpha+2)}\cdot\sqrt[8]{(\alpha+4)}\cdot\sqrt[16]{(\alpha+8)}\cdots-\alpha.$$

19 From this formula which evaluates Paul's prospective gain it follows that this value will increase with the size of Paul's fortune and will never attain an infinite value unless Paul's wealth simultaneously becomes infinite. In addition we obtain the following corollaries. If Paul owned nothing at all the value of his expectation would be

$$\sqrt[2]{1}\cdot\sqrt[4]{2}\cdot\sqrt[8]{4}\cdot\sqrt[16]{8}\cdots$$

which amounts to two ducats, precisely. If he owned ten ducats his opportunity would be worth approximately three ducats; it

---

[9] Since the number of cases is infinite, it is impossible to speak about one half of the cases, one quarter of the cases, etc., and the letter N in Bernoulli's argument is meaningless. However, Paul's expectation on the basis of Bernoulli's hypothesis concerning evaluation can be found by the same method by which, in footnote 8, Paul's classical expectation was determined. If Paul's fortune is α ducats, then, according to Bernoulli, he attributes to a gain of 2^{n-1} ducats the value $b \log \frac{\alpha+2^{n-1}}{\alpha}$. If the probability of this gain is $\frac{1}{2}^n$, his expectation is $b/2^n \log \frac{\alpha+2^{n-1}}{\alpha}$. Paul's expectation resulting from the game is therefore

$$\frac{b}{2}\log\frac{\alpha+1}{\alpha}+\frac{b}{4}\log\frac{\alpha+2}{\alpha}+\ldots+\frac{b}{2^n}\log\frac{\alpha+2^{n-1}}{\alpha}+\ldots$$
$$=b\log\left[(\alpha+1)^{1/2}(\alpha+2)^{1/4}\cdots(\alpha+2^{n-1})^{1/2n}\cdots\right]-b\log\alpha.$$

What addition D to Paul's fortune has the same value for him? Clearly, $b\log\frac{\alpha+D}{\alpha}$ must equal the above sum. Therefore

$$D=(\alpha+1)^{1/2}(\alpha+2)^{1/4}\cdots(\alpha+2^{n-1})^{1/2n}\cdots-\alpha.$$

—Karl Menger

would be worth approximately four if his wealth were one hundred, and six if he possessed one thousand. From this we can easily see what a tremendous fortune a man must own for it to make sense for him to purchase Paul's opportunity for twenty ducats. The amount which the buyer ought to pay for this proposition differs somewhat from the amount it would be worth to him were it already in his possession. Since, however, this difference is exceedingly small if α (Paul's fortune) is great, we can take them to be equal. If we designate the purchase price by x its value can be determined by means of the equation

$$\sqrt[2]{(\alpha + 1 - x)} \cdot \sqrt[4]{(\alpha + 2 - x)} \cdot \sqrt[8]{(\alpha + 4 - x)} \cdot \sqrt[16]{(\alpha + 8 - x)} \cdots = \alpha$$

and if α is a large number this equation will be approximately satisfied by

$$x = \sqrt[2]{\alpha + 1} \cdot \sqrt[4]{\alpha + 2} \cdot \sqrt[8]{\alpha + 4} \cdot \sqrt[16]{\alpha + 8} \cdots - \alpha.$$

After having read this paper to the Society[10] I sent a copy to the aforementioned Mr. Nicolas Bernoulli, to obtain his opinion of my proposed solution to the difficulty he had indicated. In a letter to me written in 1732 he declared that he was in no way dissatisfied with my proposition on the evaluation of risky propositions when applied to the case of a man who is to evaluate his own prospects. However, he thinks that the case is different if a third person, somewhat in the position of a judge, is to evaluate the prospects of any participant in a game in accord with equity and justice. I myself have discussed this problem in §2. Then this distinguished scholar informed me that the celebrated mathematician, Cramer,[11] had developed a theory on the same subject several years before I produced my paper. Indeed I have found his theory so similar to mine that it seems miraculous that we independently reached such close agreement on this sort of subject. Therefore it seems worth quoting the words with which the celebrated Cramer himself first described his theory in his letter of 1728 to my cousin. His words are as follows:[12]

"Perhaps I am mistaken, but I believe that I have solved the extraordinary problem which you submitted to M. de Montmort, in your letter of September 9, 1713, ... For the sake of simplicity I shall assume that A tosses a coin into the air and B

[10] Bernoulli's paper had been submitted to the Imperial Academy of Sciences in Petersburg. [Translator.]
[11] Cramer, Gabriel, famous mathematician, born in Geneva, Switzerland (1704–1752). [Translator.]
[12] The following passage of the original text is in French. [Translator.]

commits himself to give A 1 ducat if, at the first throw, the coin falls with its cross upward; 2 if it falls thus only at the second throw, 4 if at the third throw, 8 if at the fourth throw, etc. The paradox consists in the infinite sum which calculation yields as the equivalent which A must pay to B. This seems absurd since no reasonable man would be willing to pay 20 ducats as equivalent. You ask for an explanation of the discrepancy between the mathematical calculation and the vulgar evaluation. I believe that it results from the fact that, *in their theory*, mathematicians evaluate money in proportion to its quantity while, *in practice*, people with common sense evaluate money in proportion to the utility they can obtain from it. The mathematical expectation is rendered infinite by the enormous amount which I can win if the coin does not fall with its cross upward until rather late, perhaps at the hundredth or thousandth throw. Now, as a matter of fact, if I reason as a sensible man, this sum is worth no more to me, causes me no more pleasure and influences me no more to accept the game than does a sum amounting only to ten or twenty million ducats. Let us suppose, therefore, that any amount above 10 millions, or (for the sake of simplicity) above $2^{24} = 166777216$ ducats be deemed by him equal in value to 2^{24} ducats or, better yet, that I can never win more than that amount, no matter how long it takes before the coin falls with its cross upward. In this case, my expectations is $\frac{1}{2} \cdot 1 + \frac{1}{4} \cdot 2 + \frac{1}{8} \cdot 4$ $\cdots + \frac{1}{2} 25 \cdot 2^{24} + \frac{1}{2} 26 \cdot 2^{24} + \frac{1}{2} 27 \cdot 2^{24} + \cdots = \frac{1}{2} + \frac{1}{2} + \frac{1}{2} + \cdots$ (24 times) $\cdots + \frac{1}{2} + \frac{1}{4} + \frac{1}{8} + \cdots = 12 + 1 = 13$. Thus, my moral expectation is reduced in value to 13 ducats and the equivalent to be paid for it is similarly reduced—a result which seems much more reasonable than does rendering it infinite."

Thus far[13] the exposition is somewhat vague and subject to counter argument. If it, indeed, be true that the amount 2^{25} appears to us to be no greater than 2^{24}, no attention whatsoever should be paid to the amount that may be won after the twenty-fourth throw, since just before making the twenty-fifth throw I am certain to end up with no less than $2^{24} - 1$,[14] an amount that, according to this theory, may be considered equivalent to 2^{24}. Therefore it may be said correctly that my expectation is only worth twelve ducats, not thirteen. However, in view of the coincidence between the basic principle developed by the aforementioned author and my own, the foregoing is clearly not intended to be taken to invalidate that principle. I refer to the proposition that reasonable men should evaluate money in accord with the

[13] From here on the text is again translated from Latin. [Translator.]

[14] This remark of Bernoulli's is obscure. Under the conditions of the game a gain of $2^{24} - 1$ ducats is impossible.—Karl Menger.

utility they derive therefrom. I state this to avoid leading anyone to judge that entire theory adversely. And this is exactly what Cl. C.[15] Cramer states, expressing in the following manner precisely what we would ourselves conclude. He continues thus:[16]

"The equivalent can turn out to be smaller yet if we adopt some alternative hypothesis on the moral value of wealth. For that which I have just assumed is not entirely valid since, while it is true that 100 millions yield more satisfaction than do 10 millions, they do not give ten times as much. If, for example, we suppose the moral value of goods to be directly proportionate to the square root of their mathematical quantities, e.g., that the satisfaction provided by 40000000 is double that provided by 10000000, my psychic expectation becomes

$$\tfrac{1}{2}\sqrt{1} + \tfrac{1}{4}\sqrt{2} + \tfrac{1}{8}\sqrt{4} + \tfrac{1}{16}\sqrt{8} + \cdots = \frac{1}{2 - \sqrt{2}}.$$

However this magnitude is not the equivalent we seek, for this equivalent need not be equal to my moral expectation but should rather be of such a magnitude that the pain caused by its loss is equal to the moral expectation of the pleasure I hope to derive from my gain. Therefore, the equivalent must, on our hypothesis, amount to $\left(\dfrac{1}{2-\sqrt{2}}\right)^{2} = \left(\dfrac{1}{6-4\sqrt{2}}\right) = 2.9 \cdots$, which is consequently less than 3, truly a trifling amount, but nevertheless, I believe, closer than is 13 to the vulgar evaluation."

[15] To be translated as "the distinguished Gabriel." [Translator.]
[16] Text continues in French. [Translator.]

* * *

The great Laplace accepted Bernoulli's account of utility with enthusiasm and the general argument seems thereafter to have been widely known. The offer Peter made to Paul in §17 became especially famous and, because of the journal in which Bernoulli's work was published, it came to be called the "St. Petersburg paradox." Bernoulli's argument did not explicitly affect the thinking of psychologists and economists, however, until the second half of the nineteenth century; then in 1869, G. T. Fechner made it the basis of his psychophysical measurements of sensation, and in 1871 William Stanley Jevons made it the basis of his very psychological theory of economic behavior. It is the economic argument that we shall follow here; discussion of the psychophysical implications must be postponed to the next chapter.

Jevon's book, *The Theory of Political Economy,* was the first salvo in what was shortly to become a violent revolution in economic theory. This is no place to recite economic history,* but a few general remarks may be helpful.

By the middle of the nineteenth century, the classical economic theory developed by Adam Smith, Jeremy Bentham, Thomas Malthus, David Ricardo, John Stuart Mill, and many others, was a completed doctrine that nicely filled the textbooks, but poorly fitted the events of the day. It came under attack by Marx and Engels from one direction; then shortly afterward a swarm of brilliant theorists—Jevons, Karl Menger, Auguste Walras, Alfred Marshall, and many others—began to revise the classical theory to make it more mathematical and more psychological. It is this second revolution that concerns us here.

Among the classical economists it had been Jeremy Bentham who emphasized the importance of pleasure and pain for controlling man's behavior in the marketplace. Bentham even went so far as to talk about a "felicific calculus" whereby men could compute their maximum happiness. However, except for a few discursive uses of mathematical ideas ("the greatest happiness of the greatest number"), Bentham did not try to develop the mathematical implications of his hedonistic psychology. That step was left for Jevons and his contemporaries.

Jevons may not have been the most brilliant of the new theorists, and he certainly was not the best mathematician, yet his prose was so clear and his arguments so persuasive that he makes a most attractive representative of this stage in the history of economic theory. The following excerpts are from Jevon's book, first published in 1871.

* O. H. Taylor, *A history of economic thought.* New York: McGraw-Hill, 1960, Chap. 12.

William Stanley Jevons

Theory of Utility

Pleasure and pain are undoubtedly the ultimate objects of the Calculus of Economics. To satisfy our wants to the utmost with the least effort—to procure the greatest amount of what is desirable at the expense of the least that is undesirable—in other words, *to maximise pleasure*, is the problem of Economics. But it is convenient to transfer our attention as soon as possible to the physical objects or actions which are the source to us of pleasures and pains. A very large part of the labour of any community is spent upon the production of the ordinary necessaries and conveniences of life, such as food, clothing, buildings, utensils, furniture, ornaments, etc.; and the aggregate of these things, therefore, is the immediate object of our attention.

It is desirable to introduce at once, and to define some terms which facilitate the expression of the Principles of Economics. By a *commodity* we shall understand any object, substance, action, or service, which can afford pleasure or ward off pain. The name was originally abstract, and denoted the quality of anything by which it was capable of serving man. Having acquired, by a common process of confusion, a concrete signification, it will be well to retain the word entirely for that signification, and employ the term *utility* to denote the abstract quality whereby an object serves our purposes, and becomes entitled to rank as a commodity. Whatever can produce pleasure or prevent pain *may* possess utility. J.-B. Say has correctly and briefly defined utility as "la faculté qu'ont les choses de pouvoir servir à l'homme, de quelque manière que ce soit." The food which prevents the pangs of hunger, the clothes which fend off the cold of winter, possess

W. S. Jevons, *The theory of political economy*, (2nd ed.) London: Macmillan, 1879, Chap. 3, pp. 37–53.

incontestable utility; but we must beware of restricting the meaning of the word by any moral considerations. Anything which an individual is found to desire and to labour for must be assumed to possess for him utility. In the science of Economics we treat men not as they ought to be, but as they are. Bentham, in establishing the foundations of Moral Science in his great *Introduction to the Principles of Morals and Legislation* (page 3), thus comprehensively defines the term in question: "By utility is meant that property in any object, whereby it tends to produce benefit, advantage, pleasure, good, or happiness (all this, in the present case, comes to the same thing), or (what comes again to the same thing) to prevent the happening of mischief, pain, evil, or unhappiness to the party whose interest is considered."

This perfectly expresses the meaning of the word in Economics, provided that the will or inclination of the person immediately concerned is taken as the sole criterion, for the time, of what is or is not useful.

Economics must be founded upon a full and accurate investigation of the conditions of utility; and, to understand this element, we must necessarily examine the wants and desires of man. We, first of all, need a theory of the consumption of wealth. J. S. Mill, indeed, has given an opinion inconsistent with this. "Political economy," he says,[1] "has nothing to do with the consumption of wealth, further than as the consideration of it is inseparable from that of production, or from that of distribution. We know not of any laws of the consumption of wealth, as the subject of a distinct science; they can be no other than the laws of human enjoyment."

But is is surely obvious that Economics does rest upon the laws of human enjoyment; and that, if those laws are developed by no other science, they must be developed by economists. We labour to produce with the sole object of consuming, and the kinds and amounts of goods produced must be determined with regard to what we want to consume. Every manufacturer knows and feels how closely he must anticipate the tastes and needs of his customers: his whole success depends upon it; and, in like manner, the theory of Economics must begin with a correct

[1] *Essays on some Unsettled Questions of Political Economy*, p. 132.

theory of consumption. Many economists have had a clear perception of this truth. . . .

My principal work now lies in tracing out the exact nature and conditions of utility. It seems strange indeed that economists have not bestowed more minute attention on a subject which doubtless furnishes the true key to the problem of Economics.

In the first place, utility, though a quality of things, is *no inherent quality*. It is better described as *a circumstance of things* arising out of their relation to man's requirements. As Senior most accurately says, "Utility denotes no intrinsic quality in the things which we call useful; it merely expresses their relations to the pains and pleasures of mankind." We can never, therefore, say absolutely that some objects have utility and others have not. The ore lying in the mine, the diamond escaping the eye of the searcher, the wheat lying unreaped, the fruit ungathered for want of consumers, have no utility at all. The most wholesome and necessary kinds of food are useless unless there are hands to collect and mouths to eat them sooner or later. Nor, when we consider the matter closely, can we say that all portions of the same commodity possess equal utility. Water, for instance, may be roughly described as the most useful of all substances. A quart of water per day has the high utility of saving a person from dying in a most distressing manner. Several gallons a day may possess much utility for such purposes as cooking and washing; but after an adequate supply is secured for these uses, any additional quantity is a matter of comparative indifference. All that we can say, then, is that water, up to a certain quantity, is indispensable; that further quantities will have various degrees of utility; but that beyond a certain quantity the utility sinks gradually to zero; it may even become negative, that is to say, further supplies of the same substance may become inconvenient and hurtful.

Exactly the same considerations apply more or less clearly to every other article. A pound of bread per day supplied to a person saves him from starvation, and has the highest conceivable utility. A second pound per day has also no slight utility: it keeps him in a state of comparative plenty, though it be not altogether indispensable. A third pound would begin to be superfluous. It is clear, then, that *utility is not proportional to commodity:* the very same articles vary in utility according as we already possess more or less of the same article. The like may be said of other things. One suit of clothes per annum is necessary, a second convenient, a third desirable, a fourth not unacceptable; but we, sooner or later, reach a point at which further supplies are not desired with any perceptible force, unless it be for subsequent use.

Let us now investigate this subject a little more closely. Utility must be considered as measured by, or even as actually identical with, the addition made to a person's happiness. It is a convenient name for the aggregate of the favourable balance of feeling produced—the sum of the pleasure created and the pain prevented. We must now carefully discriminate between the *total utility* arising from any commodity and the utility attaching to any particular portion of it. Thus the total utility of the food we eat consists in maintaining life, and may be considered as infinitely great; but if we were to subtract a tenth part from what we eat daily, our loss would be but slight. We should certainly not lose a tenth part of the whole utility of food to us. It might be doubtful whether we should suffer any harm at all.

Let us imagine the whole quantity of food which a person consumes on an average during twenty-four hours to be divided into ten equal parts. If his food be reduced by the last part, he will suffer but little; if a second tenth part be deficient, he will feel the want distinctly; the subtraction of the third tenth part will be decidedly injurious; with every subsequent subtraction of a tenth part his sufferings will be more and more serious, until at length he will be upon the verge of starvation. Now, if we call each of the tenth parts *an increment,* the meaning of these facts is, that each increment of food is less necessary, or possess less utility, than the previous one. To explain this variation of utility we may make use of space-representations, which I have found convenient in illustrating the laws of Economics in my College lectures during fifteen years past.

Let the line *ox* be used as a measure of the quantity of food, and let it be divided into ten equal parts to correspond to the ten portions of food mentioned above. Upon these equal lines are

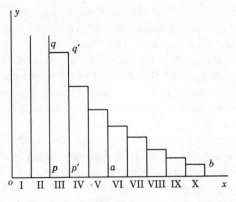

Figure 1

constructed rectangles, and the area of each rectangle may be assumed to represent the utility of the increment of food corresponding to its base. Thus the utility of the last increment is small, being proportional to the small rectangle on x. As we approach towards o, each increment bears a larger rectangle, that standing upon III being the largest complete rectangle. The utility of the next increment, II, is undefined, as also that of I, since these portions of food would be indispensable to life, and their utility, therefore, infinitely great.

We can now form a clear notion of the utility of the whole food, or of any part of it, for we have only to add together the proper rectangles. The utility of the first half of the food will be the sum of the rectangles standing on the line $oa;$ that of the second half will be represented by the sum of the smaller rectangles between a and b. The total utility of the food will be the whole sum of the rectangles, and will be infinitely great.

The comparative utility of the several portions is, however, the most important point. Utility may be treated as *a quantity of two dimensions,* one dimension consisting in the quantity of the commodity, and another in the intensity of the effect produced upon the consumer. Now, the quantity of the commodity is measured on the horizontal line ox, and the intensity of utility will be measured by the length of the upright lines, or *ordinates.*

The intensity of utility of the third increment is measured either by pq, or $p'q'$, and its utility is the product of the units in pp' multiplied by those in pq.

But the division of the food into ten equal parts is an arbitrary supposition. If we had taken twenty or a hundred or more equal parts, the same general principle would hold true, namely, that each small portion would be less useful and necessary than the last. The law may be considered to hold true theoretically, however small the increments are made; and in this way we shall at last reach a figure which is undistinguishable from a continuous curve. The notion of infinitely small quantities of food may seem absurd as regards the consumption of one individual; but, when we consider the consumption of a nation as a whole, the consumption may well be conceived to increase or diminish by quantities which are, practically speaking, infinitely small compared with the whole consumption. The laws which we are about to trace out are to be conceived as theoretically true of the individual; they can only be practically verified as regards the aggregate transactions, productions, and consumptions of a large body of people. But the laws of the aggregate depend of course upon the laws applying to individual cases.

The law of the variation of the degree of utility of food may thus be represented by a continuous curve pbq (Figure 2), and the perpendicular height of each point of the curve above the line ox, represents the degree of utility of the commodity when a certain amount has been consumed.

Thus, when the quantity oa has been consumed, the degree of utility corresponds to the length of the line ab; for if we take a very little more food, aa', its utility will be the product of aa' and ab very nearly, and more nearly the less is the magnitude of aa'. The degree of utility is thus properly measured by the height of a very narrow rectangle corresponding to a very small quantity of food, which theoretically ought to be infinitely small.

We are now in a position to appreciate perfectly the difference between the *total utility* of any commodity and *the degree of utility* of the commodity at any point. These are, in fact, quantities of altogether different kinds, the first being represented by an area, and the second by a line. We must consider how we may express these notions in appropriate mathematical language.

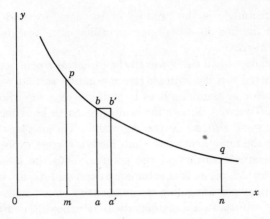

Figure 2

Let x signify, as is usual in mathematical books, the quantity which varies independently—in this case the quantity of commodity. Let u denote the *whole utility* proceeding from the consumption of x. Then u will be, as mathematicians say, *a function of x;* that is, it will vary in some continuous and regular, but probably unknown, manner, when x is made to vary. Our great object at present, however, is to express the *degree of utility*.

Mathematicians employ the sign Δ prefixed to a sign of quantity, such as x, to signify that a quantity of the same nature as x, but small in proportion to x, is taken into consideration. Thus Δx means a small portion of x, and $x + \Delta x$ is therefore a quantity a little greater than x. Now, when x is a quantity of commodity, the utility of $x + \Delta x$ will be more than that of x as a general rule. Let the whole utility of $x + \Delta x$ be denoted by $u + \Delta u$; then it is obvious that the increment of utility Δu belongs to the increment of commodity Δx; and if, for the sake of argument, we suppose the degree of utility uniform over the whole of Δx, which is nearly true owing to its smallness, we shall find the corresponding degree of utility by dividing Δu *by* Δx.

We find these considerations fully illustrated by Figure 2, in which oa represents x, and ab is the degree of utility at the point a. Now, if we increase x by the small quantity aa', or Δx, the utility is increased by the small rectangle $abb'a'$, or $\Delta u;$ and, since a rectangle is the product of its sides, we find that the length of the line ab, the degree of utility, is represented by the fraction $\Delta u/\Delta x$.

As already explained, however, the utility of a commodity may be considered to vary with perfect continuity, so that we commit a small error in assuming it to be uniform over the whole increment Δx. To avoid this we must imagine Δx to be reduced to an infinitely small size, Δu decreasing with it. The smaller the quantities are the more nearly we shall have a correct expression for ab, the degree of utility at the point a. Thus the *limit* of this fraction $\Delta u/\Delta x$, or, as it is commonly expressed du/dx, is the degree of utility corresponding to the quantity of commodity x. *The degree of utility is,* in mathematical language, *the differential coefficient of u considered as a function of x,* and will itself be another function of x.

We shall seldom need to consider the degree of utility except as regards the last increment which has been consumed, or, which comes to the same thing, the next increment which is about to be consumed. I shall therefore commonly use the expression *final degree of utility,* as meaning the degree of utility of the last addition, or the next possible addition of a very small, or infinitely small, quantity to the existing stock. In ordinary circumstances, too, the final degree of utility will not be great compared with what it might be. Only in famine or other extreme circumstances do we approach the higher degrees of utility. Accordingly, we can often treat the lower portions of the curves of variations (pbq, Figure 2) which concern ordinary commercial transactions, while we leave out of sight the portions beyond p or q. It is also evident that we may know the degree of utility at any point while ignorant of the total utility, that is, the area of the whole curve. To be able to estimate the total enjoyment of a person would be an interesting thing, but it would not be really so important as to be able to estimate the additions and subtractions to his enjoyment, which circumstances occasion. In the same way a very wealthy person may be quite unable to form any accurate statement of his aggregate wealth; but he may nevertheless have exact accounts of income and expenditure, that is, of additions and subtractions.

The final degree of utility is that function upon which the Theory of Economics will be found to turn. Economists, generally speaking, have failed to discriminate between this function and the total utility, and from this confusion has arisen much perplexity. Many commodities which are most useful to us are esteemed and desired but little. We cannot live without water, and yet in ordinary circumstances we set no value on it. Why is this? Simply because we usually have so much of it that its final degree of utility is reduced nearly to zero. We enjoy, every day, the almost infinite utility of water, but then we do not need to consume more than we have. Let the supply run short by drought, and we begin to feel the higher degrees of utility, of which we think but little at other times.

The variation of the function expressing the final degree of utility is the all-important point in economic problems. We may state as a general law, that *the degree of utility varies with the quantity of commodity, and ultimately decreases as that quantity increases.* No commodity can be named which we continue to desire with the same force, whatever be the quantity already in use or possession. All our appetites are capable of *satisfaction* or *satiety* sooner or later, in fact, both these words mean, etymologically, that we have had *enough,* so that more is of no use to us. It does not follow, indeed, that the degree of utility will always sink to zero. This may be the case with some things, especially the simple animal requirements, such as food, water, air, etc. But the more refined and intellectual our needs become, the less are they capable of satiety. To the desire for articles of taste, science, or curiosity, when once excited, there is hardly a limit.

* * *

In these paragraphs, as far as they go, Jevons adds nothing important to what Bernoulli had already said, although he does emphasize the psychological rationale that motivates his mathematics. Jevons goes on, however, to develop a theory of exchange in terms of increased utility for both parties: If you have too much A but no B, and I have too much B and no A, we can both increase our total happiness by trading some of your A for my B. In fact, you should go on trading with me until the gain in utility you get when you acquire another unit of B is exactly equal to the loss in utility that you suffer when you give up a unit of A. This point defines for you a kind of equilibrium between A and B. By arguments such as this the mathematical analysis of equilibria became a central concern in mathematic economics.

As psychology, of course, all this was quite empty. Even if one believes there are no upper or lower limits on human happiness, even if one is willing to accept as normative rather than empirical the conception of man as a pleasure-maximizing machine, still the assumption that all pleasures are commensurable—that so much of one sort of pleasure felt by one person can be equated to so much of other sorts of pleasure felt by other people—seems to go beyond anything we might establish empirically. The mathematical convenience of such assumptions is no guarantee of their truth.

Consequently, psychologists who looked at this normative theory were not favorably impressed, and eventually the economists themselves began to admit its shortcomings as a basis for descriptive studies. In the hands of Alfred Marshall and those who followed him, this kind of utility analysis was recognized as merely an enrichment, not a replacement, for the older, classical concepts. Pleasure and pain cannot be, as Jevons claimed, "the ultimate objects of the Calculus of Economics." A major part of modern economic theory must be devoted to the decisions of aggregate bodies—banks, corporations, governments, and others—where Jevons's hedonistic psychology is simply not relevant. Thus, while the mathematical innovations spread rapidly into all branches of economics, the psychological substance of these new theories inspired little interest or respect either from economists or from psychologists.

When we read Jevons today and compare his basic assumptions with those of Bernoulli more than a century earlier, we are apt to be struck by Jevons's emphasis on pleasure and happiness and his almost complete neglect of risk and probability. Perhaps equally striking to our modern eye, however, is the fact that both authors demonstrate a confident disregard for measurements. Bernoulli assumed a logarithmic function, even though any function that increases at a progressively decreasing rate would have served as well; his preference for a logarithmic function was esthetic, not empirical. Jevons argued eloquently that mathematical theory can proceed without numerical estimates, and then seemed to assume that numerical estimates would not be helpful if they did exist. Other economic theorists were equally abstract in this respect.

The development of utility measurement in recent years makes an interesting story, for it illustrates how dependent good measurement is on the prior development of good theory. Apparently the first person who tried to measure some of the magnitudes implied by the mathematical theory was the psychologist L. L. Thurstone.* In 1931 Thurstone asked some experimental subjects to compare the utilities of different bundles of commodities. A subject was given (symbolically) one bundle (eight hats and eight pairs of shoes) as the "standard" and told to compare its utility with various other bundles (nine hats and seven pairs of shoes, or ten hats and seven pairs of shoes, and so on). On the basis of such judgments Thurstone was able, by a chain of argument we need not reproduce here, to convince himself that Bernoulli's logarithmic assumption was not unreasonable. In several respects Thurstone's procedures were open to criticism, but he could scarcely have improved on them without introducing risks into the choice situation—a step that was foreign to the economic theories of that day.

It was really not until 1951 that a straightforward and explicit measurement of utility was finally made.† In 1951 Frederick Mosteller and Philip Nogee developed a measurement procedure based on ideas advanced by Neumann and Morgenstern, a procedure that reintroduced the concept of probability along with the concepts of objective value and subjective utility.

In developing their axiomatic statement of utility theory, Neu-

---

* L. L. Thurstone, *The measurement of values.* Chicago: University of Chicago Press, 1959, Chap. 12, pp. 123–144.

† F. Mosteller and P. Nogee, An experimental measurement of utility. *J. polit. Econ.*, 1951, **59**, 371–404.

mann and Morgenstern assumed that if object A is preferred to object B and object B is preferred to object C, then there must be some probability combination of A and C such that the individual is indifferent between it and B. Mosteller and Nogee considered such objects as the following:

Object A: receipt of 25 cents
Object B: neither receipt nor loss of money
Object C: loss of 5 cents

which most people will prefer in the order A, B, C. By assumption, therefore, there must be some probability combination of A and C that will have the same utility for a person as would B. This means there must be some probability p such that

$$p\, U(A) + (1 - p)\, U(C) = U(B)$$

where $U(X)$ denotes the utility of X. To use the monetary example,

$$p\, U(25\text{¢}) + (1 - p)\, U(-5\text{¢}) = U(0\text{¢})$$

In their actual measurements, Mosteller and Nogee preferred to fix only two of the monetary values (B and C) and the probability p, and to search for an A that would satisfy the equation. That is to say, for a particular probability p_0, they tried to find an A such that, for a given person,

$$p_0\, U(A) + (1 - p_0)\, U(-5\text{¢}) = U(0\text{¢})$$

Finding A thus becomes an experimental problem. It was solved in the following way. First, Mosteller and Nogee defined an arbitrary zero point and unit of measurement:

$$U(0\text{¢}) = 0 \text{ utile, and } U(-5\text{¢}) = -1 \text{ utile}$$

where "utile" is the name they invented for the unit of measurement of utility. Substituting these values into the equation and solving for $U(A)$ gives us

$$U(A) = \frac{1 - p_0}{p_0} \text{ utiles}$$

Thus, the conditions specified by the experimenters enabled them to specify the utility of A, given a known probability of winning A. For example, the object A—whatever it is—that satisfies the equation when $p_0 = \frac{1}{2}$ will have a subjective value of 1 utile.

The experimental procedure for finding A consisted of offering possible bets to people who then either agreed or refused to bet a nickel. The bets were posed in terms of a game of poker dice, but the players were informed as to the exact probabilities of winning every bet. Suppose, for example, that the probability of the subject winning the bet is $p_0 = \frac{1}{6}$; then the utility will be 5 utiles, and a payoff of $6 \times 5\cancel{c} = 30\cancel{c}$ comprises a "fair" bet. If the subject is a conservative bettor, he will not accept the bet unless winning it involves the receipt of more than $30\cancel{c}$. If he insists on being paid, say, $40\cancel{c}$, then for him $U(40\cancel{c}) = 5$ utiles. If he will accept the same bet when it pays only, say, $20\cancel{c}$, then he is an extravagant bettor and $U(20\cancel{c}) = 5$ utiles for him. By offering a series of such bets at different probabilities, Mosteller and Nogee were able to determine the utility for fifteen different individuals of small sums ranging from $5\cancel{c}$ up to about $5.00.

The traditional theory that we have seen developed above by Bernoulli and Jevons would imply that rational subjects should be conservative, and that the utility of money would increase more and more slowly as the amount increased. The college students that Mosteller and Nogee tested did follow this general pattern; the larger the bet, the more conservative they became. With subjects chosen from the National Guard, however, the opposite was the case. These subjects, whose education and economic status was less favorable than that of the college boys, were willing to accept very unfair bets if the sum they might win was large enough.

By such procedures and arguments Mosteller and Nogee were able to demonstrate that it is feasible to measure the utility of money, that different people seem to have different but relatively consistent utility functions, and that Bernoulli's logarithmic function is far too simple to account for all the facts.

One aspect of this pioneering experiment, however, remained unsettled. At bottom, the uncertainty was not one of experimental technique, but one of conceptual ambiguity. The problem can be stated as follows: If we are to distinguish between the objective value and the subjective utility of money, should we not also distinguish between objective and subjective conceptions of probability? As a matter of fact, the notion of subjective probability had already been submitted to experimental test. In 1948 M. G. Preston and P. Baratta had used gambling experiments in order to estimate what subjective probability is required before people will behave as if the true mathematical probability was some given value.* As Mosteller and Nogee pointed out, their own measurements of utility could be reinterpreted (even though their subjects were told the true probabilities) as measurements of subjective probability and compared with those of Preston and Baratta. (When this was done they found agreement in general, but some puzzling differences in detail.) The problem, therefore, was to decide which of these two psychological quantities they had actually measured, utility or subjective probability. Or could the two quantities be just different ways to talk about the same thing?

What was needed here was some way to measure utility and subjective probability simultaneously. It seemed a difficult problem, but, oddly enough, a solution had already been proposed twenty-five years earlier by an English mathematician. Mosteller and Nogee did not discover Frank P. Ramsey's essay until their own work had been completed. The crux of Ramsey's solution was to begin with an event known to have a subjective probability of one-half (or, in his terminology, an "ethically neutral proposition" having a "degree of belief" of one-half). With this quantity given, he could then use it to measure utility (or "value," as he preferred to call it).

The following passage is an excerpt from the essay Ramsey wrote in 1926. It was published posthumously in 1931.

* M. G. Preston and P. Baratta, An experimental study of the auction-value of an uncertain outcome. *Amer. J. Psychol.*, 1948, **61**, 183–193.

Frank Plumpton Ramsey

Truth and Probability

Let us now try to find a method of measuring beliefs as bases of possible actions. It is clear that we are concerned with dispositional rather than with actualized beliefs; that is to say, not with beliefs at the moment when we are thinking of them, but with beliefs like my belief that the earth is round, which I rarely think of, but which would guide my action in any case to which it was relevant.

The old-established way of measuring a person's belief is to propose a bet, and see what are the lowest odds which he will accept. This method I regard as fundamentally sound; but it suffers from being insufficiently general, and from being necessarily inexact. It is inexact partly because of the diminishing marginal utility of money, partly because the person may have a special eagerness or reluctance to bet, because he either enjoys or dislikes excitement or for any other reason, e.g. to make a book. The difficulty is like that of separating two different co-operating forces. Besides, the proposal of a bet may inevitably alter his state of opinion; just as we could not always measure electric intensity by actually introducing a charge and seeing what force it was subject to, because the introduction of the charge would change the distribution to be measured.

In order therefore to construct a theory of quantities of belief which shall be both general and more exact, I propose to take as a basis a general psychological theory, which is now universally discarded, but nevertheless comes, I think, fairly close to the truth in the sort of cases with which we are most concerned. I

F. P. Ramsey, *The foundations of mathematics.* New York: Harcourt Brace, 1931, pp. 172–184. Reprinted by permission of Humanities Press, Inc.

mean the theory that we act in the way we think most likely to
realize the objects of our desires, so that a person's actions are
completely determined by his desires and opinions. This theory
cannot be made adequate to all the facts, but it seems to me a
useful approximation to the truth particularly in the case of our
self-conscious or professional life, and it is presupposed in a great
deal of our thought. It is a simple theory and one which many
psychologists would obviously like to preserve by introducing
unconscious desires and unconscious opinions in order to bring it
more into harmony with the facts. How far such fictions can
achieve the required result I do not attempt to judge: I only
claim for what follows approximate truth, or truth in relation to
this artificial system of psychology, which like Newtonian mechanics can, I think, still be profitably used even though it is
known to be false.

It must be observed that this theory is not to be identified
with the psychology of the Utilitarians, in which pleasure had a
dominating position. The theory I propose to adopt is that we
seek things which we want, which may be our own or other people's pleasure, or anything else whatever, and our actions are
such as we think most likely to realize these goods. But this is
not a precise statement, for a precise statement of the theory can
only be made after we have introduced the notion of quantity
of belief.

Let us call the things a person ultimately desires "goods," and
let us at first assume that they are numerically measurable and
additive. That is to say that if he prefers for its own sake an
hour's swimming to an hour's reading, he will prefer two hours'
swimming to one hour's swimming and one hour's reading. This is
of course absurd in the given case but this may only be because
swimming and reading are not ultimate goods, and because we
cannot imagine a second hour's swimming precisely similar to the
first, owing to fatigue, etc.

Let us begin by supposing that our subject has no doubts about
anything, but certain opinions about all propositions. Then we
can say that he will always choose the course of action which
will lead in his opinion to the greatest sum of good.

It should be emphasized that in this essay good and bad are

never to be understood in any ethical sense but simply as denoting that to which a given person feels desire and aversion.

The question then arises how we are to modify this simple system to take account of varying degrees of certainty in his beliefs. I suggest that we introduce as a law of psychology that his behaviour is governed by what is called the mathematical expectation; that is to say that, if p is a proposition about which he is doubtful, any goods or bads for whose realization p is in his view a necessary and sufficient condition enter into his calculations multiplied by the same fraction, which is called the "degree of his belief in p." We thus define degree of belief in a way which presupposes the use of the mathematical expectation.

We can put this in a different way. Suppose his degree of belief in p is m/n; then his action is such as he would choose it to be if he had to repeat it exactly n times, in m of which p was true, and in the others false. (Here it may be necessary to suppose that in each of the n times he had no memory of the previous ones.)

This can also be taken as a definition of the degree of belief, and can easily be seen to be equivalent to the previous definition. Let us give an instance of the sort of case which might occur. I am at a cross-roads and do not know the way; but I rather think one of the two ways is right. I propose therefore to go that way but keep my eyes open for someone to ask; if now I see someone half a mile away over the fields, whether I turn aside to ask him will depend on the relative inconvenience of going out of my way to cross the fields or of continuing on the wrong road if it is the wrong road. But it will also depend on how confident I am that I am right; and clearly the more confident I am of this the less distance I should be willing to go from the road to check my opinion. I propose therefore to use the distance I would be prepared to go to ask, as a measure of the confidence of my opinion; and what I have said above explains how this is to be done. We can set it out as follows: suppose the disadvantage of going x yards to ask is $f(x)$, the advantage of arriving at the right destination is r, that of arriving at the wrong one w. Then if I should be willing to go a distance d to ask, the degree of my belief that I am on the right road is given by $p = 1 - \dfrac{f(d)}{r - w}$.

For such an action is one it would just pay me to take, if I had to act in the same way n times, in np of which I was on the right way but in the others not.

For the total good resulting from not asking each time

$$= npr + n(1 - p)w$$
$$= nw + np(r - w),$$

that resulting from asking at distance x each time

$$= nr - nf(x). \qquad \text{(I now always go right.)}$$

This is greater than the preceding expression, provided

$$f(x) < (r - w)(1 - p),$$

therefore the critical distance d is connected with p, the degree of belief, by the relation $f(d) = (r - w)(1 - p)$

$$\text{or } p = 1 - \frac{f(d)}{r - w} \qquad \text{as asserted above.}$$

It is easy to see that this way of measuring beliefs gives results agreeing with ordinary ideas; at any rate to the extent that full belief is denoted by 1, full belief in the contradictory by 0, and equal belief in the two by $\frac{1}{2}$. Further, it allows validity to betting as means of measuring beliefs. By proposing a bet on p we give the subject a possible course of action from which so much extra good will result to him if p is true and so much extra bad if p is false. Supposing the bet to be in goods and bads instead of in money, he will take a bet at any better odds than those corresponding to his state of belief; in fact his state of belief is measured by the odds he will just take; but this is vitiated, as already explained, by love or hatred of excitement, and by the fact that the bet is in money and not in goods and bads. Since it is universally agreed that money has a diminishing marginal utility, if money bets are to be used, it is evident that they should be for as small stakes as possible. But then again the measurement is spoiled by introducing the new factor of reluctance to bother about trifles.

Let us now discard the assumption that goods are additive and immediately measurable, and try to work out a system with as few assumptions as possible. To begin with we shall suppose, as before, that our subject has certain beliefs about everything; then he will act so that what he believes to be the total consequences of his action will be the best possible. If then we had the power of the Almighty, and could persuade our subject of our power, we could, by offering him options, discover how he placed in order of merit all possible courses of the world. In this way all possible worlds would be put in an order of value, but we should have no definite way of representing them by numbers. There would be no meaning in the assertion that the difference in value between α and β was equal to that between γ and δ. (Here and elsewhere we use Greek letters to represent the different possible totalities of events between which our subject chooses—the ultimate organic unities.)

Suppose next that the subject is capable of doubt; then we could test his degree of belief in different propositions by making him offers of the following kind. Would you rather have a world α in any event; or world β if p is true, and world γ if p is false? If, then, he were certain that p was true, he would simply compare α and β and choose between them as if no conditions were attached; but if he were doubtful his choice would not be decided so simply. I propose to lay down axioms and definitions concerning the principles governing choices of this kind. This is, of course, a very schematic version of the situation in real life, but it is, I think, easier to consider it in this form.

There is first a difficulty which must be dealt with; the propositions like p in the above case which are used as conditions in the options offered may be such that their truth or falsity is an object of desire to the subject. This will be found to complicate the problem, and we have to assume that there are propositions for which this is not the case, which we shall call ethically neutral. More precisely an atomic proposition p is called ethically neutral if two possible worlds differing only in regard to the truth of p are always of equal value; and a non-atomic proposition p is called ethically neutral if all atomic truth-arguments[1] are ethically neutral.

[1] I assume here Wittgenstein's theory of propositions; it would probably be possible to give an equivalent definition in terms of any other theory.

We begin by defining belief of degree $\frac{1}{2}$ in an ethically neutral proposition. The subject is said to have belief of degree $\frac{1}{2}$ in such a proposition p if he has no preference between the options (1) α if p is true, β if p is false, (2) α if p is false, β if p is true, but has a preference between α and β simply. We suppose by an axiom that if this is true of any one pair α, β it is true of all such pairs.[2] This comes roughly to defining belief of degree $\frac{1}{2}$ as such a degree of belief as leads to indifference between betting one way and betting the other for the same stakes.

Belief of degree $\frac{1}{2}$ as thus defined can be used to measure values numerically in the following way. We have to explain what is meant by the difference in value between α and β being equal to that between γ and δ; and we define this to mean that, if p is an ethically neutral proposition believed to degree $\frac{1}{2}$, the subject has no preference between the options (1) α if p is true, δ if p is false, and (2) β if p is true, γ if p is false.

This definition can form the basis of a system of measuring values in the following way:

Let us call any set of all worlds equally preferable to a given world a value: we suppose that if world α is preferable to β any world with the same value as α is preferable to any world with the same value as β and shall say that the value of α is greater than that of β. This relation "greater than" orders values in a series. We shall use α henceforth both for the world and its value.

Axioms

(1) There is an ethically neutral proposition p believed to degree $\frac{1}{2}$.

(2) If p, q are such propositions and the option

α if p, δ if not-p is equivalent to β if p, γ if not-p,

then

α if q, δ if not-q is equivalent to β if q, γ if not-q.

Def. In the above case we say $\alpha\beta = \gamma\delta$.

Theorem. If $\alpha\beta = \gamma\delta$, then $\beta\alpha = \delta\gamma$, $\alpha\gamma = \beta\delta$, $\gamma\alpha = \delta\beta$.

(2a) If $\alpha\beta = \gamma\delta$, then $\alpha > \beta$ is equivalent to $\gamma > \delta$
and $\alpha = \beta$ is equivalent to $\gamma = \delta$.

---

[2] α and β must be supposed so far undefined as to be compatible with both p and not-p.

(3) If option A is equivalent to option B and B to C, then A to C.

Theorem. If $\alpha\beta = \gamma\delta$ and $\beta\eta = \zeta\gamma$, then $\alpha\eta = \zeta\delta$.

(4) If $\alpha\beta = \gamma\delta$, $\gamma\delta = \eta\zeta$, then $\alpha\beta = \eta\zeta$.

(5) (α, β, γ). E ! $(\imath x)$ $(\alpha x = \beta\gamma)$.*

(6) (α, β). E ! $(\imath x)$ $(\alpha x = x\beta)$.*

(7) Axiom of continuity: Any progression has a limit (ordinal).

(8) Axiom of Archimedes.

These axioms enable the values to be correlated one-one with real numbers so that if α' corresponds to α, etc.

$$\alpha\beta = \gamma\delta . \equiv . \alpha' - \beta' = \gamma' - \delta'.$$

Henceforth we use α for the correlated real number α' also.

Having thus defined a way of measuring value we can now derive a way of measuring belief in general. If the option of α for certain is indifferent with that of β if p is true and γ if p is false,[3] we can define the subject's degree of belief in p as the ratio of the difference between α and γ to that between β and γ; which we must suppose the same for all α's, β's and γ's that satisfy the conditions. This amounts roughly to defining the degree of belief in p by the odds at which the subject would bet on p, the bet being conducted in terms of differences of value as defined. The definition only applies to partial belief and does not include certain beliefs; for belief of degree 1 in p, α for certain is indifferent with α if p and any β if not-p.

We are also able to define a very useful new idea—"the degree of belief in p given q." This does not mean the degree of belief in "If p then q," or that in "p entails q," or that which the subject would have in p if he knew q, or that which he ought to have. It roughly expresses the odds at which he would now bet on p, the bet only to be valid if q is true. Such conditional bets were often made in the eighteenth century.

* [Editor's note: E! $(\imath x)(\phi x)$ means "One and only one x satisfies ϕ."]

[3] Here β must include the truth of p, γ its falsity; p need no longer be ethically neutral. But we have to assume that there is a world with any assigned value in which p is true, and one in which p is false.

The degree of belief in p given q is measured thus. Suppose the subject indifferent between the options (1) a if q true, β if q false, (2) γ if p true and q true, δ if p false and q true, β if q false. Then the degree of his belief in p given q is the ratio of the difference between a and δ to that between γ and δ, which we must suppose the same for any a, β, γ, δ which satisfy the given conditions. This is not the same as the degree to which he would believe p, if he believed q for certain; for knowledge of q might for psychological reasons profoundly alter his whole system of beliefs.

Each of our definitions has been accompanied by an axiom of consistency, and in so far as this is false, the notion of the corresponding degree of belief becomes invalid. This bears some analogy to the situation in regard to simultaneity discussed above.

I have not worked out the mathematical logic of this in detail, because this would, I think, be rather like working out to seven places of decimals a result only valid to two. My logic cannot be regarded as giving more than the sort of way it might work.

From these definitions and axioms it is possible to prove the fundamental laws of probable belief (degrees of belief lie between 0 and 1):

(1) Degree of belief in p + degree of belief in $\bar{p} = 1$.

(2) Degree of belief in p given q + degree of belief in $\bar{p}$ given $q = 1$.

(3) Degree of belief in (p and q) = degree of belief in $p \times$ degree of belief in q given p.

(4) Degree of belief in (p and q) + degree of belief in (p and $\bar{q}$) = degree of belief in p.

The first two are immediate. (3) is proved as follows.

Let degree of belief in $p = x$, that in q given $p = y$.

Then ξ for certain $\equiv \xi + (1 - x)t$ if p true, $\xi - xt$ if p false, for any t.

$\xi + (1 - x)t$ if p true $\equiv$

$$\begin{cases} \xi + (1 - x)t + (1 - y)\, u \text{ if "}p \text{ and } q\text{" true,} \\ \xi + (1 - x)t - yu \text{ if } p \text{ true } q \text{ false;} \end{cases}$$

for any u.

Choose u so that $\xi + (1 - x)t - yu = \xi - xt$, i.e. let

$$u = t/y \qquad (y \neq 0)$$

Then ξ for certain $\equiv$

$$\begin{cases} \xi + (1 - x)t + (1 - y)t/y & \text{if "p and q" true} \\ \xi - xt & \text{otherwise,} \end{cases}$$

therefore degree of belief in "p and q" $=$

$$\frac{xt}{t + (1 - y)t/y} = xy. \qquad (t \neq 0)$$

If $y = 0$, take $t = 0$. Then
ξ for certain $\equiv \xi$ if p true, ξ if p false

$$\equiv \xi + u \text{ if } p \text{ true, } q \text{ true; } \xi \text{ if } p \text{ false, } q \text{ false;}$$
$$\xi \text{ if } p \text{ false}$$

$$\equiv \xi + u, pq \text{ true; } \xi, pq \text{ false}$$

therefore degree of belief in $pq = 0$.

(4) follows from (2), (3) as follows:
Degree of belief in $pq =$ that in $p \times$ that in q given p, by (3).
Similarly degree of belief in $p\bar{q} =$ that in $p \times$ that in $\bar{q}$ given p,
therefore sum $=$ degree of belief in p, by (2).

These are the laws of probability, which we have proved to be necessarily true of any consistent set of degrees of belief. Any definite set of degrees of belief which broke them would be inconsistent in the sense that it violated the laws of preference between options, such as that preferability is a transitive asymmetrical relation, and that if a is preferable to β, β for certain cannot be preferable to a if p, β if not-p. If anyone's mental condition violated these laws, his choice would depend on the precise form in which the options were offered him, which would be absurd. He could have a book made against him by a cunning better and would then stand to lose in any event.

We find, therefore, that a precise account of the nature of partial belief reveals that the laws of probability are laws of consistency, an extension to partial beliefs of formal logic, the logic of consistency. They do not depend for their meaning on any degree of belief in a proposition being uniquely determined as the rational one; they merely distinguish those sets of beliefs which obey them as consistent ones.

Having any definite degree of belief implies a certain measure of consistency, namely willingness to bet on a given proposition at the same odds for any stake, the stakes being measured in terms of ultimate values. Having degrees of belief obeying the laws of probability implies a further measure of consistency, namely such a consistency between the odds acceptable on different propositions as shall prevent a book being made against you.

Some concluding remarks on this section may not be out of place. First, it is based fundamentally on betting, but this will not seem unreasonable when it is seen that all our lives we are in a sense betting. Whenever we go to the station we are betting that a train will really run, and if we had not a sufficient degree of belief in this we should decline the bet and stay at home. The options God gives us are always conditional on our guessing whether a certain proposition is true. Secondly, it is based throughout on the idea of mathematical expectation; the dissatisfaction often felt with this idea is due mainly to the inaccurate measurement of goods. Clearly mathematical expectations in terms of money are not proper guides to conduct. It should be remembered, in judging my system, that in it value is actually defined by means of mathematical expectation in the case of beliefs of degree $\frac{1}{2}$, and so may be expected to be scaled suitably for the valid application of the mathematical expectation in the case of other degrees of belief also.

Thirdly, nothing has been said about degrees of belief when the number of alternatives is infinite. About this I have nothing useful to say, except that I doubt if the mind is capable of contemplating more than a finite number of alternatives. It can consider questions to which an infinite number of answers are possible, but in order to consider the answers it must lump them into a finite number of groups. The difficulty becomes practically relevant when discussing induction, but even then there seems to me no need to introduce it. We can discuss whether past experience gives a high probability to the sun's rising tomorrow without bothering about what probability it gives to the sun's rising each morning for evermore.

Ramsey's proposals for measuring utility and subjective probability were taken up by Davidson, Suppes, and Siegel and subjected to empirical tests in 1957.* They found that it was indeed possible to disentangle the measurement of utility from the measurement of subjective probability by following Ramsey's suggestion and starting with events having a subjective probability of $\frac{1}{2}$. (Not all events known to have an objective probability of $\frac{1}{2}$ are judged to have a subjective probability of $\frac{1}{2}$. In order to create a situation in which people really did not care which event they bet on, Davidson, Suppes, and Siegel used a six-sided die with ZEJ printed on three faces and ZOJ printed on the rest.) Their experimental results were quite encouraging; subjects made their judgments with remarkable consistency and seemed to perform according to the postulates of the theory.

Empirical studies of this sort are becoming increasingly popular among psychologists. So much of life is a gamble, so many decisions must be made under conditions of uncertainty, that the psychological implications of these theories can be made to seem almost as broad as they are precise. The normative aspects still bother some psychologists—surely it is not a law of nature that we must always maximize our subjectively expected utility—but that issue seems of less importance to many younger psychologists. "Let us first specify the underlying regularities in behavior," they seem to say. "We can argue later about whether they are natural laws or not." Viewed from this newer point of view, a far more serious objection stems from the artificiality of the gambling situations that have been used in the experimental laboratory. But now that the measurements are known to be possible in principle, perhaps in the future more realistic procedures will be adopted in practice.

The measurement of utility and of subjective probability form only one chapter in the story of the influence of mathematical economics on mathematical psychology. Another important chap-

---

* D. Davidson, P. Suppes, and S. Siegel, *Decision making.* Stanford, Calif.: Stanford University Press, 1957.

ter was written by John von Neumann and Oskar Morgenstern,* whose work we have already referred to briefly. In their *Theory of Games* Neumann and Morgenstern tried to capture the essential features of conflicting interests. The original work was published by Neumann in the late 1920's, but it stimulated little interest until the jointly authored book appeared in 1944, and the expanded second edition appeared in 1947.

The following selection is an excerpt from a long, enthusiastic review of game theory by Jacob Marschak. In it he presents some of the most important concepts in a form more readily intelligible to the nonmathematician. The review was quite influential; it attracted many new readers to the book and generally helped to introduce game theoretic ideas into the main stream of the social sciences.

* J. von Neumann and O. Morgenstern, *Theory of games and economic behavior,* 2nd ed. Princeton, N.J.: Princeton University Press, 1947.

* * *

Jacob Marschak

Neumann's and Morgenstern's New Approach to Static Economics

A Three-Person Game

Adams has offered his house for sale. Two buyers, Black and Clark, are in the market. Because of alternative uses to which Adams can put his house if unsold, he will not sell it for less than $u = \$9$ thousand. The buyers, Black and Clark, on the other hand, because of the alternative uses to which they can put their

J. Marschak, Neumann's and Morgenstern's new approach to static economics. *J. polit. Econ.,* 1946, 54, 97–107, reprinted by permission of the University of Chicago Press.

money, will not invest in the house more than $v = \$17$ thousand
and $w = \$22$ thousand, respectively. Given these three price
limits (or valuations), what will be the possible outcome of
bargaining?

The answer usually given is this: While it will pay Clark (the
more eager or potent of the two buyers) to offer any price not
exceeding $w = 22$, he has to pay at least $v = 17$ to bid Black out
of the market. Hence the house will be sold to Clark, and its
price will be between $v = 17$ and $w = 22$. (Any such price will
also satisfy seller Adams, since u $< v$.)

This answer is certainly incomplete. Instead of bidding against
his less potent or eager competitor, Clark can pay him a compensation—say $2 thousand—to stay out of the market. Seller
Adams will then have to concede Clark a price below Black's
limit of 17; if the price is depressed below this limit by as much
as, or by more than, the compensation paid to Black, i.e., if the
price is 15 or less, the deal is at least as advantageous to Clark
as what he got in the "free-market" case considered above; and
as long as the prices does not reach the seller's limit of 9, Adams
will also prefer the deal to not selling at all. Thus the outcome—
"Clark pays for the house a sum between 9 and 15 and pays
Black 2"—is as much an answer to our problem as the usual one
—"Clark pays for the house a sum between 17 and 22 and pays
Black 0." Why should there not exist many more such solutions?
In fact, what is meant by a *solution?* To define "solution," two
more elementary concepts must be defined first: "imputation"
and "domination."

Suppose the house is sold at the price $p = 19$ (no compensation paid to Black). The excess of Adams' receipts over his valu-
ation, $p - u = 10$, may be called Adams' gain, a. Correspondingly, the difference $w - p = 3$ can be called Clark's gain, c. As
to Black, his gain is $b = 0$. The triplet (a, b, c) denotes the distribution, or *imputation* of gains; in the particular example just
given the imputation is $(10, 0, 3)$. Denote this particular imputation by the letter I. If the price had been 21 instead of 19, the
imputation would have been $(12, 0, 1)$: call this imputation J.
Now there is no reason to regard the price 19 and the imputation
I which it involves as more admissible than the price 21 and the

imputation J—or vice versa. Buyer Clark naturally prefers I, seller Adams prefers J. But neither of them can enforce the preferred imputation. Hence neither of these imputations discredits, *dominates*, the other one. At the same time, there are obvious imputations dominated by I or J.

Suppose, for example, Adams sells to Black instead of to Clark. The price must then lie between $v = 17$ and $u = 9$. Let it be 11. The resulting imputation is $(2, 6, 0)$—call it K. Compared with I, i.e., with $(10, 0, 3)$, imputation K favors Black but disfavors Adams as well as Clark. Moreover, the latter two, by making a sales contract (i.e., by Adams' deserting Black) can in any case get together 13, i.e., not less than their combined gain in I; whereas Black, for whom K is more favorable, cannot enforce the gain 3 by acting alone, since Adams can always refuse to sell. This illustrates the precise definition of *domination*:

Imputation X *is said to dominate imputation* Y *if some of the participants have separately greater gains in* X *than in* Y *and can, by acting together, enforce* X. The words "enforce X" are equivalent to "secure for themselves a combined gain at least equal to that provided in X."

Apply this concept to the case in which Clark pays Black for staying out. Black's compensation may or may not eat up the extra gain (the difference $v - p$) that Clark draws from his arrangement with Black. If it does, Clark will desert Black and bid for the house in the old fashion. E.g., if Clark has to pay 12 to Adams for the house and 8 to Black for staying out, the resulting imputation is $(3, 8, 2)$—call it L. L is less favorable to Adams, as well as to Clark, than the imputation I—$(10, 0, 3)$; and these two men, by agreeing upon a sales contract at any price p', can always secure for themselves a combined gain $(22 - p') + (p' - 9) = 13$, i.e., as much as the combined gain in I. Therefore, I dominates L: it is more favorable than L to each of the members of a coalition that can enforce I. It is true that to the third man, Black (a one-man coalition, if you will), L is more favorable than I; but he cannot enforce it, since Adams can always refuse to sell.

Suppose, on the other hand, Black's compensation is small enough to make the arrangement worth Clark's while; suppose

Black is contented with a compensation 2 and Clark gets the house for 12. The resulting imputation (3, 2, 8)—call it M—is, unlike L, undominated by I. Nor does M dominate I; although (3, 2, 8) is more favorable than (10, 0, 3) for each of the two buyers, they cannot enforce it, since the seller can always refuse to sell; and, although (10, 0, 3) is more favorable than (3, 2, 8) for the seller, he cannot enforce it, since the buyers' coalition can block the sale, too. The relation between I and M is thus similar to that between I and J. The reader will agree that, to come nearer the solution of our problem, it will be necessary to determine all such situations of indifference, or mutual nondomination, and, therefore, to scrutinize systematically all cases of domination or nondomination between imputations. The precise definition of what should be meant by a "solution" is, to be sure, still ahead of us.

Remember that "domination" implies not only the preferability of one imputation to another from the point of view of some participants (as revealed by their individual gains in the two compared imputations) but also their ability to enforce the preferred imputation. List, therefore, the highest total gains that the various coalitions can secure (one-man coalitions and the all-men coalition are included for the convenience of general treatment): for example, the amount which Adams and Black can secure if acting together is g(Adams, Black) $= u - v = 8$.

The highest gains that various coalitions can secure are shown in the accompanying tabulation.

g(Adams)	0*
g(Black)	0†
g(Clark)	0†
g(Black, Clark)	0†
g(Adams, Black)	$v - u = 8$‡
g(Adams, Clark)	$w - u = 13$§
g(Adams, Black, Clark)	$w - u = 13$‖

* Each buyer can refuse to buy.
† Adams can refuse to sell.
‡ Sale at price p secures $g = (p - u) + (v - p) = v - u$.
§ Sale at price p secures $g = (p - u) + (w - p) = w - u$.
‖ House transfer to Clark gives highest total gain, regardless of money transfers.

We can now consider any triplet of nonnegative numbers and decide whether the imputation it represents does or does not dominate some other imputation. According to the definition, imputation X, (a_X, b_X, c_X), dominates imputation Y, (a_Y, b_Y, c_Y), if and only if either

$$a_X > a_Y, b_X > b_Y, a_X + b_X \leqq g(\text{Adams, Black}) = v - u = 8, \quad (1)$$

or

$$a_X > a_Y, c_X > c_Y, a_X + c_X \leqq g(\text{Adams, Clark}) = w - u = 13, \quad (2)$$

or

$$b_X > b_Y, \quad c_X > c_Y, \quad b_X + c_X \leqq g(\text{Black, Clark}) = 0. \quad (3)$$

Clearly, the condition in equation (3) that $b_X + c_X \leqq 0$ cannot be fulfilled except for a trivial case; hence the Black-Clark coalition and the case (3) need not be considered. The same is true of the one-man coalitions. The table shows further that only triplets adding up exactly to 13 need be considered. Imputations with a sum of gains larger than 13 do not exist, since the three men, even if acting together, cannot secure more than 13; while imputations in which the sum of gains falls short of 13—as was our imputation K—are, of course, dominated by any imputations in which the three men can secure for themselves at least 13.

Our three-person problem can therefore be conveniently treated graphically, using the fact that distances of any point in or on an equilateral triangle always add up to a constant, which is the altitude of the triangle. Figure 1 shows an equilateral triangle of altitude 13 $(= w - u)$. Every point—say, L—in or on the triangle represents an imputation: the point's distance from the (horizontal) basis will measure seller Adams' gain $(a,$ or in this case, $a_L = 3)$, while the distances, respectively, from the left and the right remaining side will measure the gains of the buyers Black $(b,$ or in this case $b_L = 8)$ and Clark $(c,$ or in this case $c_L = 2)$. We recognize on the figure our previous examples:

I: $(10, 0, 3)$; J: $(12, 0, 1)$; L: $(3, 8, 2)$; M: $(3, 2, 8)$

In what follows, the quantities $w - u$, $v - u$, and $w - v$ will be replaced, for brevity, by the numerical values they have in our examples: 13, 8, and 5, respectively. It will be remembered that $a + b + c = 13$. Mark on the left side of the triangle the point D having altitude $a_D = 8$ and draw DE parallel to (and

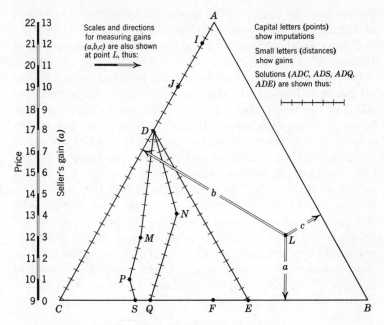

Figure 1. The case of one seller and two buyers.

obviously having distance 5 from) AB. All points in or on the triangle can then be grouped into three regions "M," "I," "L," so named in correspondence to the example-points M, I, L.

Region "M": in or on the small triangle CDE; that is, $c \geqq 5$; hence $a \leqq 8$, $b \leqq 8$, $a + b \leqq 8$.

Region "I": on line AD; that is, $c < 5$, $b = 0$; hence $a > 8$, $a + b > 8$, $a + c = 13$.

Region "L": all other points in or on large triangle ABC; that is, $c < 5$, $b > 0$; hence $a \leqq 8$, $a + b > 8$, $a + c < 13$.

(It is seen that Region "I" covers all cases when Clark bids against Black; in Region "M," Clark pays Black a compensation small enough to be profitable for Clark; in Region "L," Black's compensation makes the deal unprofitable for Clark in comparison with some case of Region "I.")

Applying the domination criteria (1) and (2) above, we find

that no point of Region "I" is dominated by any point; no point of Region "M" is dominated by points of Regions "I" or "L"; and every point of Region "L" is dominated by some points of Region "I."

One might be tempted to declare the following as a solution: all points of Regions "I" and "M," that is, the whole length of AD and the whole area CDE (including its boundary). This, however, is not satisfactory. Points of Region "M" are related to each other in a way different from the way in which the points of Region "I" are related to each other and to those of Region "M." For example, the two points M $(3, 2, 8)$ and N $(4, 3, 6)$ both belong to Region "M," as seen on the figure. But point M is dominated by point N because $a_N > a_M$, $b_N > b_M$, and $a_N + b_N \leqq 8$, i.e., criterion (1) above is satisfied. Therefore, they cannot belong to the same solution. Imputations I, J, and M belong to one solution, while imputations I, J, and N belong to another. Each solution corresponds to a different *accepted standard of behavior*. Thus each accepted standard of behavior restricts the choice of admissible imputations to one set of imputations called "solution."

The "solution" concept is perhaps best understood if we first define those imputations which are *not* elements of a given solution: *An imputation is not an element of a given solution if and only if it is dominated by some element of the solution.* (Thus point N does not belong in the solution which includes points I, J, M; and point M does not belong in the solution which includes points I, J, and N.) Or, in positive phrasing: The elements of a given solution are those and only those imputations which are undominated by any element of it.

It can be shown that any solution—in the sense just defined —of our problem consists of two parts: (α) the straight-line segment AD and (β) a curve going downward from D in a direction never deviating from the vertical by more than $30°$ ($DMPS$ and DNQ are such curves; also the straight lines DC and DE). In nongeometrical terms, part of α consists of imputations in which Black gets 0, Clark gets 5 or less, and Adams gets 8 or more; part β consists of imputations in which Clark gets 5 or more and neither Adams nor Black gets more than 8. Furthermore, seller

Adams' gain is not the same in any two imputations within the same solution; and a larger gain of seller Adams is always accompanied by a smaller gain of one buyer and a smaller or equal gain of the other buyer (i.e., b and c are nonincreasing functions of a).

Thus, while part a is common to all solutions, part β varies according to the "accepted standard of behavior" which sets the rule of allocation between the two buyers. The two parts a and β form a continuous range of imputations, each implying a different price paid to Adams (between 0 and 13) and a different compensation paid to Black (between 0 and 8). The continuous range of imputations covered by part a has been well known to economists; the present result consists in extending the range to β and showing that this can be done in an infinite number of ways, unless the "accepted standard of behavior" is given.

The causes which make the bargainers Adams and Clark stop at one particluar imputation out of one set a of equally admissible imputations have usually been regarded as beyond the economist's reach. This indeterminateness is now extended by one degree of freedom, since more than one such set has been shown to exist (e.g., the lines $ADMPS$, $ADNQ$, ADC, ADE, etc.). As is usually the case, the empirical interpretation is not so clear cut as are the formal propositions. There is no ambiguity in distinguishing between the determination of a set of solutions, the determination of a single solution within this set, and the determination of a single imputation within the chosen solution. The rules from which the first kind of determination is deduced are given the name of "rules of the game"; the second (and presumably the third) kind of determination is assigned by the authors to "accepted standards of behavior." In the empirical interpretation of these words, the "rules of the game" seem to be thought of as having a greater constancy than the "standards of behavior." The latter are vaguely identified with legal or moral codes to which the people adhere for expediency considerations; while the "rules of the game" might possibly include the physical conditions and psychological habits of individual behavior. Thus the actual stability of economic situations (where it exists) can be explained partly by appealing to the stability of legal and moral codes, which need not be further specified by the theorist, and partly by properly specifying physical and psychological data, such as differences in individual intelligence or sensitivity.

A Two-Person Game

One of the steps necessary to obtain the results of the preceding section was to state for each possible coalition the maximum amount, g, which it can enforce (see tabulation on p. 81). This amount is called *the value of the game* to the given coalition. In the case treated in the preceding section it was possible to establish it somewhat intuitively. In general, a more detailed and rigorous analysis is required.

One can consider each coalition as if it were a single person trying to maximize his gain but restricted by the similar desire of other persons. In determining the maximum gain which a coalition of certain persons can secure for itself in spite of any action of the remaining ones, one has to remember that the members of the coalition cannot prevent the other persons from forming a countercoalition, which may depress the gains of the first coalition. Therefore, the value of the game to the first coalition must be calculated under the assumption that it faces the worst, viz., a countercoalition of the remaining persons. The problem is thus reduced to a *two-person game*.

We might thus think, say, of bilateral monopoly as a case most suitable for this basic analysis. It is, however, not the simplest one because it is not a *zero-sum game*. In a two-person zero-sum game, the positive gain of one player equals the loss (negative gain) of the other. Such are many ordinary games. In economics, however, the aggregate of all players may lose or win (e.g., by producing output in excess of input, or—as in our [previous section]—by transferring goods between persons who assign them different values). Hence the necessity to consider *general games*, i.e., games in which the gains may or may not add up to zero. These can be reduced to zero-sum games if a *fictitious player* (called "Nature," if you like) is introduced: he wins or loses what the real players lose or win in the aggregate, but he is unable to control his gains either by joining coalitions or by otherwise choosing most advantageous decisions. In a simple case like the one of [the previous section], direct treatment of a nonzero game was not difficult. In general, however, the device of reduction to a zero game has to be used: an n-person general game is treated as a special sort of $(n + 1)$-person zero game, the $(n + 1)$th person being a fictitious one. (This is one of many devices used in the book to strip every problem to its essentials. It is with the help of such devices that the authors free themselves from the accident of empirical occurrence and are able to give general analysis.)

Having thus simplified the problem down to a zero-sum two-person game, the question has to be answered as to how the value of the game for each of the two players—A and B—can be determined. What is the maximum gain each of them can enforce?

A's gain depends on (1) A's decision—call it x, and (2) B's decision—call it y. Or, symbolically, A's gain $= f(x, y)$. In principle, all possible decisions can be enumerated, and thus x and y can be regarded as variables, and $f(x, y)$ as their function, in the usual sense. Geometrically, $f(x,y)$ can be represented as the altitude of a point on a map of the United States, the point having latitude x and longitude y. Player A wants to make altitude f as large as possible. But he knows that for any x he chooses, his opponent B—if B is a good player—will choose a y such as to make altitude f as small as is compatible with the chosen x. Player A knows that for the case in which he chooses 40° latitude, B has prepared himself to choose the longitude of the dip formed by the Mississippi River; and that if A names 45°, B will choose the longitude of the Great Lakes dip. A's best policy is therefore to name a latitude such that even the lowest point on it is higher than the lowest point on any other latitude. The resulting altitude, say, $g_A(A)$ equals $\text{Max}_x \text{Min}_y f(x, y)$: this expresses the fact that the function f is first minimized with respect to y (B's choice), then maximized with respect to x (A's choice)—where the words "first" and "then" mean merely the sequence of mathematical operations and do not at all mean that B's action precedes A's action in time.

Consider now the best policy for B: he will name a longitude such that even the highest point on it is lower than the highest point on any other latitude. The resulting altitude—say $g_B(A)$

equals $\text{Min}_y \ \text{Max}_x f(x, y)$: the function f is first maximized with respect to x, then minimized with respect to y. Assuming that B is a good player, $g_A(A)$ is the highest gain A can hope for; and assuming that A is a good player, $g_B(A)$ is the smallest gain (or largest loss) for A that B can hope for. Now it may happen that the values x and y, which make A's gain assume the value $g_A(A)$, coincide with those that make A's gain assume the value $g_B(A)$, i.e., that it does not matter whether f is first minimized with respect to y and then maximized with respect to x, or whether the two operations are reversed in order. In this case the surface $f(x, y)$ is said to have a *saddle-point* (think of a mountain pass, i.e., the lowest point of a ridge!). But, in general, such a point need not exist. Hence, in general, A and B will not agree upon an imputation that will express each man's best policy. There will be no unique equilibrium position.

To reconcile this result with the empirical fact that, in ordinary human affairs, equilibrium does, on the whole, exist, various changes in the postulates can be made. One is to change the rules of the game which serves as a model. For example, in the two-person zero-sum game, the rule may be added that while (as before) A has to make his decision in ignorance of what B has decided, B has full knowledge of what A decides. The quantities $g_A(A)$ and $g_B(A)$ will then both be equal to $\text{Max}_x \ \text{Min}_y f(x, y)$. Thus the outcome of the game is now determinate. Similarly, if the added rule of the game is that A knows B's decision while B is ignorant of what A decides, the outcome is also determinate: the resulting quantities $g_A(A)$ and $g_B(A)$ are both equal to $\text{Min}_y \ \text{Max}_x f(x, y)$. Furthermore, it is intuitively plausible that the player who has "found out" his adversary is at an advantage. This is confirmed mathematically by the easy theorem that $\text{Max}_x \ \text{Min}_y f(x, y)$ can never be larger than $\text{Min}_y \ \text{Max}_x f(x, y)$. Finally, it seems to us that properly stated differences in degrees of knowledge or intelligence of individual players can also be regarded as rules of the game.

However, the authors do not choose to invoke this possibility. They maintain the assumption that all players have the same capacity to draw inferences from given information. To be sure, the concept of information is defined exactly, and the possibility for a player to control the information available to other players ("signals" and "bluffing" in card games) is studied in its many interesting implications. But it is never assumed that, given the same external circumstances, one player may act differently from another (an interesting exception will be noted later and will refer not to "intelligence" but to "discernment").

Instead, the authors make the two-person zero-sum game determinate by introducing the concept of *mixed* or *statistical strategy*. One might also call it "randomized" strategy because of its analogy to techniques applied in designing an experiment. Each player, instead of choosing a single action, chooses a set of probabilities (a "probability distribution"), attaching a probability to each possible action. He will act at random, guided by the probability distribution he has chosen. For example, if there are three alternative actions, he may attach to them, respectively, the probabilities $\frac{3}{6}$, $\frac{2}{6}$, $\frac{1}{6}$ or $\frac{4}{6}$, $\frac{1}{6}$, $\frac{1}{6}$, etc. Suppose he chooses the first of these probability distributions. He arranges, then, that if, on throwing dice, he gets 1 or 2 or 3 dots, he chooses the first action; if he gets 4 or 5 dots, the second action; if 6 dots, the third. Accordingly, not the value of a single play for player A but the *long-run value of the game* for player A is considered—not a function of two single decisions x and y of the two opponents but the mathematical expectation of this function. This expectation obviously depends on the two probability distributions—say, p_x and p_y—chosen by the two players. Altitude, latitude, and longitude of a previous illustration now acquire changed meanings; altitude now means the mathematical expectation of A's gain, latitude and longitude now mean not two single numbers but the two probability distributions p_x and p_y chosen by the two players. It is then proved that in this case a saddle-point will always exist.

* * *

The theory of games was the first example of an elaborate *mathematical* development centered solely in the social sciences, clearly a remarkable achievement. This review by Marschak succeeds in communicating some of the general concepts of game theory, but it could scarcely do justice to the mathematical depth and rigor of the original presentation. Although social scientists soon began to apply game theory to their empirical problems,* the initial impact of the theory was in applied mathematics, especially in mathematical statistics.

Abraham Wald, who originated statistical decision theory,† pointed out the striking similarity between the structure of a two-person, zero-sum game and the structure of the decision problem in statistics. The experimenter (or statistician) is one player and nature is the other. The scientist has a choice of observations he can make; nature has a "choice" as to what her true state will be. The value of his research will depend on both his choice and the true state of nature. On the basis of this analogy Wald proposed that a scientist should use a minimax strategy in deciding what observations to make. That is to say, he should perform those experiments that would minimize his maximum loss. Statistical decision theory would thus appear to be a modern formulation of the ancient problem of inductive logic.

A minimax strategy, however, assumes that the opponent is another person who is also intelligent and also striving to minimize his own maximum loss. Some theorists have felt that Wald was being too cautious, that nature is not a malignant force opposing the scientist. Consequently, a variety of alternative solutions have been proposed for the scientific game against nature. Each of these proposals has certain features that recommend it, each is "rational" in its own special way, but no one solution seems clearly superior to all the others. And so we have a mathematical demonstration—if one were necessary—that the normative problem of selecting the best course of action does not always have a unique solution.

The effect of statistical decision theory on psychological re-

* See M. Shubik, *Strategy and market structures: Competition, oligopoly, and the theory of games.* New York: Wiley, 1959. See also S. Siegel and L. E. Fouraker, *Bargaining and group decision making,* New York: McGraw-Hill, 1960. For an excellent survey, see R. D. Luce and H. Raiffa, *Games and decisions,* New York: Wiley, 1957.

† A. Wald, *Statistical decision functions.* New York: Wiley, 1950.

search may be to deflect some of the psychologist's energies away from the problem of prediction. For example, when a psychological test is given to a person, what should be done with the results? Should they be used to predict his future behavior? Or should they be used as a basis for deciding what he should do, or what should be done to him? The prediction problem has been the traditional one. But some psychologists are beginning to feel that the decision problem is more realistic; they propose to modify the statistical techniques that psychologists use in such a way as to take advantage of these new advances in the theoretical foundations of mathematical statistics.*

These ideas promise to enrich psychology on at least two levels. They provide a way to describe what people are trying to do when they make decisions under uncertainty. But the psychologist also must make such decisions about his own research. It is gratifying to have a theory that describes the behavior of the theorist as well as that of his guinea pigs.

* R. M. Thrall, C. H. Coombs, and R. L. Davis, *Decision processes*. New York: Wiley, 1954. L. J. Cronbach and P. C. Gleser, *Psychological tests and personnel decisions*. Urbana: University of Illinois Press, 1957.

4

Functional Applications:
Determinate

In everyday usage the function of something is ordinarily understood to be its normal and expected mode of operation. In this sense we speak of the function of an executive, or the function of a carburetor, and so on. It is in this sense that biologists distinguish between physiology and anatomy, one studying the functions and the other the structure of different organ systems. And it is also in this sense that an American school of psychologists, following the pragmatic tradition of William James and John Dewey, called themselves functionalists because they studied the functions, rather than the content or structure of the mind.

In mathematical usage, however, a function is defined quite differently. Originally the term was introduced by mathematicians to indicate rather generally any dependence between two numerical quantities. The notation $y = f(x)$ was understood to mean that there was a rule f whereby you could calculate the value of y if you knew the value of x. In modern mathematics this definition has been generalized to any biunique relation between two sets of elements, such that for every element of set X there is at most one element of set Y related to it. In this modern sense, "is a son of" is a function relating the set of all sons to the set of all fathers—or, since fathers are themselves sons, mapping the set of all males into a subset of itself.

These two usages can become a bit confounded when functional psychologists start to use mathematical functions. It is not always easy to keep clearly in mind the difference between such statements as, "The function of behavior is to adapt the organism to its environment," and "Behavior is a function of environmental stimulation." But confusion at this discursive level is probably harmless. When the mathematical definition is seriously invoked, there is little chance of mistaking it.

For many years psychologists looked toward physics as their paradigm of what a successful science should be. This tradition led early psychologists to concentrate on experimental methods and on the expression of laws in the form of mathematical functions, both of which had been marvelously successful in the physical sciences. And, at first, these tactics seemed to work equally well in psychology, especially when Fechner (a physicist) used them to describe a functional relation between sensory magnitudes and the intensity of the stimulating energy, or when Helmholtz (a physicist and physiologist) used them to describe visual and auditory experience, and so on. As our first example of this use of mathematics in psychology, therefore, we shall consider briefly some of the history of that psychological subscience called psychophysics, the branch of psychology whose central concern is to measure psychological magnitudes of sensation as a function—a mathematical function—of physical magnitudes of stimulation.

In 1834, as part of a Latin monograph on the pulse, absorption, hearing, and touch, the German physiologist E. H. Weber noted that, "In comparing objects and observing the distinction between them, we perceive not the difference between the objects, but the ratio of this difference to the magnitude of the objects compared."* It is not the absolute, but the relative size of the difference that is important. A difference that is very obvious at a low level may be imperceptible at a high level of stimulation; at night a car's headlights illumine the whole road, but in broad daylight the driver will not even notice that they are turned on. Although the relativity of such perceptual judgments had been

* Quoted from E. B. Titchener's translation in B. Rand, *The classical psychologists*. Boston: Houghton Mifflin, 1912.

appreciated long before Weber commented on it*, today we remember this important principle as "Weber's Law." The reason Weber's name was remembered while others were forgotten is that Weber's work was more familiar to the man who created psychophysics, G. T. Fechner.

The evidence on which Weber's law rested was obtained in experimental studies of the smallest change in stimulation that was just barely noticeable (the just noticeable difference, or jnd). Weber claimed that an increment of one part in thirty was necessary before a change in weight could be detected, and, most important, this fraction was supposed to be constant regardless of whether light or heavy weights were involved. Similar results were obtained for other types of sensory differences, although with different fractions.

It was on this foundation that Fechner was to construct the science of psychophysics, a science where mathematics was to be exploited more consistently and more efficiently than anywhere else in psychology. Fechner assumed that all jnds must be subjectively equal, since they were all equally noticeable, and so could be used as units of measurement for the subjective magnitude of sensations.

The heart of Fechner's argument is contained in the following short excerpt from his famous text, *Elemente der Psychophysik*, published originally in 1860.

* G. S. Fullerton and J. McK. Cattell, On the perception of small differences. *Publ. University of Pennsylvania, Philosophy Series*, No. 2, 1892.

Gustav Theodor Fechner

The Fundamental Formula and the Measurement Formula

Although not as yet having a measurement for sensation, still one can combine in an exact formula the relation expressed in Weber's law—that the sensation difference remains constant when the relative stimulus difference remains constant—with the law, established by the mathematical auxiliary principle, that small sensation increments are proportional to stimulus increments. Let us suppose, as has generally been done in the attempts to preserve Weber's law, that the difference between two stimuli, or, what is the same, the increase in one stimulus, is very small in proportion to the stimulus itself. Let the stimulus which is increased be called β, the small increase $d\beta$, where the letter d is to be considered not as a special magnitude, but simply as a sign that $d\beta$ is the small increment of β. This already suggests the differential sign. The relative stimulus increase therefore is $d\beta/\beta$. On the other hand, let the sensation which is dependent upon the stimulus be called γ, and let the small increment of the sensation which results from the increase of the stimulus by $d\beta$ be called $d\gamma$, where d again simply expresses the small increment. The terms $d\beta$ and $d\gamma$ are each to be considered as referring to an arbitrary unit of their own nature.

According to the empirical Weber's law, $d\gamma$ remains constant when $d\beta/\beta$ remains constant, no matter what absolute values $d\beta$ and β take; and according to the a priori mathematical auxiliary principle the changes $d\gamma$ and $d\beta$ remain proportional to one another so long as they remain very small. The two relations may

G. T. Fechner, Elements of psychophysics, transl. by H. S. Langfeld. In B. Rand, *The classical psychologists*. Boston: Houghton Mifflin, 1912, pp. 562–572. Pp. 565–569 reprinted by permission of Houghton Mifflin Co.

be expressed together in the following equation: $d\gamma = \kappa d/\beta/\beta$ where κ is a constant (dependent upon the units selected for γ and β). In fact, if one multiplies βd and β by any number, so long as it is the same number for both, the proportion remains constant, and with it also the sensation difference $d\gamma$. This is Weber's law. If one doubles or triples the value of the variation $d\beta$ without changing the initial value β, then the value of the change $d\gamma$ is also doubled or tripled. This is the mathematical principle. The equation $d\gamma = \kappa d\beta/\beta$ therefore entirely satisfies both Weber's law and this principle; and no other equation satisfies both together. This is to be called the *fundamental formula,* in that the deduction of all consequent formulas will be based upon it.

The fundamental formula does not presuppose the measurement of sensation, nor does it establish any; it simply expresses the relation holding between small relative stimulus increments and sensations increments. In short, it is nothing more than Weber's law and the mathematical auxiliary principle united and expressed in mathematical symbols.

There is, however, another formula connected with this formula by infinitesimal calculus, which expresses a general quantitative relation between the stimulus magnitude as a summation of stimulus increments, and the sensation magnitude as a summation of sensation increments, in such a way, that with the validity of the first formula, together with the assumption of the fact of limen, the validity of this latter formula is also given.

Reserving for the future a more exact deduction, I shall attempt first to make clear in a general way the connection of the two formulas.

One can readily see, that the relation between the increments $d\gamma$ and $d\beta$ in the fundamental formula corresponds to the relation between the increments of a logarithm and the increments of the corresponding number. For as one can easily convince oneself, either from theory or from the table, the logarithm does not increase by equal increments when the corresponding number increases by equal increments, but rather when the latter increases by equal amounts; in other words, the increases in the logarithms remain equal, when the relative increases of the numbers remain equal. Thus, for example, the following numbers and logarithms belong together:

Number	Logarithm
10	1.000000
11	1.0413927
100	2.000000
110	2.0413927
1000	3.000000
1100	3.0413927

where an increase of the number 10 by 1 brings with it just as great an increase in the corresponding logarithm, as the increase of the number 100 by 10 or 1000 by 100. In each instance the increases in the logarithm is 0.0413927. Further, as was already shown in explaining the mathematical auxiliary principle, the increases in the logarithms are proportional to the increases of the numbers, so long as they remain very small. Therefore one can say, that Weber's law and the mathematical auxiliary principle are just as valid for the increases of logarithms and numbers in their relation to one another, as they are for the increases of sensation and stimulus.

The fact of the threshold appears just as much in the relation of a logarithm to its number as in the relation of sensation to stimulus. The sensation begins with values above zero, not with zero, but with a finite value of the stimulus—the threshold; and so does the logarithm begin with values above zero, not with a zero value of the number, but with a finite value of the number, the value 1, inasmuch as the logarithm of 1 is equal to zero.

If now, as was shown above, the increase of sensation and stimulus stands in a relation similar to that of the increase of logarithm and number, and, the point at which the sensation begins to assume a noticeable value stands in a relation to the stimulus similar to that which the point at which the logarithm attains positive value stands to the number, then one may also expect that sensation and stimulus themselves stand in a relation to one another similar to that of logarithm to number, which, just as the former (sensation and stimulus) may be regarded as made up of a sum of successive increments.

Accordingly the simplest relation between the two that we can write is $\gamma = \log \beta$.

In fact it will soon be shown that, provided suitable units of sensation and stimulus are chosen, the functional relation between both reduces to this very simple formula. Meanwhile it is not the most general formula that can be derived, but one which is only valid under the supposition of particular units of sensation and stimulus, and we still need a direct and absolute deduction instead of the indirect and approximate one.

The specialist sees at once how this may be attained, namely, by treating the fundamental formula as a differential formula and integrating it. In the following chapter one will find this done. Here it must be supposed already carried out, and those who are not able to follow the simple infinitesimal deduction, must be asked to consider the result as a mathematical fact. This result is the following functional formula between stimulus and sensation, which goes by the name of the measurement formula and will not be further discussed:

$$\gamma = \kappa \ (\log \beta - \log b)$$

In this formula κ again stands for a constant, dependent upon the unit selected and also the logarithmic system, and a second constant which stands for the threshold value of the stimulus, at which the sensation γ begins and disappears.

According to the rule, that the logarithm of a quotient of two numbers may be substituted for the difference of their logarithms, . . . one can substitute for the above form of the measurement formula the following, which is more convenient for making deductions: $\gamma = \kappa \ \log \beta/b$. From this equation it follows that the sensation magnitude γ is not to be considered as a simple function of the stimulus value β, but of its relation to the threshold value b, where the sensation begins and disappears. The relative stimulus value, β/b is for the future to be called the fundamental stimulus value, or the fundamental value of the stimulus.

Translated in words, the measurement formula reads:

The magnitude of the sensation (γ) is not proportional to the absolute value of the stimulus (β), but rather to the logarithm of the magnitude of the stimulus, when this last is expressed in terms of its threshold value (b), i.e. that magnitude considered as unit at which the sensation begins and disappears. In short, it is proportional to the logarithm of the fundamental stimulus value.

* * *

An attentive reader will hear echoes of Herbart in this discussion of thresholds and fluctuating magnitudes of sensation; and he will recognize that Fechner's Law relating subjective sensation to objective stimulation is exactly the same as D. Bernoulli's Law relating subjective utility to objective money. But Fechner's Law was immediately strengthened by his proposals for psychometric methods of measurement, whereas methods for measuring the subjective magnitudes that Bernoulli was talking about were not developed until the middle of the twentieth century. A theory is good, but a theory plus measurements is a great deal better.

It should probably be pointed out that today Weber's Law is generally stated as

$$\frac{d\beta}{\beta} = \text{constant.}$$

By restating it in the form

$$d\gamma = k \frac{d\beta}{\beta},$$

Fechner introduced the assumption that the change in sensation $d\gamma$ was equal for all jnds. It was this assumption from which his logarithmic function derived, and which is now generally called Fechner's Law.

Fechner's ideas were not accepted without resistance, however. The objections were numerous and often highly technical; we will mention here only one of several arguments that Fechner had to defend himself against.

As early as the 1850's the Belgian physicist J. A. F. Plateau,*

---

* J. A. F. Plateau, Sur la mesure des sensations physiques, et sur la loi qui lie l'intensité de ces sensations à l'intensité de la cause excitante. *Bull. Acad. roy. Belg.*, 1872, **33** (Ser. 2), 376–388.

a student of light and optics, noted that the apparent brightness
relations in a painting tend to remain constant over a wide range
of ambient illuminations. Changing the ambient illumination
changes the absolute levels, of course, but not the relative levels
of stimulation; if you keep the objective ratios constant, then
over a wide range of illuminations, the subjective ratios appear
constant, too. On this basis he proposed that the subjective ratios
must be proportional to the objective ratios in the stimulus.
Plateau's conjecture implied that the law should be

$$\frac{d\gamma}{\gamma} = k \frac{d\beta}{\beta}.$$

That is to say, whereas Fechner assumed that all jnds represent
constant *differences* in sensation, Plateau's hypothesis implied
that they represent constant *ratios* in sensation. In 1874 the phil-
osophical psychologist F. Brentano* advanced the same idea in
a more explicit form.

Fechner, however, showed that the constant-ratio hypothesis
led not to the logarithmic function that he had derived from
Weber's Law, but rather to a power function of the general form

$$\gamma = k \, \beta^n,$$

and he vehemently rejected it for that reason. The difference between these rival hypotheses was not easily submitted to experimental test, but Fechner, by virtue of his vigorous and persuasive
defense, eventually managed to carry the day. The logarithmic
law became widely known and generally accepted by most workers interested in sensory psychology.

And so Fechner's psychophysical adventures prospered during
the early days of the "new" (that is, experimental) psychology.
In 1905 when E. B. Titchener published his authoritative and
highly respected texts in experimental psychology, Fechner's
ideas held a prominent position. The following excerpt from
Titchener, which summarizes the Fechnerian argument in a brief
but lucid form, was studied scrupulously by a whole generation
of experimental psychologists.

* F. Brentano, *Psychologie vom empirischen Standpunkt.* Leipzig: Dunker
& Hunbolt, 1874.

Edward Bradford Titchener

Fechner's Psychophysics

If Weber laid the foundation stone of experimental psychology, Gustav Theodor Fechner (1801–1887) may be said to have planned, and in large measure to have erected, a whole building. His work covers a period of full fifty years, from the after-image investigations of 1838 to the Psychische Massprincipien of 1887. We are here concerned only with its quantitative side, i.e., with the writings which led up to and grew out of the *Elemente der Psychophysik* (1860: reprinted under Wundt's auspices, with notes and bibliography, 1889).

It was on the 22d Oct., 1850, Fechner tells us, as he lay awake in bed before getting up, that the thought came to him of "making the relative increase of bodily energy the measure of the increase of the corresponding mental intensity." The general idea of measuring the intensity of mental activity in terms of the underlying physical activity had long occupied him, but had hitherto led to no fruitful result. The new thought was definite; it gave him a starting point; thrown into mathematical form, it even gave him two formulae which later on play a large part in the *Elemente*. But it did not, of course, give him any measure of sensation. The stimuli could be measured; their precise correlation with sensation was a matter of hypothesis. The only thing to do, in default of a sensation measure, was to assume the correctness of the rule, and to put it to empirical test under conditions where measurement was not needed: e.g., in the observation of simple increase or decrease of sense intensity, of extremes of sensation, of sensations of equal intensity. Fechner therefore con-

E. B. Titchener, *Experimental psychology: A manual of laboratory practice.* Vol. 2, Part 2, Instructor's Manual. New York: Macmillan, 1905, pp. xx–xxix.

tented himself, for the time being, with a brief mention of his new ideas in the *Zend-Avesta* (1851)—a work which, as he gravely remarks, "does not pretend to the character of exact research."

The exact research followed, in the shape of the classical experiments on brightness and lifted weights, on visual and tactual distances, in many of which Fechner was loyally assisted by A. W. Volkmann. While these were in progress, he lighted upon Weber's generalisation, and his own principle forthwith became Weber's Law. Confirmation of the law was sought—and found—in various places: notably in the astronomical classification of the fixed stars by visible magnitude. The fact of the limen, "a datum of everyday experience which has attracted little observation, but on which the whole of the night side of mind depends," supplied the last link in the chain of mathematical reasoning. Last, not least, the three psychophysical metric methods, of just noticeable differences, of right and wrong cases, and of average error, were worked out with such care and subtlety as to raise psychology, once and for all, to the dignity of an experimental science.

Of all this work we hear nothing until 1858, when Fechner published a paper on mental measurement, a sort of author's review of the forthcoming *Elemente*. In 1859 appeared a detailed inquiry into the validity of the law in the sphere of visual intensity, which furnished material for the discussion in ch. ix. of the *Elemente*. Finally, in 1860, came the *Psychophysik* itself. We must devote some little space to its analysis.

Fechner defines Psychophysics as "an exact science of the functional relations or relations of dependency between body and mind." Its sphere is thus as wide as the sphere of psychology; there will be a psychophysics of sensation, of perception, of feeling, of action, of attention, etc. In the present state of our knowledge, however, it will be wise for us to occupy ourselves primarily with sensations, which we may classify as intensive and extensive. All sensations possess magnitude and form, termed in the intensive domain "intensity" and "quality." We shall be concerned chiefly with their magnitude.

The first step in psychophysical metrics is the establishment of the metric principle of sensitivity. Sensitivity is a special form of organic irritability or excitability, the organism's capacity of response to stimulation; it may be defined as the degree of correspondence between sensation and adequate stimulus. "One and the same stimulus may, even if applied in the same manner, be sensed more or less strongly by one observer or one organ than by another, or by the same observer or organ at different times; and, contrariwise, stimuli of different magnitude may, under certain circumstances, be sensed equally strongly. We then attribute to the one observer or organ, or to the single observer or organ at one time, a greater or less sensitivity than to the other, or to the same at another time." Now we can measure stimuli; and we are perfectly well able to say whether two given sensations are "equal" or "alike." Hence we can measure sensitivity: it is inversely proportional to the magnitude of the stimuli which arouse sensations of equal magnitude. Suppose that you can just sense a pressure of 2 gr. at a certain part of the skin, and that I, at the corresponding part, can sense nothing below 4 gr.; then your sensitivity is twice as great as mine. Suppose that (as Weber found) a pressure of 1.5 oz. on the lips is equal to a pressure of 4 oz. on the forehead; the sensitivities of the two parts stand to one another in the ratio 8:3. It must be understood that, in "measuring sensitivity," we are always measuring stimuli, not sensation; we determine what stimuli (or stimulus differences) arouse sensations (or sensation differences) of equal magnitude. And it is clear that "the measure of sensitivity, as a measure of mere capacity of sensation, is not to be confused with a measure of sensation itself. Nor does it presuppose any such measure, but only the observation of instances of equal sensations, under like or different conditions of stimulation." . . .

"Since sensitivity is a variable matter, we have not to measure it as we should measure a constant; but we can seek to determine (1) its extreme and (2) its mean values; we can investigate (3) the dependency of its changes upon circumstances; and we can (4) make search for laws which hold throughout its variations. These laws are the most important thing."

Our measurement of sensitivity is a necessary first step, but still only a first step, towards the measurement of sensation.

"The possibility of establishing the equality of small differences of sensation, or small increments of sensation, under changed conditions of stimulation, is the main prerequisite of measurement," but does not guarantee measurement. To measure sensation we must be able to say, not only that our present pain is much more severe than our pain of yesterday, not only that the illumination of two rooms is sensibly the same, but that our pain is 2, 3, 4, . . . times as great as the previous pain, that the brightness of the light is 10, 15, 20, . . . times as great as that of the brightness unit. And we must be able to say this in terms of sensation itself, not merely in terms of the stimulus which arouses sensation. How are we to arrive at exact statements of this kind?

"The difference between two R-magnitudes may always be considered as a positive or negative increment of the one or the other R-magnitude; and a total R may be regarded, mathematically, as made up by positive increments from zero, increment being constantly added to the sum of former increments, until the full R is present.* In the same way, a sensation difference may be considered, mathematically, as positive or negative increment of the one or the other sensation, and a total sensation may be regarded as made up of positive increments from zero to its full intensity. If we know the functional relation between the sum of the R-increments from zero onwards, and the sum of the corresponding S-increments, we have it *eo ipso* for the total R and the S which the R releases." We may, then, get over the difficulty of sense measurement by "having recourse to the relation between the elementary increments out of which we may regard the R and S as built; this requires no measurement of sensation, but only . . . a judgment of the equality of S-differences or S-increments which correspond to given, measurable, variable R-increments; from it we derive the functional relation of the sums of the increments, and thus obtain the measure of S in terms of the measured R." We mark off an S-magnitude in units of its own kind; that is essential to measurement; but the scale which we lay upon the S-magnitude is physical, an R-scale. "In principle, therefore, our measurement of S comes to this: that we split up every S into equal divisions, *i.e.*, the equal increments out of

* [Editor's note: R = stimulus, S = sensation.]

which it is built up from the zero-point of its existence, and consider the number of these equal divisions to be determined (as if by the inches of a yard-stick) by the corresponding variable *R*-increments which can produce the equal *S*-increments. . . . We determine the magnitude of the *S*, which we cannot determine directly, as a multiple of the equal parts which we can determine directly; but we read off the number of parts not from the *S*, but from the *R* which brings the *S* with it, and which can be more easily read." . . .

It is a fact of everyday experience that the increase of a given *R* which shall effect a noticeable change of the corresponding *S* depends on the magnitude which *R* has already attained: the stars give no light in the daytime, but give a good deal of light on a moonless night. Weber found that this increase of *R*, expressed as a fraction of the total *R*, remains approximately constant over a wide range of absolute *R*-intensities. This, so far as Weber himself is concerned, is Weber's Law: this and nothing more. Fechner treats the facts on the hypotheses (1) that the *S*, as a magnitude, may be regarded as a sum of *S*-units; (2) that, in investigations which aim at the determination of the j. n. d., these units are conveniently given in the j. n. d. themselves, which as "sensed differences" or "difference sensations" are equal at all parts of the *R*-scale; and (3) that Weber's Law may be transferred from the sphere of "sensed differences" to that of "differences of sensation." On these assumptions mathematical treatment becomes possible.

Let *R* be the original stimulus, and *dR* a small increment of *R*,—the *d* not standing for any particular magnitude, but simply indicating that the increment *dR* is very small: cf. its use as the sign of differentiation. Then the relative *R*-increase is dR/R. In the same way, let *S* be the sensation corresponding to *R*, and *dS* the *S*-increment corresponding to *dR*. We need a formula which shall satisfy (*a*) the requirement of Weber's Law, that *dS* remains constant so long as dR/R is constant, and (*b*) the mathematical requirement that *dS* and *dR* vary proportionally so long as they are very small. The formula is:

$$d\,S = c\,\frac{dR}{R}$$

where c is a constant, depending on the unit-values chosen for S and R. This is the *fundamental formula* of mental measurement.

From the fundamental formula, together with the fact of the stimulus limen, a second formula may be derived, which "expresses a general quantitative relation between the R-magnitude, summed from R-increments, and the S-magnitude, summed from S-increments." Consider the fundamental formula as a differential equation, and integrate. Then:

$$S = c \ log. \ nat. \ R + C,$$

where C is the constant of integration. Now introduce the limen; i.e., the determination that S vanishes when R has the liminal value r. The formula becomes:

$$0 = c \ log. \ nat. \ r + C$$

in other words:

$$C = -c \ log. \ nat. \ r$$

and therefore:

$$S = c \ (log. \ nat. \ R - log. \ nat. \ r).$$

Translating into the language of common logarithms, we have:

$$S = k \ (log. \ R - log. \ r)$$

in other words:

$$S = k \ log. \ \frac{R}{r}$$

where k is a constant including the modulus of the common system. If we make r, the liminal stimulus value, $= 1$, we may write:

$$S = k \ log. \ R,$$

the form in which the metric formula, as Fechner terms it, usually appears in the text-books. Put into words the formula reads: "the magnitude of sensation (S) stands in relation not to the absolute magnitude of stimulus (R) but to the logarithm of the magnitude of stimulus, when the unit of stimulus is defined as its liminal value (r), i.e., as that magnitude at which sensation appears and disappears." If we call the value R/r the fundamental stimulus value, we may say that S-magnitudes are proportional to the logarithms of the corresponding fundamental R-values. If we make $r = 1$, we may say simply that sensation is proportional to the logarithm of stimulus.

The metric formula accords with empirical results: "(1) in the cases of *equality* where an S-difference remains the same with change of the absolute intensity of the R (Weber's Law): (2) in the limiting cases where S itself and where change of S cease to be noticeable or considerable [stimulus limen and neighbourhood of terminal stimulus]. . ; (3) in the cases of *opposition* between sensations which attain and do not attain to noticeability, in a word, between conscious and unconscious S." In it, we have "a relation of dependency that obtains universally, not merely for equal cases of S, between the magnitude of the fundamental R-value and the magnitude of the corresponding S, and which allows us to calculate from quantitative ratios of the former the number of units (*das Wievielmal*) in the latter: wherewith the measure of sensation is given."

*   *   *

For more than half a century Fechner's work set the standard for what mathematical psychology could be, and even today many of the most powerful uses of mathematical reasoning seem to center in and around these problems of sensory measurement. Oddly enough, however, there were flaws in Fechner's mathematics, flaws that were not pointed out until 1958 when Luce and Edwards* showed that Fechner's assumption that all jnds are subjectively equal is too weak to generate an interval scale for measuring sensation, and that a somewhat stronger assumption—that equally often noticed differences are equal unless always or never noticed—is actually required. The enthusiasm for Fechner's accomplishment apparently led psychologists for many years to overlook some of the finer points in the theoretical argument.

* R. D. Luce and W. Edwards, The derivation of subjective scales from just noticeable differences. *Psychol. Rev.*, 1958, **65**, 222–237.

The consequences of Fechner's Law for the young science of experimental psychology were quite pervasive, but only two of them will concern us here.

First, if the differential threshold was to be adopted for the unit of subjective measurement, then it was essential to have accurate experimental methods to determine it. Many workers contributed to the painstaking process of methodological refinement*—Fechner himself adapted several existing procedures and invented others—but to recount this history here would lead us far afield. The aspect of this story that is of some mathematical interest concerns the statistical procedures that were used to estimate the threshold values. The threshold is not a sharp boundary that separates a noticeable change from an unnoticeable change. Instead, there is a range of stimulus values over which the probability of noticing the change gradually increases. The methodological problem is to obtain accurate estimates of those probabilities, to plot the probabilities as a *psychometric function* of the stimulus increments, and to define an appropriate level of probability as corresponding to the threshold. Behind this methodological problem, therefore, lies an intriguing theoretical problem of formulating adequate mathematical models for the psychometric functions obtained with the various methods. Since the threshold is a statistical concept, however, we shall postpone our discussion of this topic to the next chapter.

A second consequence of Fechner's argument that concerns us here is the question of how we should measure psychological magnitudes in general. We have already mentioned a particular instance of this general question when we asked whether the sensory magnitude as a *psychophysical function* of the stimulus magnitude was logarithmic or exponential. The more general issue, however, has expanded in scope and importance as psychology has expanded and as psychologists have attempted to assign numbers to an ever-widening range of psychological phenomena.

In response to this general problem of providing a rationale

* J. P. Guilford, *Psychometric methods,* 2nd ed. New York: McGraw-Hill, 1954.

for psychological measurements there has grown up a sizable technical literature devoted to the theory of scaling.*

The cornerstone of the psychological theory of scale construction was laid by L. L. Thurstone in a famous series of papers that appeared in 1927.† Thurstone generalized and extended Fechner's ideas beyond the relatively narrow field of psychophysics into areas such as attitude measurement where continuously variable physical quantities are not available for measuring the magnitudes of stimulation. Thurstone's argument, however, was essentially statistical in nature, and so it, too, is better postponed to the next chapter.

One of the pioneers in this field has been S. S. Stevens, who in 1946‡ proposed a scheme for classifying the various possible scales of measurement in terms of their mathematical properties. In the following excerpt Stevens summarizes this system of classification in the context of psychophysical measurement; the implications of this classification, however, extend well beyond the bounds of psychophysics.

* W. S. Torgeson, *Theory and method of scaling*. New York: McGraw-Hill, 1958.
† L. L. Thurstone, *The measurement of values*. Chicago: University of Chicago Press, 1959.
‡ S. S. Stevens, On the theory of scales of measurement. *Science*, 1946, **103**, 679–680.

Stanley Smith Stevens

The Quantification of Sensation

Measurement

The eminent scholars who have said that sensation cannot be measured comprise a long and distinguished list. Some have asserted it flatly, as a truth too obvious for argument. Others have suggested reasons. The well-known claim of William James is perhaps the most quotable: "Our feeling of pink is surely not a portion of our feeling of scarlet; nor does the light of an electric arc seem to contain that of a tallow candle in itself."

That sentence was written some seventy years ago. The fact that sensations cannot be separated into component parts, or laid end to end like measuring sticks, was once a telling argument against their measurability. But that was before there was general recognition of the fact that measurement is not limited to counting. It was in fact before many scientists had become fully aware that mathematics with its number system is a game of signs and rules, man-made and arbitrary, like the game of chess. The formal emancipation of mathematics, its complete decoupling from matters of empirical, earthy fact, was destined to fashion a new outlook on the problem of measurement.

Our understanding of the profound difference between science and mathematics took many centuries to develop, mainly because the operations of both measurement and mathematics had seemed at first to be one and the same process. The earliest scales of measurement were schemes for the counting of goods and chat-

S. S. Stevens, The quantification of sensation. *Daedalus*, 1959, **88**, 606–621. Pp. 608–618, reprinted by permission of author and the American Academy of Arts and Sciences.

tels, pebbles and beads, friends and enemies. The numbers themselves, with their rules of combination and all the paraphernalia that grew into modern mathematics, originated as a simple model invented to mirror what was done with collections of objects, to aid in the measurement of numerosity. Since arithmetic was invented to serve the purposes of measurement, it is not surprising that the isomorphic correspondence between certain arithmetical operations and the more elementary empirical operations of counting was tight and satisfying. It was, in fact, too much so, for man soon found himself a slave to his invention: the properties of the model began to dictate what was and what was not to be considered measurement. But with the ultimate decoupling of the formal, arbitrary, empty, gamelike aspects of mathematics from the empirical pursuits of the "concrete" disciplines it became clear that the province of measurement extends to wherever our ingenuity can contrive systematic rules for pinning numbers on things.

The number system is merely a model, to be used in whatever way we please. It is a rich model, to be sure, and one or another aspect of its syntax can often be made to portray one or another property of objects or events. It is a useful convention, therefore, to define as measurement the assigning of numbers to objects or events in accordance with a systematic rule. Since there are different kinds of rules, there are different kinds of measurements; but for each kind some degree of isomorphism obtains between the empirical relations among objects and the formal relations among numbers.

Among the empirical properties of the world for which numbers may serve as models the most important are these:

(1) *Identity:* numbers may serve as names or labels to identify items or classes;
(2) *Order:* numbers may serve to reflect the rank order of items;
(3) *Intervals:* numbers may serve to reflect differences or distances among items;
(4) *Ratios:* numbers may serve to reflect ratios among items.

Corresponding to each of these uses there is a type of scale: nominal, ordinal, interval, and ratio, as set forth in Table 1, along with definitions and examples. The key to the nature of

TABLE 1. *A Classification of Scales of Measurement*

Scale	Basic empirical operations	Mathematical group-structure	Permissible statistics (invariantive)	Typical examples
Nominal	Determination of equality	Permutation group $x' = f(x)$ where $f(x)$ means any one-to-one substitution	Numbers of cases Mode "Information" measures Contingency correlation	"Numbering" of football players Assignment of type or model numbers to classes
Ordinal	Determination of greater or less	Isotonic group $x' = f(x)$ where $f(x)$ means any increasing monotonic function	Median Percentiles Order correlation (type 0: interpreted as a test of order)	Hardness of minerals Grades of leather, lumber, wool, and so forth Intelligence-test raw scores
Interval	Determination of the equality of intervals or of differences	Linear or affine group $x' = ax + b$ $a > 0$	Mean Standard deviation Order correlation (type I: interpreted as r) Product moment (r)	Temperature (Fahrenheit and Celsius) Position on a line Calendar time Potential energy Intelligence-test "standard scores" (?)
Ratio	Determination of the equality of ratios	Similarity group $x' = cx$ $c > 0$	Geometric mean Harmonic mean Percent variation	Length, numerosity, density, work, time intervals, and so forth Temperature (Kelvin) Loudness (sones) Brightness (brils)

Measurement is the assignment of numbers to objects or events according to rule. The rules and the resulting kinds of scales are tabulated above. The basic operations needed to create a given scale are all those listed in the second column, down to and including the operation listed opposite the scale. The third column gives the mathematical transformations that leave the scale form invariant. Any number x on a scale can be replaced by another number x′ where x′ is the function of x listed in column 2. The fourth column lists, cumulatively downward, examples of statistics that show invariance under the transformations of column 3 (the mode, however, is invariant only for discrete variables).

these different scales lies in a powerful but simple principle: the concept of invariance. When we have carried out a set of empirical operations (such as comparisons, matchings, balancings, orderings, etc.) we assign a set of numbers to reflect the outcome of the operations. Then comes the crucial question: in what ways can we transform the numbers without loss of empirical information?

As shown in Table 1, each of the four scales has its characteristic group of permissible transformations. For our present purposes, the group of greatest interest is the one that defines the ratio scale, for this is the most useful type of scale. Here we can only multiply by a constant, as we do in converting inches to centimeters, or seconds to minutes. Any more radical transformation would distort the picture that the ratio scale serves to portray.

The measurement of sensation on the most interesting type of scale would call, therefore, for a procedure for assigning numbers to sensations in such a way that anything more drastic than multiplication by a constant would cause a loss of information. Such a scale would be a ratio scale, and with it we could tell how sensory magnitude grows with the stimulus input. The numbers on this scale would allow us to specify, for example, when one sensation is twice as intense as another. . . .

Quality versus Quantity

There is ready agreement among all observers that sensations come in so many and such varied forms as to elude complete description. All the richness of the daily sights and sounds and tastes and smells and feelings to which our sense organs admit us can no more be captured within a formula than can the intricate dancing of a falling leaf. Nevertheless, once a few basic distinctions are made, there emerge some simple and engaging principles that relate certain aspects of sensation to certain properties of the impinging forces of the environment. Perhaps the chief of these distinctions is the one between quantity and quality, or magnitude and kind, or size and sort. No pair of common words quite fits the distinction; but what it means concretely is that sweet is different from sour, although both may vary from strong to weak.

It is only fair to point out that psychophysics, the science of sensation, has little to say as yet about qualitative variations among sensations. This aspect of the sensory world confronts us with a succession of baffling and discontinuous leaps as we go from quality to quality, as well as from one sense of modality to another—and no one quite knows why. The various colors, tastes, smells, and feelings seem not to lie on a continuum, but to exist in more or less complete independence of one another. In terms of the scales of measurement listed in Table 1, the sensory qualities provide a first-rate example of measurement at the nominal level —the most primitive type of measurement, where all we can do is identify and label. Sometimes a crude ordering seems possible, but for the most part the qualities are just what they are, and the best we can do is to name them.

Quite different opportunities present themselves for those aspects of sensation that appear to lie on a continuum of some sort. Here we can usually order sensations on a scale from faint to intense, or on some other dimension, and for many continua a form of measurement stronger than ordinal may readily be achieved. It would of course simplify the problem if a common set of rules governed all perceptual continua, but this turns out not to be the case. At least one basic distinction must be made between two kinds of continua.

The prototypes of the two kinds of continua are exemplified by loudness and pitch. Loudness is an aspect of sound that has about it what can best be described as degrees of magnitude or quantity. Pitch does not. Pitch varies from high to low; it has a kind of position, and in a sense it is a qualitative continuum. Loudness may be called a *prothetic* continuum, and pitch a *metathetic* one. The criteria that define these two classes of continua reside wholly in how they behave in psychophysical experiments, but the names themselves are suggested by the nature of the physiological processes that appear to underlie each of them.

Sensory discrimination may be mediated by two processes: the one additive, the other substitutive. Additional excitation may be added to an excitation already present, or new excitation may be substituted for excitation that has been removed. An observer can tell, for example, when a light pressure becomes a strong pressure at a given point on the arm, and he can also tell when the stimulus is moved from that point to another location. Different sets of general laws govern these two types of sensory discrimination.

The metathetic, positional, qualitative continua seem to concern *what* and *where* as opposed to *how much*. They include such things as pitch, apparent position, apparent inclination, and apparent proportion. Perhaps they also include visual saturation and visual hue—at least to whatever extent hue may be made to behave as a continuum. All in all, the metathetic continua do not seem to comprise a neat and orderly class of perceptual variables, and as yet they have not been very thoroughly explored.

The prothetic continua, on the other hand, have lately yielded rich rewards for the systematic efforts made to scale their magnitudes. Some two dozen continua have been examined, always with the same outcome: the sensation magnitude ψ grows as a power function of the stimulus magnitude ϕ. In terms of a formula,

$$\psi = k\phi^n$$

In this equation, the constant k depends on the units of measurement and is not very interesting; but the value of the exponent n may vary from one sensory continuum to another. As a matter of fact, perhaps the most interesting thing about a sensory continuum is (as we shall see) the value of the exponent n. . . .

The Power Law

Perhaps the easiest way to elicit the relevant behavior from an observer is to stimulate his eye, say, with a variety of different intensities, and to ask him to assign a number proportional to the apparent magnitude of each brightness, as he sees it. Most observers, once they understand the problem, carry out this process (called magnitude estimation) with reasonable success. Not that all observers make the same estimates, or even feel any great confidence in what they are doing, but the average result for a group of normal observers turns out to be quite stable and reproducible. After all, it is the reaction of the typical (median) observer that interests us here, for we are not concerned, at the outset at least, with the fact that people differ, or that some are blind and some are photophobic. Psychophysics wants to know, first of all, what the typical input-output operating characteristics of the sensory systems are.

The typical input-output relation for all prothetic continua thus far tested is a power function. To date, the observed values of the exponent in the relation $\psi = k\phi^n$ have ranged from about 0.33 for brightness to about 3.5 for the apparent intensity of electric shock applied to the fingers. The exponent of the power function determines its curvature. If the exponent is exactly 1, the function is a straight line, and the output (reported sensation) varies linearly with the intensity of the stimulus. But when the exponent is greater than 1, the line representing the function ascends in an ever steeper slope. When it is less than 1, the curvature is the other way and the line becomes ever more horizontal.

These relations are illustrated in Figure 1, which shows examples of three perceptual continua, each having a different exponent. Electric current produces a sensation whose intensity grows more and more rapidly as the current increases, whereas brightness seems to grow less rapidly with increasing physical intensity. As we might expect, the apparent length of a line seems to grow very nearly in direct proportion to the physical length. One foot looks about half as long as two feet—not quite, it seems, but almost.

A felicitous feature of power functions is the form they assume when graphed in log-log coordinates (logarithmic scales on both axes). The plot of a power function then becomes a straight line, and the slope of the line is a direct measure of the exponent. We can see how this works out if we make a log-log plot of the same three functions shown in Figure 1. We find that the differences in curvature in Figure 1 becomes differences in slope in Figure 2.

The nature of these power functions and the universality of their application testify to the existence of a profoundly simple relation between stimulus and sensory response: equal stimulus

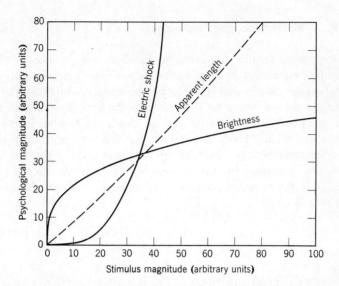

Figure 1. The apparent magnitudes of shock, length, and brightness follow different curves of growth. Their exponents are 3.5, 1.1, and 0.33, respectively. The units of the scales have been chosen arbitrarily in order to show the relative form of the curves on a single plot.

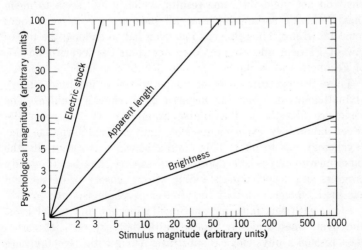

Figure 2. When the curves in Figure 1 are plotted against logarithmic coordinates, they become straight lines. The slope of the line corresponds to the exponent of the power function that governs the growth of the sensation.

ratios produce equal subjective ratios. That is the essence of the psychophysical law. For example, it requires approximately a ninefold increase in energy to double the apparent brightness of a light, no matter where we start from in the first place. Doubling the apparent intensity of an electric shock requires an increase in current of only about 20 per cent, but this percentage increase is approximately the same all up and down the scale. On all continua governed by the power law, a constant percentage change in the stimulus produces a constant percentage change in the sensed effect. . . .

*   *   *

Stevens's direct procedure of magnitude estimation yields a ratio scale for the measurement of sensory magnitudes, whereas the most that can be claimed for Fechner's indirect procedure of summing jnds is that it yields an interval scale. Moreover, on what he calls prothetic continua the two methods of measurement do not yield the same results, which would seem to mean that Fechner's assumption that all jnds are subjectively equal must be wrong. Thus Stevens has been led to endorse the power law of Plateau and Brentano, rather than the logarithmic law of Fechner. And so the century-old debate continues.

These few excerpts do scant justice to the volume and quality of mathematical reasoning inspired by Fechner's problem. The topic provides the best available example of the interplay between laboratory experiments and mathematical formulae that psychology has to offer. This approach, which is essentially the experimental physicist's approach to science, has led to steady progress and deeper understanding of our sensory processes, and has justified the faith that the pioneer psychologists had in it.

Along with this faith in experimentation and functional laws, moreover, went a closely related faith that psychological processes rest on a physiological substrate. Along with psychophysics went psychophysiology. Research on sensory physiology developed rapidly during the nineteenth century; the genius of such men as Hermann von Helmholtz made it possible to account for many subjective phenomena in terms of objective processes and structures in the sensory systems. The following passage is an example—one of a large variety of possible examples—of an attempt to "explain" a subjective sensory phenomenon in terms of an objective physiological process in the receptor organ. It introduces equations that are appropriate to describe a physiological process and boldly assumes that they must also be appropriate to describe its subjective correlate.

The author was Selig Hecht, a visual physiologist whose work has inspired much of our modern research on the visual processes. This selection has been taken out of a chapter that Hecht contributed in 1929 to a handbook of experimental psychology.

* * *

Selig Hecht

The Nature of the Photoreceptor Process

An environmental disturbance which starts a receptor process can vary in three ways: in intensity, in duration, and in composition. Let us leave composition to one side for a moment, since I shall devote a separate section to it later, and consider first the relationships which exist between time and intensity.

In general, in order for an outside agent such as light to produce a given sensory effect, the intensity required is an inverse function of the duration of its application. The exact relation between the two is still unsettled in its final form for the human eye and it varies to some extent from organism to organism; but in all cases it is true that the lower the intensity, the longer is

S. Hecht, Vision: II, The nature of the photoreceptor process. In C. Murchison (Ed.), *The foundations of experimental psychology.* Worcester, Mass.: Clark University Press, 1929. Pp. 218–222 reprinted by permission of the publisher.

the time necessary for it to act, and, conversely, the higher the intensity, the shorter is the time required to elicit an effect.

Such a relationship is a commonplace of photochemistry. In its simplest form it is the Bunsen-Roscoe law which holds for many photochemical reactions; it states that to produce a given photolytic effect a constant amount of energy is necessary, regardless of its distribution in time. If I is the intensity and t the time of its action then

$$It = C \qquad (1)$$

where C is a constant. As here given, or in a modified form the inverse relationship applies to a great variety of photolytic processes.

The relation between time and intensity in the photoreceptor process brings to light a significant property of vision, namely, the threshold. For a given animal and under constant conditions there can be found a low, but measurable intensity which produces an effect after a reasonably long exposure, but below which even an extremely prolonged exposure fails to elicit a sensory effect. This intensity is the threshold.

What does the presence of an intensity threshold tell us about the photosensory process? The production of a given sensory effect undoubtedly means the formation of a certain physical or chemical change in the contents of the sense-cell. In the photosensory process the first effect of the light is obviously the conversion of a light-sensitive but inactive substance into an active substance which starts the train of events culminating in a nervous discharge. The first thing then that we learn from the existence of a threshold intensity is that this primary photochemical reaction is accompanied by another reaction, not photochemical in nature, which tends to remove the products of the photochemical reaction. If the first part of the photoreceptor process were merely a simple, direct, photochemical reaction, we should never have a threshold. The reciprocity law of Bunsen and Roscoe would probably hold rigorously, as it does in the irreversible bleaching of visual purple among other things, and exposures would be cumulative as they are in the photographic plate. Like the astronomer who can expose a photographic plate to light of the same dim star several evenings in succession and get a developable image, we should be able to see a light no matter how low its intensity, provided the exposure were prolonged sufficiently. The effects of light, however, do not accumulate this way in the sense-cells. Therefore, there must be a process which tends to remove or render inactive the photochemical products as they are formed by the light.

One may put the whole matter in the following way. Let us describe the photosensitive material in the sense-cell as S and suppose that light changes S into its photochemical product, which may be one substance P, or more substances P, A, B, etc. We may write $S \to P$ as this reaction. It is P which starts the series of events ending in the outgoing impulse to the nerve. The associated process demanded by the existence of a threshold may then be of the following kind. P may diffuse away from the scene of action. P may combine with some constituent of the cell and be rendered inactive. Or, finally, P, by itself or by combining with some material furnished by the cell or by the surrounding fluids, may become reconverted into the original sensitive material S and be used over again.

On the basis of the information so far presented, one cannot decide which of these conditions is the most probable. But for purposes of understanding the data which describe the properties of the threshold they may be treated mathematically in a practically identical manner. Assume an intensity I shining on such a system. The light will be absorbed by the substance S, which will be changed from its initial concentration a to a concentration a—x where x is the concentration of S converted into P. Since this is a threshold change, it will be small, and we may write its average velocity as

$$v_1 = k_1 I (a-x) \tag{2}$$

where k_1 is a velocity constant which includes the absorption coefficient. Now assume that P diffuses away, or combines with another substance, or is changed back to S. The velocity of the process will be proportional to the concentration of the reactants, P, A, B . . . , which in case of chemical reactions would be x, or x^2, or x^n depending on whether there are 1, 2, or n number of different photolytic products. This velocity

$$v_2 = k_2 x^n \tag{3}$$

must be subtracted from the photochemical velocity in order to describe the actual velocity

$$\frac{x}{t} = k_1 I (a—x) - k_2 x^n \qquad (4)$$

with which the products P accumulate in the sense-cell. We are not interested particularly in this velocity, but in the relations between the intensity I and the time t which are required to result in a given constant amount x of photochemical products accumulating in the sense-organ. Equation (4) may be arranged as follows:

$$It = \frac{x}{k_1 (a—x)} + \frac{k_2 x^n}{k_1 (a—x)} t \qquad (5)$$

to give us the desired information. Since x is taken as a constant amount of material, $(a — x)$ is also constant, and equation (5) may be written

$$It = C + Dt \qquad (6)$$

where C and D are constants.

Equation (6) has been derived somewhat differently by Lasareff and by Pütter, but, aside from its derivation, it and its predecessor equation (5) have many interesting properties. The velocity constant k_2 of the negative reaction is most likely smaller than the velocity constant k_1 of the photochemical reaction; otherwise it would require enormous intensities to effect any measurable accumulation of products P in the sense-cell. Thus the constant D is probably smaller than C. Moreover, for threshold values x is a small fraction of a; any power of x must therefore be smaller than x, which makes the value of D still smaller. Finally, with small values of the exposure time t, the term Dt in (6) becomes negligible in relation to C, and the equation becomes

$$It = C \qquad (1)$$

which is the Bunsen-Roscoe law all over again. What this means in words is that, in spite of the presence of the extra reaction which removes P, we might expect the relation between time and intensity in the photosensory system to follow the very simple equation (1) for short exposures, and the slightly more involved equation (6) for longer exposures. This is essentially what has been found by a variety of investigators.

Bloch first found that for *short flashes* of light the relation between I and t for the human eye conformed to equation (1). This has been confirmed by Rutenberg and Braunstein, Table 1

TABLE 1. *Relation between Intensity I and Time t for Short Exposures to Produce a Minimal Sensory Response in Mya and in the Human Eye*

Data for the eye are from Braunstein; for Mya from Hecht.

| I | Eye | | I | Mya | |
	t	I·t		t	I·t
1	.0210	.021	54	0.104	5.62
2	.0098	.020	76	0.073	5.55
4	.0047	.019	112	0.053	5.94
8	.0024	.019	194	0.030	5.82
16	.0012	.019	238	0.023	5.47
			334	0.016	5.34

gives Braunstein's data from which the results may be judged. A similar application of the Bunsen-Roscoe law has been found for short flashes of light in the ascidian *Ciona intestinalis*, the clam *Mya arenaria*, and by Loeb for a small range of intensities with the polyp *Eudendrium*. In Table 1 there is included the data for *Mya*. In some organisms the relation $It = C$ holds over such an enormous range of time and intensity that it is fairly certain there is no accessory reaction to remove the photolytic products as they are formed. Blaauw showed for wheat seedlings that a given phototropic response is caused by the same amount of energy, about 20 meter-candle-seconds, when the exposure time varies between 0.001 second and 43 hours, and the intensity between 26,520 and 0.00017 meter-candles. Over such a range this seems never to have been found with an animal.

When the exposures become longer than the short flashes already considered, it has been shown by a number of observers that equation (6) applies. Blondel and Rey found that for exposures between 0.001 and 3.0 seconds their data for the human eye may be expressed by the equation $It = 0.065 + 0.31t$, using arbitrary values of the intensity. This relation has been confirmed by various experimenters. For extremely short exposures it seems not to hold, as both Piéron and Reeves have shown. Apparently other factors enter. In the case of Mya, Piéron believed that for a larger range of exposures than those given in Table 1 the simple It relation does not hold. Unfortunately Piéron's experiments are vitiated by his use of an episcotister for varying the intensity; since this device produces a series of short flashes, it obviously cannot be used for short exposures; and, furthermore, there is implicit in it the assumption that I and t are interchangeable, which is the question at issue. Curiously enough, for the longer exposures, where one might expect an episcotister to be useful, Piéron's data show that for Mya equation (6) applies and that $It = 3.5 + 1.2t$.

There is an interesting consequence of the difference in the relation between time and intensity for short and for long exposures. The physicochemical reason that It is constant for short exposures may be that, since the straight photochemical reaction is so rapid, the comparatively slow removal process hardly gets under way before the sensory response is over. Under such conditions the initial process may be treated as a purely photochemical reaction. It has become almost axiomatic to say, since Goldberg first showed it to be true, that photochemical reactions possess low temperature coefficients very near 1 for 10°C., in contrast to ordinary chemical reactions whose temperature coefficients for 10°C. are between 2 and 3. For short flashes of light it should therefore be true that the value of It obtained for the photosensory process at different temperatures should yield a coefficient near unity. Using a constant exposure of 0.016 second, I determined the minimum intensity necessary to elicit a response from Mya at four temperatures between 13° and 31°C. The results with four separate experiments gave values for the temperature coefficient for 10°C. as follows: 1.04, 1.06, 1.07, and 1.06, which bear out the idea that for short flashes the first reaction is primarily photochemical.

These examples show that the existence of a threshold, if interpreted even in the most general terms, is enough to furnish information about the structure of the receptor process. The assumption of a removal or recovery process accompanying the principal, photochemical reaction has enabled us to derive equations which describe as a first approximation the known data of the relation between time and intensity in the visual process.

The characteristic of the threshold which is to be emphasized is that intensity is the limiting factor, and not time. Below a certain intensity, no matter how long the exposure may be, no sensory effect is produced. Consider this in terms of equation (4) describing the velocity of the reaction as a whole. If the reaction proceeds for infinite time, $t = \infty$ and x/t becomes 0. Equation (4) then becomes

$$\frac{k_1}{k_2} I = \frac{x^n}{a-x} \tag{7}$$

from which time is completely eliminated. A given concentration x of P can be formed, according to this equation, only as the result of a certain intensity I, even at infinite exposure.

The conception of the photoreceptor process which we have so far suggested has been deliberately general. It has been specific in the one respect only, that it has involved the existence of a process which accompanies the main photochemical process and removes its products. It is possible to be even more specific about this reaction, but in order to do so we must consider other characteristics of the photoreceptor process and the data that belong to them.

*   *   *

Hecht's description of what was happening in the light-sensitive cells in the retina of the eye was highly persuasive. Moreover, many of the effects he described seemed to parallel closely the subjective phenomena of vision. This parallel was counted as a success for the "photochemical theory" of vision, but to some people it was a rather puzzling success. If the subjective phenomena of vision can be explained by mathematical functions describing processes in the peripheral receptor, then what is the purpose of all that vastly complicated and highly specialized nervous system that follows after the retina? A visual system has no right to be as simple as Hecht said it was. No effective protest was voiced, however, until 1940 when W. J. Crozier tried to put the emphasis on neural rather than photochemical processes. But that attempt is better left to the next chapter.

This is as far as we will pursue the use of determinate functions for sensory systems. It was good science by any standard and it set a high level of aspiration for psychologists working in other areas. But, unfortunately, in other areas of psychology the twin tools of experimentation and functional laws—even when supported by physiology—seemed to move forward much more slowly.

In order to illustrate some of the difficulties encountered elsewhere, we will shift now from sensory processes to learning and memory. In this area the attempts to use mathematics developed more slowly and were, by and large, far less successful than in psychophysics or in sensory psychophysiology.

The modern experimental science of learning and memory is built on a foundation created by three men: Hermann Ebbinghaus, who developed methods for studying rote memorization; Ivan Petrovich Pavlov, who discovered and explored conditioning; and Edward Lee Thorndike, who emphasized the importance of the learner's motivation. All three of these men created experimental situations in which quantitative measures of performance could be obtained, but none of them was particularly adept as a mathematician. Ebbinghaus, it is true, did make a gesture in the direction of a functional law. In the description of his famous study on memory for lists of nonsense syllables, published in 1885, he proposed the equation

$$Y = \frac{100k}{(\log_{10}t)^c + k}$$

to describe the course of forgetting. Here Y was his measure of per cent retained, t $(\geqq 1)$ was the time in minutes after the end of the learning period, and c and k were arbitrary constants which, for his data, were $c = 1.25$ and $k = 1.84$. But he offered no rationalization to explain why this equation, rather than any other, should fit the data. His formula was simply a precise way to say that as time passed the amount recalled declined, rapidly at first, then more and more slowly as it approached zero. "Of course," he said, "this statement and the formula upon which it rests have here no other value than that of a shorthand statement of the above results."*

In the quarter of a century following the publication of Ebbinghaus's work, the amount of experimentation on learning and memory increased steadily, but no serious effort was made to develop a formal theory of learning or forgetting. The few attempts that were made to use mathematics to describe learning† were highly tentative and empirical. Today they are usually dismissed scornfully as mere "curve-fitting," since no rationale was offered for the particular equations that were proposed.

Students of the learning process like to plot the number of errors or the number of correct responses on successive trials in order to keep track of improvements in performance as a function of practice. This function—traditionally called a "learning curve," although "performance curve" would be a better name for it—has been a primary target for mathematical attacks on the learning process. As an example of the initial attempts to determine this function, consider the following excerpt from L. L. Thurstone, written in 1919.

* H. Ebbinghaus, *Memory,* transl. by H. A. Ruger. New York: Teachers College, Columbia University, 1913, p. 79.
† See H. Gulliksen, A rational equation of the learning curve based on Thorndike's law of effect. *J. gen. Psychol.,* 1934, 11, 395–434.

Louis Leon Thurstone

The Learning Curve Equation

Purpose of the Equation

When the learning function for a simple coordination proceeds undisturbed by external or internal distraction it usually follows a law of diminishing returns. In the majority of learning curves the amount of attainment gained per unit of practice decreases as practice increases. Exceptions to this tendency are found in studying the learning of complex processes such as a foreign language, and when successive generalizations are involved such as puzzle solving and the like. These exceptions sometimes take the form of a positive acceleration at the initial stage of the learning, plateaus during the course of learning and erratic advance of attainment. But these irregularities should not stand in the way of an attempt to express the learning function as a law provided that we do it with due conservatism in its interpretation. All we can hope to do in thus expressing the learning function is to formulate what can with considerable certainty be considered as the typical relation between practice and attainment.

Besides giving the satisfaction of formulating the relation between practice and attainment, the use of an equation for this relation enables one to predict the limit of practice before it has been attained, provided that the learning follows the law of diminishing returns. It also enables one to differentiate for various purposes the rate of learning from the limit of practice since these two attributes are undoubtedly independent. It enables us to state how much preceding practice the subject has experi-

L. L. Thurstone, The learning curve equation. *Psychol. Monogr.*, 1919, **26**, No. 114, 51 pp. Pp. 11–13 reprinted by permission of the American Psychological Association.

enced under the assumption that the learning function followed the same law before and after the formal measurements. Another use for which the equation can be of service is in the analysis of the relation between the variability in learning and other mental attributes. The problems of formal discipline may be investigated by ascertaining whether a succession of learning processes, all of the same type, yields any rise in the limit of practice, or a higher rate of learning, or a greater consistency of learning in the successive learning processes. Some of these coefficients may be more susceptible than others to modification by successive repetition of the same type of learning. This would in reality be studying the problems of learning how to learn. All questions of transfer of training may be investigated by the learning equation and the transfer effect may be differentiated into psychological components. Thus, continued practice in learning poetry may show no rise of the practice limit, but a considerable rise in the rate at which that limit is approached and in a decrease of the variability of the learning. Relearning may be found to approach the same limit of practice as the initial learning but it may proceed at a higher rate, and this rate can be stated as a coefficient which is independent of the amount of previous practice in each learning process. The laws of forgetting are expressible in terms quite similar to those here used for the learning function. It is not at all unlikely that these coefficients may come to be significant in individual psychology quite apart from their immediate utility as descriptive attributes of the learning function. The preceding remarks have, I hope, justified my attempt to devise a method for investigating the learning, memory, and forgetting functions.

The Equation

After experimenting with some forty different equations on published learning curves I have selected a form of the hyperbola as being for practical purposes the most available. It takes the form

$$Y = \frac{L \cdot X}{X + R} \tag{1}$$

in which $Y = attainment$ in terms of the number of successful
acts per unit time.

$X = formal \ practice$ in terms of the total number of
practice acts since the beginning of formal practice.

$L = limit \ of \ practice$ in terms of attainment units.

$R = rate \ of \ learning$ which indicates the relative rapid-
ity with which the limit of practice is being approached. It is numerically high for a low rate of
approach and numerically low for a high rate of
approach.

Equation 1 represents a learning curve which passes through
the origin, i.e., it starts with a zero score at zero formal practice.
The majority of learning curves start with some finite score even
at the initial performance. For learning curves which do not pass
through the origin, the equation becomes

$$Y = \frac{L(X + P)}{(X + P) + R} \tag{2}$$

in which $P = equivalent \ previous \ practice$ in terms of formal
practice units. . . .

Equation 1 may be rectified as follows:

$$Y = \frac{L \cdot X}{X + R}$$

$$XY + RY = LX$$

$$X + R = L\left(\frac{X}{Y}\right) \tag{3}$$

This equation is linear if X/Y is plotted against X. Similarly
equation 2 may be rectified when written in the form

$$X + (R + P) = L \frac{(X + P)}{Y} \tag{4}$$

which becomes linear when $(X + P)/Y$ is plotted against X.

When so rectified, the constants L, R, and P may be determined by several different methods, the choice between which
depends on the scatter of the data, the desired accuracy, and the
number of curves one has to calculate.

Although Thurstone offers no rationale for his equation, other than to say that it fits his data, obviously his choice was not a matter of mere whimsy. Behind nearly all of the equations that have been offered to describe the learning curve there lies a simple schema that may help the reader to organize and remember them.* The amount of work X that is required to learn a task of difficulty R to a degree of mastery M is $X = RM$, for some appropriate choice of units. The problem is to remember what choice of units each theorist proposes. In Thurstone's case, we merely define the measure of mastery as $M = Y/(L - Y)$ in order to obtain his equation (1). Even Ebbinghaus's equation for forgetting falls into this pattern if we assume that during recall the amount of practice has been fixed at $X = k$, that the difficulty $R = (\log t)^c$, and that $M = Y/(100 - Y)$.

Another type of learning equation is obtained if we take as the measure of mastery $M = \log L/(L - Y)$. Then the $X = RM$ schema becomes

$$X = R \log \frac{L}{L - Y}$$

and when we solve this equation for Y we obtain

$$Y = L \left(1 - e^{-X/R}\right)$$

This equation has proved, over the years, to be a special favorite of learning theorists. One well-known advocate of this version was Clark Hull, who made it an important part of his general theory of behavior. But more than a century earlier Herbart had used this same equation.† Herbart used an exponential growth function to express the rise of a concept into consciousness; Hull used it to express the rise of habit strength. This should remind us that mathematical functions are psychologically neutral; the

* E. G. Boring, The beginning and growth of measurement in psychology. *Isis*, 1961, **52**, 238–257. See p. 249.

† D. Bakan, The exponential growth function in Herbart and Hull. *Amer. J. Psychol.*, 1952, **65**, 307–308.

same function can be pressed into service by theorists of violently different persuasions.

Hull's use of the exponential growth function is indicated in the following short excerpt.

*   *   *

Clark Leonard Hull

Habit Strength and Number of Reinforcements

The process of reinforcement sets up a connection in the nervous system whereby an afferent receptor discharge ($\dot{s}$) originally involved in a reinforcement is able to initiate the efferent discharge (r) also involved in the reinforcement. But since the afferent discharge ($\dot{s}$) is initiated by the action of a stimulus energy ($\dot{S}$) on the receptor, and since the efferent discharge (r) in due course enters the effector system, producing a reaction (R), we have the sequence,

$$\dot{S} \to \dot{s} \dashrightarrow r \to R.$$

The habit organization is represented by the arrow with broken shaft between the neural processes $\dot{s}$ and r. If we replace this arrow as a representation of habit with the more convenient and somewhat more appropriate letter H, we have the full and explicit notation for expressing the various relationships involved in the concept of habit strength:

$$\dot{S} \to {}_s H_r \to R.$$

However, under most circumstances there is a close approximation to a one-to-one correspondence, parallelism, or constancy

C. L. Hull, *Principles of behavior*. New York: D. Appleton-Century-Company, Inc., 1943. Copyright, 1943. D. Appleton-Century-Co., Inc. Pp. 111–119 reprinted by permission of the publisher.

between $\dot{S}$ and $\dot{s}$ on the one hand and between r and R on the other. Accordingly, for purposes of coarse molar analysis $\dot{S}$ or $\dot{s}$ may be used interchangeably, as is the case with r and R. Since we shall be dealing with gross stimulus situations and the gross results of molar activity in the early stages of the present analysis, we shall usually employ the symbol,

$$_sH_R.$$

Later, when we reach a point requiring a more precise and detailed analysis, it will be necessary not only to employ the notation
$$_sH_r,$$

thus explicitly representing the neural impulse, but to distinguish the stimulus and the response situations. For example, $\dot{S}$ and $\dot{s}$ represent S and s when considered as in the process of being conditioned, whereas the dots will never be used when S and s are considered as performing the function of response evocation.

Having decided to employ the construct $_sH_R$, we proceed at once to the problem of determining the presumptive quantitative nature of its functional relationship to its various antecedent determiners. The first of these to be considered will be the relationship of $_sH_R$ to the number of reinforcements (N), This type of determination presents certain difficulties . . . [but] . . . it is concluded that very probably:

1. Habit function is an increasing function of the number of reinforcements.

2. This function increases up to some sort of physiological limit beyond which no more increase is possible.

3. As habit strength approaches this physiological limit with continued reinforcements the increment $(\Delta \,_sH_R)$ resulting from each additional reinforcement decreases progressively in magnitude.

Now, there are numerous algebraic expressions which yield results conforming to the above specifications. One of these, however, has a rather special promise because it is known to approximate closely a very large number of observable empirical relationships in all sorts of biological situations involving growth and decay. . . . The basic principle of the simple positive growth function is that *the amount of growth resulting from each unit of growth opportunity will increase the amount of whatever is growing by a constant fraction of the growth potentiality as yet unrealized.* . . .

From the foregoing it is evident that the rate of habit growth is dependent upon three factors or *parameters:*

1. The physiological limit of maximum (M).

2. The ordinal number (N) of the reinforcement producing a given increment to the habit strength $(\Delta \, _sH_R)$.

3. The constant factor (F) according to which a portion $(\Delta \, _sH_R)$ of the unrealized potentiality is transferred to the actual habit strength at a given reinforcement.

There must also be devised a unit in which to express habit strength. This is taken arbitrarily as 1 per cent of the physiological maximum (M) of habit strength attainable by a standard organism under optimal conditions. In order to make the name of the unit easy to remember, it will be called the *hab,* a shortened form of the word *habit.* Thus under the conditions stated above there would be 100 habit units, or habs, between zero and the physiological limit, i.e., one hab $= \dfrac{M}{100}$ . . . .

It may be shown by rather simple mathematical procedures that $\Sigma\Delta_sH_R$ as a function of the number of repetitions (N) is given by the equation:

$$_s^N H_R = M - Me^{-iN}$$

where $M = 100$, N is the number of reinforcement repetitions, e is 10, and

$$i = \log \frac{1}{1 - F}$$

where F is the reduction constant. . . .

This is all Hull offers to justify his use of the "simple positive growth function" as a basic axiom in his theory. It is remarkable that as late as 1943 an outstanding theorist in this field of psychology, especially one as devoted to the "mathematico-deductive method" as Hull was known to be, would have been satisfied with an empirical equation at the very heart of his theory. As we will see in the next chapter, other psychologists had already made considerable progress toward rational equations for the learning curve. Hull ignored their work and began his own theory by postulating what others thought he should have ended by proving.

During the period from 1929 until his death in 1952, Clark Hull exerted a profound influence on the psychology of learning. As he grew older he became increasingly fond of expressing his ideas in logical and mathematical form, and he published extensive systems of axioms complete with theorems and corollaries. Whether his efforts in this direction actually contributed significantly to the forward progress of mathematical psychology, however, is a debatable question. Certainly Hull was a better psychologist than mathematician. His troubles with formal notation have usually been excused because, it was said, his great prestige helped to make mathematical theories respectable in psychology and so paved the way for more elegant work later. Unfortunately, this picture of the aging psychologist making an honest woman of the Queen of the Sciences has not seemed convincing to all his critics. The profound influence of Hull's theory on American psychology was felt more through the endless variety of observations and experiments that it suggested than in the mathematics it used. Some critics, however, have felt that the ultimate purpose of a theory is not to stimulate experiments, but to make experiments unnecessary. It is scarcely to his credit that he helped to spread the myth that mathematical theories are necessarily more precise or more testable than other kinds of theories.

By way of contrast, it is amusing to compare Clark Hull with

Nicolas Rashevsky. In almost every respect except their mutual confidence in the power of functional laws the two men were complete opposites. Hull is a psychologist with little facility at mathematics; Rashevsky knows almost nothing about psychology, but has a breath-taking ability to spin out equations as fast as he can talk. Hull's ideas were tested exhaustively by a whole generation of experimental psychologists; Rashevsky's may have led to a few scattered studies, but for most psychologists his books mean little more than a difficult exercise in mathematics. When Hull wants an equation to describe the learning curve, he simply postulates it; when Rashevsky wants effectively the same equation,* he begins by describing a particular neural network and assuming thresholds of activation for each neuron, then writes equations governing the activity of each neuron in the net until finally he deduces the desired result.

Rashevsky's network approach may sound more rational than it really is. It is obviously sensible to try to use what is known about smaller units (neurons) when trying to describe their corporate activity, and such attempts have an obvious contribution to make to neurophysiology, but it will probably take much more than good mathematics to bridge the enormous gap between the behavior of individual neurons and the behavior of a human being. If a political scientist tried to explain what happened in a national election by analyzing a hypothetical conversation among five voters, we might find the results interesting, but hardly compelling. Apparently most psychologists have had exactly that reaction to Rashevsky's neurological explanations and analyses. An argument that begins with neural networks is interesting, but it will have to be strengthened by a great deal more neurophysiological evidence before many psychologists will be persuaded to stop their own work and test Rashevsky's ideas. Until a stronger case can be made, therefore, this very ambitious and imaginative attempt to provide a rationale for our psychological formulas will probably have little influence on the development of mathematical psychology.

To contrast with Clark Hull's preoccupation with the precise

* N. Rashevsky, *Mathematical biophysics.* Chicago: University of Chicago Press, 1938. See Chapter 25, especially eq. (22), p. 255.

numerical magnitudes obtained in experimental measurements, we should now examine an example of functional mathematics done in the grand manner, where the equations are used, not to look at the data, but to look through them at the underlying relations that must hold for any possible set of numerical data. Rashevsky provided several such examples, but his extensive system of definitions and equations is so tightly woven that it is difficult to find a suitable passage that is both short and self-contained. Fortunately, there are other examples of this style in mathematical psychology, although it has generally been less popular among psychologists than among physicists and economists. The following passage taken from the writings of Herbert A. Simon illustrates some of the possibilities.

* * *

Herbert Alexander Simon

The Construction of Social Science Models

Motivation and Learning

In psychological formulations of adaptive human behavior, the concepts of motivation and learning are central. The notion of motivation is closely connected with the "criterion" in the models of optimization, while learning is connected with changes in such limitations on rationality as "state of information" and "technology." In the present model we shall not attempt any further exact translation from the previous concepts, but will start afresh.

The "Berlitz" Model

We suppose that there is an activity in which an individual engages from time to time, and that he can engage in varying amounts of it each day. As he engages in it, it becomes progressively easier for him (this is our "learning" assumption). To the extent that he finds it pleasant, he engages in it more frequently; to the extent he finds it unpleasant, he engages in it less frequently. Its pleasantness depends on how easy it is for him. (The latter two statements comprise our "motivation" assumption.)

As a concrete example, we may suppose that our individual has subscribed to a correspondence course to learn French by the Berlitz method. Each day he spends a certain amount of time in practice. As he practices, the language becomes easier; so long as the difficulty is greater than a certain level, he finds the work unpleasant, and tends to shorten his practice sessions. (We assume our student to be a kind of hedonist.) If he reaches a certain level of skill, however, the work becomes pleasant, and he will tend to practice for a longer period.

Let x be the rate (say, in hours per day) at which the activity is performed. Let D be the level of difficulty, and let us assume (learning) that the difficulty decreases logarithmically with practice:

$$dD/dt = -aDx \qquad (1)$$

Let us assume that at any given level of difficulty, practice is pleasurable up to a certain point, and unpleasant beyond that point, and that $x = \bar{x}(D)$ is this satiation level of activity. We assume then (motivation) that:

$$dx/dt = -b(x - \bar{x}) \qquad (2)$$

The two equations for dD/dt and dx/dt permit us to predict the time paths of D and x if we know their initial values, D_0 and x_0 at time t_0. Several representative time paths are shown in Figure 1.

The figure shows that whether our student eventually becomes discouraged and fails to complete his course, or whether he is successful in learning French depends on his starting point (and, of course, on the relative magnitudes of a and b and the shape of $\bar{x}(D)$). The value of D_0 represents the difficulty of the language

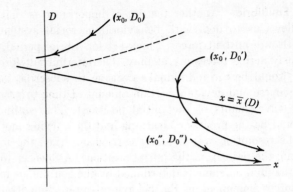

Figure 1

to him at the outset, and x_0 the amount of time he initially de-
votes to practice, If the point (x_0, D_0) lies above the dotted line,
he will ultimately become discouraged and give up his lessons;
if, instead, he begins at (x_0', D_0'), between the dotted line and the
line $x = \bar{x}(D)$, he will suffer some discouragement at the outset,
but practice will ultimately become pleasant and he will learn
the language. If he begins at (x_0'', D_0''), practice will be pleasant
from the outset, and he will learn.

Clearly one would want to refine this model before trying to
verify it from actual situations, but even in its highly simple
form it exhibits some of the qualitative features we would expect to find in such situations, and illustrates in what a natural
manner differential equations can be employed in a model of
adaptive behavior.

Prediction and Verification.   One interesting feature of a model
of this sort is that it permits qualitative predictions to be made
that are very easy to test empirically. We do not need to trace out
in detail the time path of the system, but merely to observe
whether the activity terminates before learning was completed,
or whether it ends in mastery of the language. With such observations we can test, over a sample of cases, a prediction like:
*the activity is likely to persist until learning has been achieved
only if the initial rate of practice is above a certain critical level.*

Multiple Equilibria. Another feature of importance is that the model allows us to deal with behavioral or social systems in which both intermittent forces, which act for a brief period, and continuously acting forces are at play. The intermittent force in this case would be the individual's decision to subscribe to the language course and devote a certain amount of time to practice (i.e., the determinants of the initial position). The continuous forces would be the process of learning and the varying motivation as the resolution was actually carried out (i.e., the forces determining the path from the initial position). A Spencer would say that the final outcome is determined by the continuous interplay of forces immanent in the behavioral interaction itself; a Bentham would say that the outcome is determined by the intermittent intervention—the determination of the initial conditions. The two views are in fact not contradictory provided the system has more than one position of final equilibrium. In this case an intervention can "jar" the system from one position of equilibrium to another.

A possible application of this notion is to the theory of political and social "reform" movements. It is notorious that such movements are short-lived, at least in their active and influential phases. If they are effective, it must be through disturbance of a system of forces previously in equilibrium, and a sufficient shift in initial conditions to permit the system to move toward a new equilibrium with a different stable constellation of forces.

There would seem to be a wide class of social phenomena that could be studied in terms of a model embodying this feature of multiple equilibria. Gunnar Myrdal's theory of social change appears to be of this sort, as do most theories of revolution. The relationship between "formal" organization (which operates in considerable part through intermittent pressures) and "informal" organization might also be expressed in these terms.

A Social Interpretation of the "Berlitz" Model. It might appear that we are not justified in discussing the applicability to social systems of a model that represents, after all, the behavior of a single human being. In fact, however, the writer was originally led to construct this model in order to represent a social situation. In an organization where accountants were given the task of providing accounting information to operating executives, it

was found that if understanding between accountants and operators was good, they tended to communicate frequently with each
other; when it was bad, less frequently. Moreover, frequent communication, by helping them understand each others' languages,
made communication easier. By renaming the variable x "frequency of communication between accountants and operators,"
and the variable D "difficulty of communication between accountants and operators," we obtain in the model a clear representation of this social system.

Further Comments on Motivation

If we compare the notion of motivation in the present model
with the notion of a preference field, discussed earlier, we find
one important difference that has not been mentioned. In a preference field we can say that one alternative is preferable or
"more pleasant" than another, but there is no natural zero-point
for pleasantness: we can distinguish more or less of pleasantness,
but cannot speak of pleasantness and unpleasantness in any absolute sense. In the "Berlitz" model, the function $\bar{x}(D)$ does define such a dividing line, or zero separating pleasantness from
unpleasantness.

We can reconcile the present viewpoint with the earlier one by
supposing that our student, if he does not study his language, can
engage in some other activity which, when $x > \bar{x}$, is more pleasant than the work on his language. Then to say that an activity
is "unpleasant" simply means that there is an alternative that
is preferable. The zero-point of preference for an activity is defined by what the economist would call the "opportunity cost" of
the activity.

From the standpoint of psychological theory, however, it would
appear that a "natural" zero-point can be defined with respect to
motivation. This zero-point arises from two related psychological
mechanisms. The first of these is the dependence of strength of
motivation upon the relationship between the level of aspiration
and the level of achievement. The second of these is the qualitative change in motivation that takes place under conditions of
frustration.

We take as our independent variable the difference between

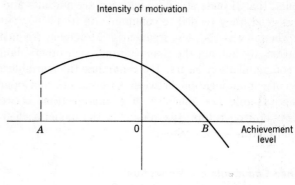

Figure 2

the actual level of skill of an individual in performing a task and the level of skill to which he aspires. If achievement exceeds aspiration, this variable will be positive; if the two are equal, zero; if aspiration exceeds achievement, negative. Now the psychological evidence would appear to indicate that the strength of drive toward the activity is related to achievement in somewhat the fashion indicated in Figure 2.

As the achievement level exceeds B, the drive toward improvement of skill disappears. We may call this "satiation." On the other hand, as the achievement level falls below A, the drive changes its character. Instead of engaging in rational, adaptive behavior, the individual in his frustration engages in behavior best described as non-adaptive or "neurotic."

The evidence generally indicates that frustration will not occur if there are alternative activities available that are regarded as desirable. In this case the aspiration level for the first activity will simply fall, until point B is reached. Frustration occurs when *all* alternatives are regarded by the individual as distinctly unpleasant—when he is faced with a dilemma rather than a choice. But this distinction between dilemma and choice suggests, again, a natural zero of motivation which is distinct from the zero of satiation. The latter would seem to correspond best with the notion of zero opportunity cost.

Equilibrium in Group Interaction

The previous section suggests that in the study of human and social adaptive systems we may be interested not only in the mechanism of adaptation, but also in the possible states of equilibrium of the system. In the present section we will examine a system of social interaction with primary emphasis on equilibrium, and will return more specifically to the question of adaptation in the next section.

The Homans Model

The system to be examined has some intrinsic interest in that it appears to represent fairly well in a formal model some of the theoretical relations postulated by George Homans in *The Human Group*. Homans' system contains four variables (his treatment of them is, of course, verbal rather than mathematical):

(1) The intensity of interaction (or communication) among the members of a group; we will designate it by $T(t)$.

(2) The amount of friendliness (or group identification) among group members; we will designate it by $I(t)$.

(3) The total amount of activity carried on by a member of the group; we will designate it by $W(t)$.

(4) The amount of activity imposed on the group by its external environment (the amount required for its survival); we will designate it by $F(t)$. (Homans also calls it the activity required for survival, the "external system.")

Each of the variables is written as a function of time, and each of the first three is supposed to be some kind of average of the levels for the individual members of the group. Homans nowhere explicitly states his postulates regarding the interrelations of these variables, but the postulates he actually employs would seem to be contained in the following statements:

"If the scheme of activities is changed, the scheme of interaction will, in general, change also, and vice versa."

"Persons who interact frequently with one another tend to like one another."

"If the interactions between the members of a group are frequent in the external system, sentiments of liking will grow up between them, and these sentiments will lead in turn to further interaction over and above the interactions of the external system."

"Persons who feel sentiments of liking for one another will express those sentiments in activities over and above the activities of the external system, and these activities may further strengthen the sentiments of liking."

"The more frequently persons interact with one another, the more alike in some respects both their activities and their sentiments tend to become."

Now these five statements can be approximately translated into three equations among our four variables. The first equation will be algebraic—representing an "instantaneous" or very rapid adjustment. The other two will be differential equations determining paths over time.

$$T = a_1 I + a_2 W \tag{3}$$

$$\frac{dI}{dt} = b(T - \beta I) \tag{4}$$

$$\frac{dW}{dt} = c_1 (I - \gamma W) + c_2 (F - W) \tag{5}$$

The first equation may be translated, roughly: interaction will be reproduced by friendliness and/or group activity. The second: friendliness will tend to increase or decrease as the amount of interaction is disproportionately large or disproportionately small, respectively, in relation to the existing level of friendliness. (The two variables will be in adjustment when $T = \beta I$.) The third: group activity will tend to increase as the level of friendliness is high relative to the existing level of activity (the two being in equilibrium when $I = \gamma W$), and as the requirements of the external system are high relative to the existing level of activity, otherwise group activity will tend to decrease.

By studying these translations—or better, by studying the equations themselves—in relation to Homans' postulates, the reader can judge for himself how well we have succeeded in capturing the essential features of Homans' system in our equations. In any event it is unnecessary to concern ourselves here with the exactness of the representation or the empirical correctness of his postulates.

Now systems of the kind we have just written down (linear differential equations with constant coefficients) are well known to the mathematician, and he can provide us with a well-stocked kit of tools for analysing their behavior. Without going into details of method or result, it may be stated that he can easily find: (1) the equilibrium position of this system, (2) the conditions under which this equilibrium is stable and unstable, and (3) the precise time path the system will follow from any initial position.

Social Disintegration. Among the conclusions that can be drawn from the purely mathematical properties of the system is the following:

If the system represented by equations (3)–(5) is dynamically stable, then as the system of externally imposed activities, F, decreases toward zero, the amounts of interaction, friendliness, and group activity will decrease toward zero (with a lag).

But this is precisely the hypothesis that Homans employs to explain social disintegration in Hilltown, and to explain the difference in extension between the primitive and modern family. Our formal model permits us to demonstrate rigorously that this is not an independent hypothesis, but follows logically from the other postulates if only the system is assumed to be dynamically stable.

Morale and "Anomie." We will cite one further example of the conclusions that mathematical reasoning permits us to draw from the model. One of Homans' empirical statements is that a social group will tend to develop a system of activities more elaborate than that needed to satisfy the requirements of the external system. In one sense we have already incorporated this statement in equation (5)—for this equation says that W will tend to increase not only if F is greater than W, but also when I is greater than γW. That is, friendliness, as well as external requirements can be a source of group activity. But does it follow from this that, when the system has attained equilibrium, W will be greater than F?

Let us define a group as possessing "positive morale" if, when the group is in a state of equilibrium, W exceeds F—the actual level of activity is higher than that required for survival. When this condition is not satisfied, we will say that the group possesses "negative morale." It can be shown from equations (3)–(5) that the group will possess positive morale if and only if $a_2 > \gamma(\beta - a_1)$. To see what the condition means we note that, in particular, it will be satisfied if a_2 is sufficiently large—that is, if the amount of interaction required per unit of group activity is large. This can be stated in still another way: group morale will be positive if there is a sufficiently high degree of interrelation among the members' tasks, requiring much communication for their performance. But this is, in substance, the central proposition of Durkheim's theory of *anomie*—a proposition that has received considerable empirical verification in work situations from the Hawthorne studies and their successors.

5

Functional Applications:

Statistical

During the 1930's mathematical psychology in America went statistical with a vengeance.

That is not to say that psychologists were innocent of statistics before 1930. Many of them, especially those who studied individual differences, were quite good statisticians. They had inherited the statistical tools of their trade from Francis Galton and Karl Pearson, who in turn had fashioned them from the mathematical theory of probability developed during the eighteenth and nineteenth centuries. "Statistics," wrote Galton, "are the only tools by which an opening can be cut through the formidable thicket of difficulties that bars the path of those who pursue the Science of Man." Those who followed Galton's path in psychology—Alfred Binet, James McKeen Cattell, Edward Lee Thorndike, Emil Kraepelin, Charles Spearman, Lewis M. Terman, William Stern, and many others—were less interested in the universal than in the differential aspects of mental life. Inspired by Darwinism, they searched for the kind of individual variability that makes evolution possible. And in the pursuit of such interests Galton was surely correct; statistics are the only tools.

Galton—himself a sometime psychologist—contributed one of the most valuable tools when in 1889 he summarized a decade of statistical work in his book on *Natural Inheritance*. He was concerned with measuring the hereditary resemblance of children to their parents, and his problem led him to discover the theory of regression and of correlation. His book attracted three students to Galton: F. Y. Edgeworth, W. F. E. Weldon, and Karl Pearson. Among them they gave the theory of correlation its present mathematical form, began a new journal *Biometrika* to publish their research, and established the modern science of mathematical statistics as a thriving enterprise. From the very first Galton seemed to know how important his discovery would be. "I have a great subject to write upon," he said in the introduction to his 1889 book. "It is full of interest of its own. It familiarizes us with the measurement of variability, and with curious laws of chance that apply to a vast diversity of social subjects."

In the best of all possible laboratories, $y = f(x)$ would be a precise function. Of course, there would usually be some small discrepancies between the theoretically computed value of y and its measured value. As early as 1885 Ebbinghaus had discussed the errors of measuring memory in these general terms. There was a true or *mean* value, but the actual observations were distributed on either side of it according to a bell-shaped curve of errors; the size of the error—how broad or how narrow the bell-shaped distribution was—could be measured by the *standard deviation* of the distribution. Such errors could, in principal at least, be reduced to whatever level an experimenter required and had the patience to attain. Unfortunately, however, in any real psychological laboratory this ideally precise function is seldom seen. Given some particular value of x, repeated measurements of y will generally produce a statistical distribution with a great deal more dispersion around the average (a larger standard deviation) than the experimenter could possibly eliminate. There is often a functional relation lurking somewhere behind the variability, but it is a heavily statistical kind of relation. That is to say, predictions of y based on a knowledge of x will have only a statistical validity; they will be about right on the average, but in any individual instance they may be far wide of the mark.

For example, consider the function relating the heights of parents to the heights of their children. Let x be the average for the two parents and y be the value for the child. What is the function f

that predicts y from a knowledge of x? Several facts are obvious: Some kind of relation exists, because children do bear a resemblance to their parents. But it is equally obvious that the relation is not precise, because several children all of the same parents will not all have precisely the same heights. Moreover, the source of this variability is not some careless error of measurement, because the ruler can be accurately applied to every member of the family without eliminating the dispersion. Finally, it is obvious that the problem is a symmetrical one, because the children's heights could just as well be used to predict the parent's. In addition to $y = f(x)$, we must have $x = g(y)$, where the function g is in some sense the reciprocal of the function f. Yet it is not precisely true that $g = f^{-1}$ because of a phenomenon that Galton termed "regression" toward the mean.

Galton noticed that when he made the best prediction he could of y on the basis of x he often got a linear function f, and when he predicted x on the basis of y he got another linear function g. If s represents a slope constant, then $f(x) = s_1 x$ and $g(y) = s_2 y$ (where x and y are expressed as deviations above or below their general average). The closer the relation between the two variables x and y, the closer slope s_1 came to the reciprocal of slope s_2. In the special case when the relation was absolutely precise, $s_1 = 1/s_2$. It was possible, therefore, to use the slopes of these two functions as the basis for a measure of how tightly one variable was tied to the other. This was Galton's insight. The mathematical details were put in order a few years later by Karl Pearson, who developed the formula for computing the product-moment *correlation coefficient* r that expressed the degree of relation between the two variables: $r = \pm\sqrt{s_1 s_2}$. This coefficient equals $+1.0$ when the correlation is perfect; when there is only a tendency for the two variables to go together, then r becomes a fraction that decreases as the tendency decreases; when the variables are completely independent, $r = 0$; and when one variable increases as the other decreases, r becomes negative, with -1 being a perfectly precise inverse function.

Correlational analysis quickly developed as an important technique of applied mathematics, not just in psychology but in all branches of science and technology where precise functional relations were not easily demonstrated. The first psychologists to exploit the new idea were those interested in measuring intelligence, for it enabled them to say in a relatively precise fashion how similar any two sets of measurements were. Because many different tests were proposed as indicators of intelligence, this enterprise involved many different sets of measurements. And for n sets of measurements there would be $n(n-1)/2$ correlation coefficients. The problem quickly became one of discovering some structure underlying these large collections of correlation coefficients—but that is a development we will postpone until the next chapter.

It should be noted, however, that the correlation coefficient does not tell us what the functional relation is between two variables (the regression equations in f and g tell us that), but merely indicates how closely related the variables are, how predictable one is from the other.

Another kind of statistical competence among psychologists grew up around the study of psychophysics. The threshold, which was so central to all psychophysical analysis, turned out to be a statistical concept. When the difference between two stimuli is very small, an observer will have only a 50–50 chance of judging it correctly; but when it is large enough the probability is nearly perfect. The appropriate statistics to use for analyzing this psychometric function were an object of much study and debate.

At first psychologists reasoned that there must be two distinct phenomena involved in the psychometric function, one that governs the true size of the threshold and another that introduces more or less random errors of measurement. As early as 1900, however, L. M. Solomons* realized that these are not distinct phenomena, but that inherent variability is the basic fact that accounts for the existence of a threshold.

Solomons argued that the receptivity of the sensory centers in the brain fluctuates from moment to moment. The sensation S that results must depend on both the stimulus magnitude s and "the brain state I"—Solomons assumed that $S = sI$—so the sensation S will also vary as the brain state I varies. "If we are

* L. M. Solomons, A new explanation of Weber's Law. *Psychol. Rev.*, 1900, **7**, 234–240.

affected in succession by two stimuli of the same intensity," he wrote,

sometimes one, sometimes the other will seem to be greater, depending on the value of I at the moment. In general one will seem to be greater as often as the other, so that if in fact there is a very slight difference between the stimuli the judgment will be correct as often as incorrect. As this difference increases, however, the proportion of correct judgments will increase; for as the differences in the value of I are of all grades, it will often happen that the actual difference in the value of s will counteract the difference in the value of I and a stimulus be correctly judged as greater than the preceding, though the value of I be less. For any given difference between the stimuli there will be a corresponding percentage of correct judgments, the percentage depending upon the extent and distribution of the variations in I. The probability of a given difference being perceived is the probability of the difference between the two values of I being less than the difference between the stimuli.

This is a remarkably modern idea to have been conceived in 1900, when the psychophysical theories of Wilhelm Wundt and G. E. Müller still dominated the field. It took more than a quarter of a century before this statistical argument gained general acceptance. Yet Solomons's explanation of Weber's Law was so simple: if $S = sI$, then "the variations of S due to I are given by the equation $dS = sdI$," Solomons continued, "while those due to the actual change of s by $dS = Ids$. For the threshold these values must be equal, which gives $Ids = sdI$, whence $ds = sdI/I$." This is, of course, Weber's Law, which states that $ds/s =$ constant, but with the constant now being interpreted as the ratio of the variation of I to the value of I—that is, the relative variation in the condition of the sensory system. To Solomons, Weber's Law simply meant that sensory variability is constant, independent of the intensity of stimulation.

In 1900, however, psychology was not yet ready for statistical explanations. It was not ready until 1927 when L. L. Thurstone, apparently quite independently, developed the same argument, dressed it in more formal attire, and generalized it to many problems of measurement other than the narrowly psychophysical ones. Before Thurstone was finished with it a whole new attitude toward statistical theories had developed in psychology.

Statistical thinking began to permeate all aspects of psychological theory. After 1930 the idea began to spread among psychologists that there is something intrinsically interesting about the unpredictability of living systems, that randomness is something a successful organism must cope with—and may even learn to take advantage of. This new attitude permitted psychologists to introduce statistical concepts into the basic axioms of their theories, rather than tacking them on afterwards as annoying perturbations in an otherwise determinate process.

Once psychologists generally accepted the challenge of statistical reasoning, a whole new style of mathematical psychology became possible. Thurstone at the University of Chicago was the leader in developing this new style. In the period from 1927 to 1931 Thurstone (1) rewrote psychophysics around his conception of "discriminal dispersion" and (2) made his argument the basis for a method of measuring attitudes.* He also (3) formulated the first truly statistical theory of learning, and (4) developed multi-factor analyses, a method for exploring the structure underlying a matrix of correlation coefficients. It was an amazingly productive period in Thurstone's life. Mathematical psychology has never been the same since.

Thurstone regarded his papers on psychophysical analysis as his best contribution to psychology; he held this opinion in spite of the much greater quantity of work inspired by his formulation of multiple-factor analysis. Thurstone's psychophysical argument begins just as Solomons's did by assuming that there is some intrinsic variability in an organism's response to a stimulus. Thurstone's addition to this idea, however, was his realization that the standard deviation of that variability could be used as a unit of measurement. This was, essentially, a statistical reformulation of Fechner's original insight. Fechner had said that the difference threshold, or jnd, could be used as a unit for psychological measurement. Once the difference threshold was explained in terms of the variability of discrimination, therefore, Fechner's original unit became transformed into Thurstone's

* A collection of 27 of Thurstone's articles on these topics have been published under the title *The measurement of values*. Chicago: University of Chicago Press, 1959.

standard deviation. As Thurstone presented the argument, however, it became obvious that this unit was entirely independent
of any physical measurements of the stimulus; the unit could be
applied to attitudes just as easily as to sensations. And so the
pleasures of mathematical reasoning were made available to a
much larger number of psychologists.

In his first paper* on this topic Thurstone derived the basic
equation underlying his law of comparative judgment. If stimulus 1 produces an effect with a mean of S_1 and a standard deviation of σ_1, and if stimulus 2 produces an effect with a mean of
S_2, and a standard deviation of σ_2, then it is a straightforward
statistical argument to show that the distribution of the differences in the effects of stimuli 1 and 2 will have a mean value of
$S_1 - S_2$ and a standard deviation of $\sqrt{\sigma_1 + \sigma_2 - 2\,r\sigma_1\sigma_2}$ where r
is the correlation (if any) between judgments of the two stimuli.
If we use this standard deviation as the unit of measurement, we
have

$$\frac{S_1 - S_2}{\sqrt{\sigma_1 + \sigma_2 - 2r\sigma_1\sigma_2}} = x_{12},$$

where x_{12} is the number of standard deviation units separating S_1
from S_2. If we assume, as Thurstone did, that the distribution of
differences is normal (or "Gaussian"), x_{12} will correspond to a
certain proportion of judgments that S_1 is greater (or less) than
S_2, and this proportion can be found by looking it up in a table
of the normal probability integral. In practice, of course, the procedure is just the reverse: the experiment gives us a proportion
of judgments of greater (or less), and from the probability table
we determine x_{12}. If we know the values of x_{ij} for several pairs of
stimuli, therefore, we can solve a set of simultaneous equations to
determine S_i and σ_i for each of the stimuli.

In the following excerpt Thurstone reviews the rationale for
this law and then proceeds to consider five cases that result from
making various simplifying assumptions.

* L. L. Thurstone. Psychophysical analysis. *Amer. J. Psychol.*, 1927, **38**,
368–389.

Louis Leon Thurstone

A Law of Comparative Judgment

The object of this paper is to describe a new psychophysical law which may be called the *law of comparative judgment* and to show some of its special applications in the measurement of psychological values. The law of comparative judgment is implied in Weber's law and in Fechner's law. The law of comparative judgment is applicable not only to the comparison of physical stimulus intensities but also to qualitative comparative judgments such as those of excellence of specimens in an educational scale and it has been applied in the measurement of such psychological values as a series of opinions on disputed public issues. The latter application of the law will be illustrated in a forthcoming study. It should be possible also to verify it on comparative judgments which involve simultaneous and successive contrast.

The law has been derived in a previous article and the present study is mainly a description of some of its applications. Since several new concepts are involved in the formulation of the law it has been necessary to invent several terms to describe them, and these will be repeated here.

Let us suppose that we are confronted with a series of stimuli or specimens such as a series of gray values, cylindrical weights, handwriting specimens, childrens drawings, or any other series of stimuli that are subject to comparisons. The first requirement is of course a specification as to what it is that we are to judge or compare. It may be gray values, or weights, or excellence, or any other quantitative or qualitative attribute about which we

L. L. Thurstone, A law of comparative judgment, *Psychol. Rev.*, 1927, **34**, 273–286.
Pp. 273–282 reprinted by permission of the American Psychological Association.

can think "more" or "less" for each specimen. This attribute which may be assigned, as it were, in differing amounts to each specimen defines what we shall call the *psychological continuum* for that particular project in measurement.

As we inspect two or more specimens for the task of comparison there must be some kind of process in us by which we react differently to the several specimens, by which we identify the several degrees of excellence or weight or gray value in the specimens. You may suit your own predilections in calling this process psychical, neural, chemical, or electrical but it will be called here in a non-committal way *the discriminal process* because its ultimate nature does not concern the formulation of the law of comparative judgment. If then, one handwriting specimen *seems* to be more excellent than a second specimen, then the two discriminal processes of the observer are different, at least on this occasion.

The so-called "just noticeable difference" is contingent on the fact that an observer is not consistent in his comparative judgments from one occasion to the next. He gives different comparative judgments on successive occasions about the same pair of stimuli. Hence we conclude that the discriminal process corresponding to a given stimulus is not fixed. It fluctuates. For any handwriting specimen, for example, there is one discriminal process that is experienced more often with that specimen than other processes which correspond to higher or lower degrees of excellence. This most common process is called here *the modal discriminal process for the given stimulus*.

The psychological continuum or scale is so constructed or defined that the frequencies of the respective discriminal processes for any given stimulus form a normal distribution of the psychological scale. This involves no assumption of a normal distribution or of anything else. The psychological scale is at best an artificial construct. If it has any physical reality we certainly have not the remotest idea what it may be like. We do not assume, therefore, that the distribution of discriminal processes is normal on the scale because that would imply that the scale is there already. We *define* the scale in terms of the frequencies of the discriminal processes for any stimulus. This artificial construct, the psychological scale, is so spaced off that the frequencies of the discriminal processes for any given stimulus form a normal distribution on the scale. The separation on the scale between the discriminal process for a given stimulus on any particular occasion and the modal discriminal process for that stimulus we shall call *the discriminal deviation* on that occasion. If on a particular occasion, the observer perceives more than the usual degree of excellence or weight in the specimen in question, the discriminal deviation is at that instant positive. In a similar manner the discriminal deviation at another moment will be negative.

The standard deviation of the distribution of discriminal processes on the scale for a particular specimen will be called its *discriminal dispersion.*

This is the central concept in the present analysis. An ambiguous stimulus which is observed at widely different degrees of excellence or weight or gray value on different occasions will have of course a large discriminal dispersion. Some other stimulus or specimen which is provocative of relatively slight fluctuations in discriminal processes will have, similarly, a small discriminal dispersion.

The scale difference between the discriminal processes of two specimens which are involved in the same judgment will be called *the discriminal difference* on that occasion. If the two stimuli be denoted A and B and if the discriminal processes corresponding to them be denoted a and b on any one occasion, then the discriminal difference will be the scale distance $(a - b)$ which varies of course on different occasions. If, in one of the comparative judgments, A seems to be better than B, then, on that occasion, the discriminal difference $(a - b)$ is positive. If, on another occasion, the stimulus B seems to be the better, then on that occasion the discriminal difference $(a - b)$ is negative.

Finally, the scale distance between the modal discriminal processes for any two specimens is the separation which is assigned to the two specimens on the psychological scale. The two specimens are so allocated on the scale that their separation is equal to the separation between their respective modal discriminal processes.

We can now state the law of comparative judgment as follows:

$$S_1 - S_2 = x_{12} \cdot \sqrt{\sigma_1{}^2 + \sigma_2{}^2 - 2r\sigma_1\sigma_2}, \tag{1}$$

in which S_1 and S_2 are the psychological scale values of the two compared stimuli.

> x_{12} = the sigma value corresponding to the proportion of judgments $p_{1>2}$. When $p_{1>2}$ is greater than .50 the numerical value of x_{12} is positive. When $p_{1>2}$ is less than .50 the numerical value of x_{12} is negative.
>
> σ_1 = discriminal dispersion of stimulus R_1.
>
> σ_2 = discriminal dispersion of stimulus R_2.
>
> r = correlation between the discriminal deviations of R_1 and R_2 in the same judgment.

This law of comparative judgment is basic for all experimental work on Weber's law, Fechner's law, and for all educational and psychological scales in which comparative judgments are involved. Its derivation will not be repeated here because it has been described in a previous article.[1] It applies fundamentally to the judgments of *a single observer* who compares a series of stimuli by the method of paired comparison when no "equal" judgments are allowed. It is a rational equation for the method of constant stimuli. It is assumed that the single observer compares each pair of stimuli a sufficient number of times so that a proportion, $p_{a>b}$, may be determined for each pair of stimuli.

For the practical application of the law of comparative judgment we shall consider five cases which differ in assumptions, approximations, and degree of simplification. The more assumptions we care to make, the simpler will be the observation equations. These five cases are as follows:

Case I.   The equation can be used in its complete form for paired comparison data obtained from a single subject when only two judgments are allowed for each observation such as "heavier" or "lighter," "better" or "worse," etc. There will be one observation

---

[1] L. L. Thurstone, Psychophysical analysis. *Amer. J. Psychol.*, July, 1927.

equation for every observed proportion of judgments. It would be written, in its complete form, thus:

$$S_1 - S_2 - x_{12} \cdot \sqrt{\sigma_1{}^2 + \sigma_2{}^2 - 2r\sigma_1\sigma_2} = 0. \qquad (1)$$

According to this equation every pair of stimuli presents the possibility of a different correlation between the discriminal deviations. If this degree of freedom is allowed, the problem of psychological scaling would be insoluble because every observation equation would introduce a new unknown and the number of unknowns would then always be greater than the number of observation equations. In order to make the problem soluble, it is necessary to make at least one assumption, namely that the correlation between discriminal deviations is practically constant throughout the stimulus series and for the single observer. Then, if we have n stimuli or specimens in the scale, we shall have $\frac{1}{2} \cdot n(n-1)$ observation equations when each specimen is compared with every other specimen. Each specimen has a scale value, S_1, and a discriminal dispersion, σ_1, to be determined. There are therefore $2n$ unknowns. The scale value of one of the specimens is chosen as an origin and its discriminal dispersion as a unit of measurement, while r is an unknown which is assumed to be constant for the whole series. Hence, for a scale of n specimens there will be $(2n-1)$ unknowns. The smallest number of specimens for which the problem is soluble is five. For such a scale there will be nine unknowns, four scale values, four discriminal dispersions, and r. For a scale of five specimens there will be ten observation equations.

The statement of the law of comparative judgment in the form of equation 1 involves one theoretical assumption which is probably of minor importance. It assumes that all positive discriminal differences $(a - b)$ are judged $A > B$, and that all negative discriminal differences $(a - b)$ are judged $A < B$. This is probably not absolutely correct when the discriminal differences of either sign are very small. The assumption would not affect the experimentally observed proportion $p_{A>B}$ if the small positive discriminal differences occurred as often as the small negative ones. As a matter of fact, when $p_{A>B}$ is greater than .50 the small positive discriminal differences $(a - b)$ are slightly more frequent than the negative perceived differences $(a-b)$. It is probable that rather refined experimental procedures are necessary to isolate this effect. The effect is ignored in our present analysis.

Case II. The law of comparative judgment as described under Case I refers fundamentally to a series of judgments *of a single observer*. It does not constitute an assumption to say that the discriminal processes for a single observer give a normal frequency distribution on the psychological continuum. That is a part of the definition of the psychological scale. But it does constitute an assumption to take for granted that the various degrees of an attribute of a specimen perceived in it by *a group* of subjects is a normal distribution. For example, if a weight-cylinder is lifted by an observer several hundred times in comparison with other cylinders, it is possible to define or construct the psychological scale so that the distribution of the apparent weights of the cylinder for the single observer is normal. It is probably safe to assume that the distribution of apparent weights for *a group* of subjects, each subject perceiving the weight only once, is also normal on the same scale. To transfer the reasoning in the same way from a single observer to a group of observers for specimens such as handwriting or English Composition is not so certain. For practical purposes it may be assumed that when *a group* of observers perceives a specimen of handwriting, the distribution of excellence that they read into the specimen is normal on the psychological continuum of perceived excellence. At least this is a safe assumption if the group is not split in some curious way with prejudices for or against particular elements of the specimen.

With the assumption just described, the law of comparative judgment, derived for the method of constant stimuli with two responses, can be extended to data collected from a group of judges in which each judge compares each stimulus with every other stimulus only once. The other assumptions of Case I apply also to Case II.

Case III. Equation 1 is awkward to handle as an observation equation for a scale with a large number of specimens. In fact the arithmetical labor of constructing an educational or psychological scale with it is almost prohibitive. The equation can be simplified if the correlation r can be assumed to be either zero or unity. It is a safe assumption that when the stimulus series is very homogeneous with no distracting attributes, the correlation between discriminal deviations is low and possibly even zero unless we encounter the effect of simultaneous or successive contrast. If we accept the correlation as zero, we are really assuming that the degree of excellence which an observer perceives in one of the specimens has no influence on the degree of excellence that he perceives in the comparison specimen. There are two effects that may be operative here and which are antagonistic to each other.

(1) If you look at two handwriting specimens in a mood slightly more generous and tolerant than ordinarily, you may perceive a degree of excellence in specimen A a little higher than its mean excellence. But at the same moment specimen B is also judged a little higher than its average or mean excellence for the same reason. To the extent that such a factor is at work the discriminal deviations will tend to vary together and the correlation r will be high and positive.

(2) The opposite effect is seen in *simultaneous contrast*. When the correlation between the discriminal deviations is negative the law of comparative judgment gives an exaggerated psychological difference $(S_1 - S_2)$ which we know as simultaneous or successive contrast. In this type of comparative judgment the discriminal deviations are negatively associated. It is probable that this effect tends to be a minimum when the specimens have other perceivable attributes, and that it is a maximum when other distracting stimulus differences are removed. If this statement should be experimentally verified, it would constitute an interesting generalization in perception.

If our last generalization is correct, it should be a safe assumption to write $r = 0$ for those scales in which the specimens are rather complex such as handwriting specimens and childrens drawings. If we look at two handwriting specimens and perceive one of them as unusually fine, it probably tends to depress somewhat the degree of excellence we would ordinarily perceive in the comparison specimen, but this effect is slight compared with the simultaneous contrast perceived in lifted weights and in gray values. Furthermore, the simultaneous contrast is slight with small stimulus differences and it must be recalled that psychological scales are based on comparisons in the subliminal or barely supraliminal range.

The correlation between discriminal deviations is probably high when the two stimuli give simultaneous contrast and are quite far apart on the scale. When the range for the correlation is reduced to a scale distance comparable with the difference limen, the correlation probably is reduced nearly to zero. At any rate, in order to simplify equation 1 we shall assume that it is zero. This represents the comparative judgment in which the evaluation of one of the specimens has no influence on the evaluation of the other specimen in the paired judgment. The law then takes the following form.

$$S_1 - S_2 = x_{12} \cdot \sqrt{\sigma_1{}^2 + \sigma_2{}^2}. \tag{2}$$

Case IV. If we can make the additional assumption that the discriminal dispersions are not subject to gross variation, we can considerably simplify the equation so that it becomes linear and therefore much easier to handle. In equation (2) we let

$$\sigma_2 = \sigma_1 + d,$$

in which d is assumed to be at least smaller than σ_1 and preferably a fraction of σ_1 such as .1 to .5. Then equation (2) becomes

$$\begin{aligned}
S_1 - S_2 &= x_{12} \cdot \sqrt{\sigma_1{}^2 + \sigma_2{}^2} \\
&= x_{12} \cdot \sqrt{\sigma_1{}^2 + (\sigma_1 + d)^2} \\
&= x_{12} \cdot \sqrt{\sigma_1{}^2 + \sigma_1{}^2 + 2\sigma_1 d + d^2}.
\end{aligned}$$

If d is small, the term d^2 may be dropped. Hence

$$\begin{aligned}
S_1 - S_2 &= x_{12} \cdot \sqrt{2\sigma_1{}^2 + 2\sigma_1 d} \\
&= x_{12} \cdot \sqrt{2\sigma_1} (\sigma_1 + d)^{\frac{1}{2}}.
\end{aligned}$$

Expanding $(\sigma_1 + d)^{1/2}$ we have

$$(\sigma_1 + d)^{1/2} = \sigma_1{}^{1/2} + \tfrac{1}{2}\sigma_1{}^{-(1/2)}d - \tfrac{1}{4}\sigma_1{}^{-(3/2)}d^2$$

$$= \sqrt{\sigma_1} + \frac{d}{2\sqrt{\sigma_1}} - \frac{d^2}{4\sqrt{\sigma_1{}^3}}.$$

The third term may be dropped when d^2 is small. Hence

$$(\sigma_1 + d)^{1/2} = \sqrt{\sigma_1} + \frac{d}{2\sqrt{\sigma_1}}.$$

Substituting,

$$S_1 - S_2 = x_{12} \cdot \sqrt{2\sigma_1} \left[\sqrt{\sigma_1} + \frac{d}{2\sqrt{\sigma_1}} \right]$$

$$= x_{12} \left[\sigma_1\sqrt{2} + \frac{d}{\sqrt{2}} \right].$$

But $d = \sigma_2 - \sigma_1$;

$$\therefore S_1 - S_2 = x_{12} \frac{\sigma_2}{\sqrt{2}} + x_{12} \frac{\sigma_1}{\sqrt{2}}$$

or

$$S_1 - S_2 = .707x_{12}\sigma_2 + .707x_{12}\sigma_1. \tag{3}$$

Equation (3) is linear and very easily handled. If $\sigma_2 - \sigma_1$ is small compared with σ_1, equation (3) gives a close approximation to the true values of S and σ for each specimen.

If there are n stimuli in the scale there will be $(2n - 2)$ unknowns, namely a scale value S and a discriminal dispersion σ for each specimen. The scale value for one of the specimens may be chosen as the origin or zero since the origin of the psychological scale is arbitrary. The discriminal dispersion of the same specimen may be chosen as a unit of measurement for the scale. With n specimens in the series there will be $\frac{1}{2}n(n-1)$ observation equations. The minimum number of specimens for which the scaling problem can be solved is then four, at which number we have six observation equations and six unknowns.

Case V. The simplest case involves the assumption that all the discriminal dispersions are equal. This may be legitimate for rough measurement such as Thorndike's handwriting scale or the Hillegas scale of English Composition. Equation (2) then becomes

$$S_1 - S_2 = x_{12} \cdot \sqrt{2\sigma^2}$$

$$= x_{12}\sigma \cdot \sqrt{2}.$$

But since the assumed constant discriminal dispersion is the unit of measurement we have

$$S_1 - S_2 = 1.4142x_{12}. \qquad (4)$$

This is a simple observation equation which may be used for rather coarse scaling. It measures the scale distance between two specimens as directly proportional to the sigma value of the observed proportion of judgments $p_{1\,>2}$. This is the equation that is basic for Thorndike's procedure in scaling handwriting and children's drawings although he has not shown the theory underlying his scaling procedure. His unit of measurement was the standard deviation of the discriminal differences which is $.707\sigma$ when the discriminal dispersions are constant. In future scaling problems equation (3) will probably be found to be the most useful.

* * *

Most applications of Thurstone's law of comparative judgment have used Case V, which is the simplest of all. As subsequent authors* have pointed out, the simplifying assumptions for Case V need not be quite as strong as Thurstone makes them look. In particular, nothing is changed but an irrelevant scale factor if we assume that the correlation is not necessarily zero, but simply that it is constant between all pairs of stimuli.

Thurstone's fertile contributions were one of the main reasons that mathematical psychology took on a statistical flavor and began to flourish during the 1930's. But there were other forces working in the same direction. That was also the decade when psychologists were learning the statistical methods of R. A. Fisher†—small sample statistics, analysis of variance, design of

* L. Guttman, An approach for quantifying paired comparisons and rank order. *Annals math. Stat.*, 1946, **17**, 144–163. F. Mosteller, Remarks on the method of paired comparisons: I. The least squares solution assuming equal standard deviations and equal correlations, *Psychometrika*, 1951, **16**, 3–9.

† The first edition of Fisher's *Statistical Methods for Research Workers* was published in 1925, but its first impact on American psychology was felt during the 1930's. His book *The Design of Experiments* appeared in 1935.

experiments, and so on—which quickly became a required topic in every psychology curriculum.

Thurstone and Fisher together were more than enough to revolutionize mathematical psychology, but there were still other influences moving in the same general direction.

In a nearby discipline George Kingsley Zipf was vigorously pursuing his statistical studies in language.* Zipf found remarkably stable distribution functions governing the frequencies of occurrence of various words. Moreover, they were laws that seemed universal, that held for different people, even for different languages. These were the kinds of universal laws that many psychologists had dreamed of finding—and they were statistical in nature.

Meanwhile, attitude measurement and public-opinion polling, which began with Thurstone, were blossoming into a profitable business. There was considerable interest among sociologists and social psychologists in these new techniques of sampling and scaling. And in 1936 J. P. Guilford published his influential text, *Psychometric Methods,* which pulled together the psychophysical and mental-testing traditions and placed them both, in the manner of Thurstone, on a statistical foundation.

It was also during the 1930's that Egon Brunswik began to emphasize the statistical aspects of the stimulus energies that impinge on an active organism. Before Brunswik began to ponder the fickle and inconstant world we live in, T-maze experiments had been relatively simple. Food was always placed in one arm of the T; a hungry rat was then released at the foot of the T and allowed to explore one of the two arms. If he took the correct turn, he always found food; if not, he found nothing. But Brunswik felt this was highly unrealistic. In his T-maze, therefore, a rat might find food 75 per cent of the times he turned one way, but only 25 per cent of the times he turned the other way. Brunswik's rat had to discriminate, not presence from absence, but high probability from low.† How the rat's probabilities come

* G. K. Zipf, *The psycho-biology of language.* Boston: Houghton Mifflin, 1935.

† E. Brunswik, Probability as a determiner of rat behavior. *J. exp. Psychol.,* 1939, **25,** 175–197.

into equilibrium with the experimenter's probabilities in this situation has ever since been a favorite topic for various statistical theories of learning. For Brunswik, however, it was merely one example of his probabilistic conception of psychology. The environment, he argued, is full of imperfectly correlated processes; our task is to learn to use some processes as cues for others, and so eventually through much experience to construct a valid picture of the world around us.

But a semi-erratic environment is not the only source of randomness in our psychological theories. Another great and obvious source lies within the organism itself. The nervous system is a vast collection of individual nerve cells whose activities may be dependable on the average, but which must certainly be unpredictable in isolation. One of the first biologists to take a statistical view of the nervous system was the visual physiologist W. J. Crozier, who objected strongly to the simple photochemical theory of vision proposed by Selig Hecht and his students. Crozier was convinced that the higher centers in the nervous system must also be taken into account. But how can such a tremendously complicated neural system be summarized by a few simple equations? Crozier thought he had found his answer in statistics. The general drift of his ideas can be seen in the following excerpt from a research paper published in 1940.

* * *

William John Crozier

ΔI as a *Function of Intensity*

The nature of the functional dependence of the sensorially least discriminable increment of intensity (ΔI) upon the magnitude of

W. J. Crozier, On the law for minimal discrimination of intensities, IV: ΔI as a function of intensity. *Proc. Natl. Acad. Sci.*, 1940, 26, 382–386 reprinted by permission of the National Academy of Sciences.

the prevailing intensity level (I_1) has long been recognized as presenting a problem of fundamental interest. The literature concerning it, experimental and theoretical, is full of tantalizing curiosities, and is voluminous to the point of generating stupefaction. Although enormous labor, in the aggregate, has been directed toward establishing a rational basis for the data of differential sensitivity, no even approximately satisfactory solution has been proposed thus far. The chief reason for this is to be found, I suspect, in the curious fascination of the "Weber fraction" $\Delta I/I$. The intensity of Fechner's realization of the psychophysical significance of the properties of ΔI largely succeeded in fastening attention on the seductive possibilities supposed to follow upon the fact that the "Weber fraction" might be (or "ought" to be) a constant. The chief consequence of this was that the academic and essentially artificial problem of the constancy or inconstancy of the ratio $\Delta I/I$ came to dominate a very considerable area of psychophysics.

A certain degree of sanity was introduced into this matter by Hecht's insistence that the more realistic problem, and the theoretical opportunity, is found not in the "constancy" of $\Delta I/I$ but in the reasons for its systematic behavior as a function of intensity. The rational theory of intensive discrimination has continued to be very largely occupied with the consideration of the properties of $\Delta I/I$ or sometimes of $I/\Delta I$.

The reasons leading to a rejection of these considerations are of two general sorts. I am referring to the rejection of what I have just termed the current rational theory of intensive discrimination; I am not discussing those attempted formulations of the data which depend only on the use of more or less convenient but not experimentally supported equations, because any number of such formulations can be found and consequently no one of them has of itself any real analytical significance; moreover, none of them thus far detected actually describes the data or takes adequate account of their known properties. The current rational theory of intensive discrimination has had a considerable (although not a completely inclusive) success in giving descriptive formulae for the dependence of visual $\Delta I/I$ upon I. The data of visual intensive discrimination cover a wider range of intensities, in more different kinds of organisms, than are available with other types of sensory excitation; and they are in some important respects less complicated by the mechanical conditions of sensory reception. For reasons which Hecht has discussed in detail it has been attractive to suppose that the quantity ΔI is (visually) one which produces a certain amount or rate of decomposition of photosensory receptor substance in a system adapted to I_1. The main reasons for rejecting this approach are (1) that there is no necessity for assuming that the magnitude or the properties of ΔI are determined peripherally in the receptor, and (2) there is no reason whatever to accept the assumption that the threshold effect is a physically constant effect. While the resulting equations provide a certain (but incomplete) description of the data, this is surely no argument for their uniqueness and does not by itself validate the assumptions from which they are derived.

The matter may be approached in a quite different way, with the help of simple assumptions for which there is now considerable direct support of a totally different sort. These assumptions avoid most, if not indeed all, of the general difficulties already referred to. The chief assumptions are: (1) the relation of sensory effect E to $\log I$ is given by a normal probability integral; the various aspects of "effect produced" as a function of intensity, when objectively measurable, do adhere to this formulation, and the reason for it is deducible in an elementary way; (2) the reciprocal of the exciting intensity measures the capacity to be excited under the conditions and with reference to the end-point of effect employed; the types of justification for this assumption are numerous, and include especially the rational behavior of the three parameters of the probability summation involving $1/I$, under various experimental treatments. Viewed in this way the derivative curve of $dE/d \log I$ as a function of $\log I$ is of course a frequency distribution of elements of neural effects (and not of the intensity thresholds of excitable neural units).

If an assemblage of neural units is adapted to an intensity I_1 the corresponding mean total effect is E_1. Excitability with respect to the production of any further sensory effect by increasing I must clearly depend on the range of the distribution of

$d \log I$ still open to activitation, and the range of additional effect potentially achievable will be drawn from and will be equivalent to $E_{\max} - E_1$.

The increment of intensity producing a noticeable effect beyond that due to I_1 is ΔI. It corresponds in quantitative properties to the "absolute threshold" ΔI_0 when $I_1 = 0$; the only difference is that with I_1 finite the test starts from a certain level of light adaptation and I_1 is (usually) still present for comparison. Among important properties in which the essential similarity of mean values of ΔI and ΔI_0 are manifest is the rectilinear proportionality to their indices of dispersion in repeated tests, the homologous types of dependence on retinal area and on exposure time, and on the level of light adaptation. Analysis demonstrates that $1/\Delta I_0$, like effect E, gives a normal probability summation as a function of exposure time. In a similar way, the "differential excitability" $1/\Delta I$ is regarded as determined by the summation of neural effects from that part of the total potential population not already excited by I_1. In other words, the capacity to be excited, which is measured by $1/\Delta I$, is determined by (and thus measurable in terms of) the remaining number of unexcited elements. If effect E is a probability integral in $\log I$, then $1/\Delta I$ must be a similar probability integral with reversed slope, since at each I_1 we will have $1/\Delta I$ equivalent to $E_{\max} - E_1$.

It will be noticed that an essential part of this argument involves simply the *number* of elements of neural effect $(dE/d \log I)$ and makes no reference to any fixity of the individual unit thresholds in terms of $\log I$; in the deduction of the probability summation for these cases it is explicitly presumed that the thresholds of these units fluctuate at random. As a matter of fact, the relation between ΔI and $\sigma_{\Delta I}$ permits another method of obtaining the form of the ΔI function, which emphasizes the significance of fluctuating variation of performance in the neural units concerned in statistically determining the nature of the law for sensory effect as a function of intensity; its results are essentially the same as those about to be described.

The tests of this formulation must ultimately involve a good deal more than its ability to apparently describe the data, particularly since customary criteria of curve fitting are of very doubtful utility for such data. Valid tests must be particularly directed toward examining the properties of the parameters of the function. Among the most interesting of such tests are those theoretically possible by altering the organism's temperature. But certain other tests, although in some respects less decisive, can readily be applied. The derivation of the probability summation for $1/\Delta I$ makes no reference to anatomical specificities of receptor or central nervous organization; it makes no appeal to the photochemical (or perhaps photoelectric) basis of the primary excitation of individual visual cells; it is concerned solely with the fact that the determination of visual response is brought about through the activation of groups of neural units which fluctuate in performance and in accommodation.

* * *

Thus the statistical argument penetrated even into the biological foundation of psychology. Whether one considered populations of stimuli as Brunswik did, or populations of neurons as Crozier did, or populations of responses as Thurstone did, statistical tools promised a way to deal with the kind of order-in-the-midst-of-chaos-and-complexity that is so characteristic of all living systems.

It is not really surprising that probability axioms entered into the foundations of mathematical psychology during the 1930's. The wonder is that it did not happen earlier. In the much admired science of physics Boltzmann's combination of statistical and mechanical principles was well-known. And biologists had long been saying that the orderly species had evolved out of disorderly matings, mutations, and competitions. All psychologists understood how Darwin had explained the slow process of adaptation from one generation to the next, yet not until 1930 did they apply this same kind of probabilistic reasoning to the more rapid process of adaptation within a single life span.

There was a statistical conception of intelligence by 1900, but a statistical formulation of learning did not appear until 1930, and a statistical formulation of reaction times did not appear until well into the 1950's. Yet if one considers these three topics intuitively, reaction times would seem to be the most obviously statistical in nature, and intelligence the least. It is such puzzles that add spice to the history of psychology.

The use of statistical axioms in psychology, which got so healthy a boost during the 1930's, was interrupted by war during the early 1940's. The story of statistical psychology does not resume until after the war, but by that time a number of new statistical ideas had emerged.

One new development that appeared during the postwar period was the theory of games, already mentioned in Chapter 3. It was significant that these theorists reintroduced risk and uncertainty into their measurements of preference and utility.

Another innovation was the statistical theory of communication which Claude Shannon presented so effectively in 1948,* and which Norbert Wiener incorporated as a fundamental part of his new science of cybernetics.†

One feature of the new theory of communication was a formula—borrowed from thermodynamics—that defined the amount of selective information in any message in terms of the mean logarithmic probability of that message. This definition excited considerable interest among psychologists during the 1950's, although most of it has since subsided or been assimilated into related problems. The following selection introduces some of the basic ideas of the theory and tries to suggest why psychologists became interested in them.

* C. E. Shannon, A mathematical theory of communication. *Bell Syst. tech. J.*, 1948, **27**, 379–423, 623–656.
† N. Wiener, *Cybernetics*. New York: Wiley, 1948.

George Armitage Miller

What Is Information Measurement?

In recent years a few psychologists, whose business throws them together with communication engineers, have been making considerable fuss over something called "information theory." They drop words like "noise," "redundancy," or "channel capacity" into surprising contexts and act as if they had a new slant on some of the oldest problems in experimental psychology. Little wonder that their colleagues are asking, "What is this 'information' you talk about measuring?" and "What does all this have to do with the general body of psychological theory?"

The reason for the fuss is that information theory provides a yardstick for measuring organization. The argument runs like this. A well-organized system is predictable—you know almost what it is going to do before it happens. When a well-organized system does something, you learn little that you didn't already know—you acquire little information. A perfectly organized system is completely predictable and its behavior provides no information at all. The more disorganized and unpredictable a system is, the more information you can get by watching it. Information, organization, and predictability room together in this theoretical house. The key that unlocks the door to predictability is the theory of probability, but once this door is open we have access to information and organization as well.

The implications of this argument are indeed worth making a fuss about. Information, organization, predictability, and their synonyms are not rare concepts in psychology. Each place they occur now seems to be enriched by the possibility of quantifica-

G. A. Miller, What is information measurement? *Amer. Psychologist*, 1953, **8**, 3–11.
Reprinted by permission of the American Psychological Association.

tion. One rereads familiar passages with fresh excitement over their experimental possibilities. Well-worn phrases like "perceptual organization," "the disorganizing effects of emotion," "knowledge of results," "stereotyped behavior," "reorganization of the problem materials," etc., begin to leap off the pages.

In the first blush of enthusiasm for this new toy it is easy to overstate the case. . . .

Most of the careless claims for the importance of information theory arise from overly free associations to the word "information." This term occurs in the theory in a careful and particular way. It is not synonymous with "meaning." Only the *amount* of information is measured—the amount does not specify the content, value, truthfulness, exclusiveness, history, or purpose of the information. The definition does not exclude other definitions and certainly does not include all the meanings implied by the colloquial usages of the word. . . . Imagine a child who is told that a piece of candy is under one of 16 boxes. If he lifts the right box, he can have the candy. The event—lifting one of the boxes—has 16 possible outcomes. In order to pick the right box, the child needs information. Anything we tell him that reduces the number of boxes from which he must choose will provide some of the information he needs. If we say, "The candy is not under the red box," we give him just enough information to reduce the number of alternatives from 16 to 15. If we say, "The candy is under one of the four boxes on the left end," we give more information because we reduce 16 to 4 alternatives. If we say, "The candy is under the white box," we give him all the information he needs—we reduce the 16 alternatives to the one he wants.

The amount of information in such statements is a measure of how much they reduce the number of possible outcomes. Nothing is said about whether the information is true, valuable, understood, or believed—we are talking about *how much* information there is.

Bit. . . . Every time the number of alternatives is reduced to half, one unit of information is gained. This unit is called one "bit" of information. If one message reduces k to k/x, it contains one bit less information than does a message that reduces k to

$k/2x$. Therefore, the amount of information in a message that reduces k to k/x is $\log_2 x$ bits.

For example, if the child's 16 boxes are reduced to two, then x is 8 and $\log_2 8$ is three bits of information. That is to say, 16 has been halved three times: 16 to 8, 8 to 4, and 4 to 2 alternative outcomes.

Source. The communication engineer is seldom concerned with a particular message. He must provide a channel capable of transmitting any message that a source may generate. The source selects a message out of a set of k alternative messages that it might send. Thus each time the source selects a message, the channel must transmit $\log_2 k$ bits of information in order to tell the receiver what choice was made.

If some messages are more probable than the others, a receiver can anticipate them and less information needs to be transmitted. In other words, the frequent messages should be the short ones. In order to take account of differences in probability, we treat a message whose probability is p as if it was selected from a set of $1/p$ alternative messages. The amount of information that must be transmitted for this message is, therefore, $\log_2 1/p$, or $- \log_2 p$. (Note that if all k messages are equally probable, $p = 1/k$ and $- \log_2 p = \log_2 k$, which is the measure given above.) In other words, some messages that the source selects involves more information than others. If the message probabilities are $p_1, p_2, \ldots, p_k$, then the amounts of information associated with each message are $- \log_2 p_1, - \log_2 p_2, \ldots, - \log_2 p_k$.

Average Amount of Information. Since we want to deal with sources, rather than with particular messages, we need a measure to represent how much information a source generates. If different messages contain different amounts of information, then it is reasonable to talk about the average amount of information per message we can expect to get from the source—the average for all the different messages the source may select. This expected value from source x is denoted $H(x)$:

$$H(x) = \text{the mean value of } (- \log_2 p_i)$$

$$= \sum_{i=1}^{k} p_i (- \log_2 p_i)$$

This is the equation that occurs most often in the psychological applications of information theory. $H(x)$ in bits per message is the mean logarithmic probability for all messages from source x. In all that follows we shall be talking about the average amount of information expected from a source, and not the exact amount in any particular message.

Related Sources. Three gentlemen—call them Ecks, Wye, and Zee—are each making binary choices. That is to say, Ecks chooses either heads or tails and simultaneously Wye also makes a choice and so does Zee. They repeat their synchronous choosing over and over again, varying their choices more or less randomly on successive trials. Our job is to predict what the outcome of this triple-choice event will be.

With no more description than this we know that there are eight ways the triple-choice can come out: HHH, HHT, HTH, HTT, THH, THT, TTH, and TTT. Thus our job is to select one out of these eight possible outcomes. If all eight were equally probable, we would need three bits of information to make the decision. . . .

Suppose that, as will usually be the case when we apply these ideas, Ecks and Wye are partially but not perfectly correlated. If we know what Ecks will do, we can make a fairly reliable guess what Wye will do, and vice versa. Some but not all of the information we get from Ecks duplicates the information we get from Wye. . . .

The situation is pictured in Figure 1. The left circle is the information we get from Ecks and the right circle is the information from Wye. The symbols $H(x)$ and $H(y)$ denote the average amounts of information in bits per event expected from sources Ecks and Wye respectively. The overlap of the two circles represents the common information due to the correlation of Ecks and Wye and its average amount in bits per event is symbolized by T. The left half of the left circle is information from Ecks alone, and the right half of the right circle is information from Wye alone. The symbols $H_y(x)$ should be taken to mean the average amount of information per event that remains to be gotten from source Ecks after Wye is already known. The total area enclosed in both circles together represents all the information that both

Ecks and Wye can provide. This total amount in bits per event is symbolized by $H(x,y)$.

$H(x)$ is calculated from the probabilities for Ecks' choices according to the equation given above. The same equation is used to calculate $H(y)$ from the probabilities for Wye's choices. And the same equation is used a third time to calculate $H(x,y)$ from the joint probabilities of the double-choices by Ecks and Wye together. Then all the other quantities involved can be calculated by simple arithmetic in just the way Figure 1 would suggest. For example:

$$H_y(x) = H(x,y) - H(y)$$
or $$T = H(x) + H(y) - H(x,y).$$

It will be seen that T has the properties of a measure of the correlation (contingency, dependence) between Ecks and Wye. In fact, $1.3863\ nT$ (where n is the number of occurrences of the event that you use to estimate the probabilities involved) is essentially the same as the value of chi square you would compute to test the null hypothesis that Ecks and Wye are independent.

These are the basic ideas behind the general theory. There are many ways to adapt them to specific situations depending on the way the elements of the specific situation are identified with the several variables of the theory. In general, however, most applications of the theory seem to fall into one or the other of two types. I shall refer to these two as the *transmission situation* and the *sequential situation*.

When information is communicated from one place to another, it is necessary to have a channel over which it can travel. If you put a message in at one end of the channel, another message comes out the other end. So the communication engineer talks about the "input" to the channel and the "output" from the channel. For a good channel, the input and the output are closely related but usually not identical. The input is changed, more or less, in the process of transmission. If the changes are random, the communication engineer talks about "noise" in the channel. Thus the output depends upon both the input and the noise.

Now we want to identify the variables in this transmission situation with the various quantities of information pictured in

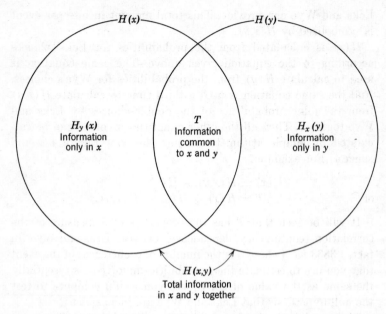

Figure 1. Schematic representation of the several quantities of information that are involved when messages are received from two related sources.

Figure 1. In order to do this, we let x be the source that generates the input information and let y be the source that generates the output information. That is to say, y is the channel itself. Since x and y are related sources of information, the overlap or common information is what is transmitted. $H(x)$ is the average amount of input information, $H(y)$ is the average amount of output information, and T is the average amount of transmitted information. (To keep terms uniform, we might refer to T as the average amount of "throughout" information.)

What interpretation can we give to $H_y(x)$ and $H_x(y)$? $H_y(x)$ is information that is put in but not gotten out—it is information *lost* in transmission. $H_y(x)$ is often called "equivocation" because a receiver cannot decide whether or not it was sent. Similarly, $H_x(y)$ is information that comes out without being put in—it is information *added* in transmission. $H_x(y)$ is called "noise" with the idea that the irrelevant parts of the output interfere with good communications.

Finally, $H(x,y)$ is the total amount of information you have when you know both the input and the output. Thus $H(x,y)$ includes the lost, the transmitted, and the added information,

$$H(x,y) = H_y(x) + T + H_x(y)$$

equivocation plus transmission plus noise.

This interpretation of the basic concepts of information theory is ordinarily used with the object of computing T, the amount of information transmitted by the channel. A characteristic of most communication channels is that there is an upper limit to the amount of information they can transmit. This upper limit is called the "channel capacity" and is symbolized by C. As the amount of information in the input is increased, there comes a point at which the amount of transmitted information no longer increases. Thus as $H(x)$ increases, T approaches an upper limit, C. This situation is shown graphically in Figure 2, where T is plotted as a function of $H(x)$.

The obvious psychological analogy to the transmission situation is between the subject in an experiment and a communication channel, between stimuli and inputs, and between responses and outputs. Then $H(x)$ is the stimulus information, $H(y)$ is the response information, and T measures the degree of dependence of responses upon stimuli. It turns out that T can be considered as a measure of discrimination, and C is the basic capacity of the subject to discriminate among the given stimuli. That is to say, C can be interpreted as a sort of modern version of the traditional Weber-fraction.

In order to explain how T and C measure the discriminative abilities of the subject, a simple example is useful. Imagine a subject can discriminate perfectly among four classes of stimuli. Any two stimuli in the same class are indistinguishable to him, but two stimuli from different classes are never confused. If we pick the stimuli carefully from different classes, therefore, he can distinguish perfectly which one of two, of three, or of four alternative stimuli we present. However, there is no way we can pick five or more stimuli so that he can discriminate them without any mis-

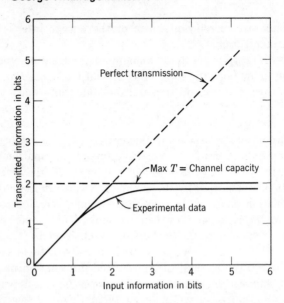

Figure 2. Illustrative graph showing the amount of transmitted information as a function of the amount of input information for a system with a channel capacity of 2 bits.

takes; at least two must be from the same class and so will be confused. If we select k stimuli to test him with, the best he can do is to reduce k to $k/4$ by saying which of his four classes each stimulus belongs in. He can never reduce the range of possible inputs to less than $k/4$. Thus his channel capacity, C, is $\log_2 4$, or 2 bits, and this is the maximum value of T we can get from him. Since 2^C is the maximum number of discriminably different classes of stimuli for this subject, C is a measure of his basic discriminative capacity. . . .

In all that has been said so far it has been implicitly assumed that successive occurrences of the event are independent. When we are dealing with behavioral processes, this assumption is never better than a first approximation. What we are going to do is conditioned by what we have just done, whether we are carrying out the day's work, writing a letter, or producing a random sequence of digits.

Although any behavioral sequence can be analyzed to discover its conditional probabilities, the most interesting example is our own verbal behavior. To take an obvious case, imagine that you are typing a letter and that you have just typed, "I hope we will see you again very." You need at least one more word to complete the sentence. You cannot open the dictionary at random to get this next word. The whole context of the sentence constrains your freedom of choice. The next word depends on the preceding words. Your most probable choice is "soon," although you might choose "often" or "much." You will certainly not choose "blue-jay," or "the," or "take," etc. The effect of these constraints built into normal English usage is to reduce the number of alternatives from which successive words are chosen. We have already seen that when the number of possible outcomes of a choice is reduced, some information has been communicated. That is to say, by reducing the range of choice, the context gives us information about what the next item is going to be. Thus when the next word occurs, some of the information it conveys is identical with information we have already received from the context. This repeated information is called "redundancy."

How can the variables in this sequential situation be identified with the various quantities of information pictured in Figure 1? In order to relate them we let x be the source that generates the context and let y be the source that generates the next word. Since x and y are related sources of information, the overlap or common information from x and y is the redundancy. $H(x)$ is the average amount of information in the first $n-1$ words (the context), $H(y)$ is the average amount of information in the nth word, and T is the average amount of redundant information. $H_y(x)$ is the average amount of information in the context that is unrelated to the next word. $H_x(y)$ is the average amount of information in the next word that cannot be obtained from the context. $H(x,y)$ is the total amount of information we have when all n words, the context plus the next word, are known.

When this interpretation of the basic concepts is used, the quantity of major interest is ordinarily $H_x(y)$, the average amount of information per word when the context is known. $H_x(y)$ can be thought of as the additional information we can expect from each new word in the sequence. Thus $H_x(y)$ is closely related to the *rate* at which information is generated by the source; it measures the average number of bits per unit (per word).

If the successive units in a sequence are chosen independently, then the redundancy T is zero and the context tells us nothing about the next unit. If the next unit is completely determined by the context—for example, in English a "q" is always followed by "u"—then the new information $H_x(y)$ is zero and the occurrence of the next unit adds nothing to what we already know.

Sequences of letters in written English have been studied with this model. It has been estimated that a context of 100 letters will, on the average, reduce the effective number of choices for the next letter to less than three possibilities. That is to say, $H_x(y)$ is about 1.4 bits per letter in standard English. We can compare this result with what would happen if successive letters were chosen independently; then each letter would be chosen from 26 alternatives and would carry $\log_2 26$, or about 4.7 bits of information. In other words, we encode about one-fourth as much information per letter as we might if we used our alphabet more efficiently. Our books seem to be about four times as long as necessary.

It is reasonable to ask why we are so redundant. The answer lies in the fact that redundancy is an insurance against mistakes. The only way to catch an error is to repeat. Redundant information is an automatic mistake-catcher built into all natural languages. Of course, if there is no chance of error, then there is no need for redundancy. The large amount of redundancy that we seem to insist on reflects our basic inefficiency as information-handling systems. Compared with the thousands or millions of bits per second that electronic devices can handle, man's performance figures (always less than 50 bits per second and usually much lower if memory is involved) can charitably be called puny. By making our languages redundant we are able to decrease the rate, $H_x(y)$, to a point where we can cope with what is being said.

Knowledge of the redundancy of English is knowledge about our verbal habits. Since so much of man's behavior is conditioned by these verbal habits, any way to measure them should interest a psychologist. For example, a verbal learning experiment might compare the memorization of ten consonant-vowel-consonant nonsense syllables (30 letters in all) with the memorization of a 30-letter sentence from English text. Since the successive letters in the nonsense syllables are effectively independent, the learner faces many more possible sequences than he does if he knows that the 30 letters are English text. Since he has already learned the redundancies of English, he is required to assimilate less new information from the sentences than from the nonsense syllables. A knowledge of the information in sequences of letters in English text thus gives us an independent, quantitative estimate of previous learning. In short, the sequential application of information concepts enables us to calibrate our verbal learning materials and so to control in a quantitative way factors that we have always discussed before in qualitative terms.

It is not necessary to confine the sequential interpretation to verbal behavior. It can be applied whenever an organism adopts a reasonably stable "course of action" that can be described probabilistically. If the course of action is coherent in such a way that future conduct depends upon past conduct, we say the behavior is predictable or, to some degree, stereotyped. In such cases the redundancy T can be used to measure the stereotypy. Arguments about the degree of organization in emotional behavior, for example, might be clarified by such a measure.

Taken together, the sequential and the transmission situations suggest a wide range of possible applications in psychology.

*   *   *

Information measurement was only one of several new ideas that psychologists inherited after World War II. Still another postwar innovation occurred in psychophysics. During the early 1940's a tremendous technological effort was made to develop radar for military purposes. The range of any radar was limited, of course, by the magnitude of the radar signal; the efficiency of the system depended on receiving and detecting very faint echoes. Initially, detection was done by human operators, but the engineers suspected that more sensitive and reliable detection might be possible with automatic devices. And so they set about developing a general theory of threshold signals that would support their efforts to design optimal detection systems.* At first these efforts focused primarily on matters of power, on the ratio of the signal power to the noise power at the receiver. Later, with the development of statistical decision theory, the work grew more and more statistical in nature.

In the simplest cases, deciding whether a particular reception does or does not contain a signal is exactly the same problem a statistician faces when he tries to decide whether a particular observation came from one or the other of two possible populations. Given this insight it becomes possible to apply mathematical statistics directly to the detection problem.

As statisticians well know, there are two kinds of mistakes that can occur in making such binary decisions. Let H_0 represent the *null hypothesis* that no signal was present. Then a Type I error occurs if H_0 is rejected although it is in fact true. And a Type II error occurs if H_0 is accepted although it is in fact false. In terms of signal detection, a Type I error is a false alarm, and a Type II error is a miss. The statistical problem is to set the decision level at some optimal point (that is, to construct a "test"), where the notion of what is optimal is open to considerable debate. One common procedure is to fix the probability of a Type I error arbitrarily at .01 or .05, subject to the condition that the Type II error be as small as possible. The probability of a Type I error is the *significance* level of the test, and 1 — probability of a Type II error is the *power* of the test. When this theory is applied to signal detection, however, the arbitrary fixing of the significance level is not generally acceptable, because a false alarm may be much more costly than a miss, or vice versa. If a false alarm is much more expensive, then we should set the decision level fairly high, so that we reduce the probability of false alarms and increase the probability of misses. Or, if a miss is more expensive,

* J. L. Lawson and G. E. Uhlenbeck, *Threshold signals.* New York: McGraw-Hill, 1950.

we should lower our threshold and improve our probability of detecting all signals, even though we will also increase the probability of false alarms.

Thus the notion of costs and values are introduced. Given any particular signal-to-noise ratio, we can set our threshold for any level we like. We can, in fact, draw a curve for that signal-to-noise ratio representing the probability of a correct detection (the power of the test) as a function of the probability of a false alarm (the significance of the test). Engineers have called this function a receiver-operating-characteristic, or *ROC curve*. From it we can see at a glance what price we must pay in false alarms in order to attain any given level of correct detections. But exactly what level we choose must depend on the costs attached to the errors we will make.

This situation can be thought of as a zero-sum, two-person game played between the source and the receiver. The source has the option of either sending or not sending a signal on any given play of the game; presumably, his strategy is random with probabilities known in advance. The receiver has a choice of setting his detection level anywhere between $-\infty$ (accept everything) and $+\infty$ (accept nothing); his problem is to set his acceptance level in such a way that he will maximize the value of the game. If the receiver knows what the probability of a signal will be, it is a straightforward matter to compute his optimum strategy; if the probability is unknown, the receiver can proceed as if the source were using the strategy that would be least favorable for the receiver, and so he can set his detection level to minimize his maximum loss. Thus, a normative flavor was introduced into psychophysics, which had for almost a century been one of the prime examples of a descriptive use of mathematics in psychology.

The statistical theory of signal reception was actively developed by many mathematicians and engineers during the 1950's.* It was inevitable that psychologists working with communications engineers would hear of this theory, would recognize its relation to the statistical theories of psychophysics, and would try to apply it to human observers. One of the first published ac-

* D. Middleton, *An introduction to statistical communication theory.* New York: McGraw-Hill, 1960.

counts of this work appeared in 1954 when W. P. Tanner and
J. A. Swets* used it to report their research on the detection of
visual signals. The following selection, however, is an excerpt
from one of their later papers, chosen because it contains a somewhat clearer and fuller statement of the underlying theory.

* W. P. Tanner, Jr., and J. A. Swets, A decision-making theory of visual
detection. *Psychol. Rev.*, 1954, **61**, 401–409. This work was based on a formulation of detection proposed by W. W. Peterson and T. G. Birdsall, The
theory of signal detectability, Electronic Defense Group, University of
Michigan, *Tech. Rep.*, No. 13, Sept. 1953.

*   *   *

John Arthur Swets, Wilson Pennell Tanner, Jr., and
Theodore Gerald Birdsall

Decision Processes in Perception

The Theory

Statistical Decision Theory

Consider the following game of chance. Three dice are thrown.
Two of the dice are ordinary dice. The third die is unusual in
that on each of three of its sides it has three spots, whereas on its
remaining three sides it has no spots at all. You, as the player of
the game, do not observe the throws of the dice. You are simply
informed, after each throw, of the total number of spots showing
on the three dice. You are then asked to state whether the third
die, the unusual one, showed a 3 or a 0. If you are correct—that
is, if you assert a 3 showed when it did in fact, or if you assert a
0 showed when it did in fact—you win a dollar. If you are in-

J. A. Swets, W. P. Tanner, Jr., and T. G. Birdsall, Decision processes in perception.
Psychol. Rev., 1961, **68**, 301–340. Pp. 302–310 reprinted by permission of the authors and the American Psychological Association.

correct—that is, if you make either of the two possible types of errors—you lose a dollar.

How do you play the game? Certainly you will want a few minutes to make some computations before you begin. You will want to know the probability of occurrence of each of the possible totals 2 through 12 in the event that the third die shows a 0, and you will want to know the probability of occurrence of each of the possible totals 5 through 15 in the event that the third die shows a 3. Let us ignore the exact values of these probabilities, and grant that the two probability distributions in question will look much like those sketched in Figure 1.

Realizing that you will play the game many times, you will want to establish a policy which defines the circumstances under which you will make each of the two decisions. We can think of this as a *criterion* or a cutoff point along the axis representing the total number of spots showing on the three dice. That is, you will want to choose a number on this axis such that whenever it is equaled or exceeded you will state that a 3 showed on the third die, and such that whenever the total number of spots showing is less than this number, you will state that a 0 showed on the third die. For the game as described, with the a priori probabili-

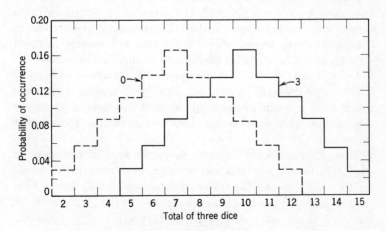

Figure 1.   The probability distributions for the dice game.

ties of a 3 and a 0 equal, and with equal values and costs associated with the four possible decision outcomes, it is intuitively
clear that the optimal cutoff point is that point where the two
curves cross. You will maximize your winnings if you choose this
point as the cutoff point and adhere to it.

Now, what if the game is changed? What, for example, if the
third die has three spots on five of its sides, and a 0 on only one?
Certainly you will now be more willing to state, following each
throw, that the third die showed a 3. You will not, however, simply state more often that a 3 occurred without regard to the
total showing on the three dice. Rather, you will lower your
cut-off point: you will accept a smaller total than before as representing a throw in which the third die showed a 3. Conversely,
if the third die has three spots on only one of its sides and 0's on
five sides, you will do well to raise your cutoff point—to require
a higher total than before for stating that a 3 occurred.

Similarly, your behavior will change if the values and costs
associated with the various decision outcomes are changed. If it
costs you 5 dollars every time you state that a 3 showed when in
fact it did not, and if you win 5 dollars every time you state that
a 0 showed when in fact it did (the other value and the other
cost in the game remaining at one dollar), you will raise your
cutoff to a point somewhere above the point where the two distributions cross. Or if, instead, the premium is placed on being
correct when a 3 occurred, rather than when a 0 occurred as in
the immediately preceding example, you will assume a cutoff
somewhere below the point where the two distributions cross.

Again, your behavior will change if the amount of overlap of
the two distributions is changed. You will assume a different
cutoff than you did in the game as first described if the three
sides of the third die showing spots now show four spots rather
than three.

This game is simply an example of the type of situation for
which the theory of statistical decision was developed. It is intended only to recall the frame of reference of this theory. Statistical decision theory—or the special case of it which is relevant
here, the theory of testing statistical hypotheses—specifies the
optimal behavior in a situation where one must choose between

two alternative statistical hypotheses on the basis of an observed event. In particular, it specifies the optimal cutoff, along the continuum on which the observed events are arranged, as a function of (a) the a priori probabilities of the two hypotheses, (b) the values and costs associated with the various decision outcomes, and (c) the amount of overlap of the distributions that constitute the hypotheses.

According to the mathematical theory of signal detectability, the problem of detecting signals that are weak relative to the background of interference is like the one faced by the player of our dice game. In short, the detection problem is a problem in statistical decision; it requires testing statistical hypotheses. In the theory of signal detectability, this analogy is developed in terms of an idealized observer. It is our thesis that this conception of the detection process may apply to the human observer as well. The next several pages present an analysis of the detection process that will make the bases for this reasoning apparent.

Fundamental Detection Problem

In the fundamental detection problem, an observation is made of events occurring in a fixed interval of time, and a decision is made, based on this observation, whether the interval contained only the background interference or a signal as well. The interference, which is random, we shall refer to as *noise* and denote as *N;* the other alternative we shall term *signal plus noise, SN.* In the fundamental problem, only these two alternatives exist— noise is always present, whereas the signal may or may not be present during a specified observation interval. Actually, the observer, who has advance knowledge of the ensemble of signals to be presented, says either "yes, a signal was present" or "no, no signal was present" following each observation. In the experiments reported below, the signal consisted of a small spot of light flashed briefly in a known location on a uniformly illuminated background. It is important to note that the signal is always observed in a background of noise; some, as in the present case, may be introduced by the experimenter or by the external situation, but some is inherent in the sensory processes.

Representation of Sensory Information

We shall, in the following, use the term *observation* to refer to the sensory datum on which the decision is based. We assume that this observation may be represented as varying continuously along a single dimension. Although there is no need to be concrete, it may be helpful to think of the observation as some measure of neural activity, perhaps as the number of impulses arriving at a given point in the cortex within a given time. We assume further that any observation may arise, with specific probabilities, either from noise alone or from signal plus noise. We may portray these assumptions graphically, for a signal of a given amplitude, as in Figure 2. The observation is labeled x and plotted on the abscissa. The left-hand distribution, labeled $f_N(x)$, represents the probability density that x will result given the occurrence of noise alone. The right-hand distribution, $f_{SN}(x)$, is the probability density function of x given the occurrence of signal plus noise. (Probability density functions are used, rather than probability functions, since x is assumed to be continuous.) Since the observations will tend to be of greater magnitude when a signal is presented, the mean of the SN distribution will be greater than the mean of the N distribution. In general, the greater the amplitude of the signal, the greater will be the separation of these means.

Observation as a Value of Likelihood Ratio

It will be well to question at this point our assumption that the observation may be represented along a single axis. Can we, without serious violation, regard the observation as unidimensional, in spite of the fact that the response of the visual system probably has many dimensions? The answer to this question will involve some concepts that are basic to the theory.

One reasonable answer is that when the signal and interference are alike in character, only the magnitude of the total response of the receiving system is available as an indicator of signal existence. Consequently, no matter how complex the sensory information is in fact, the observations may be represented in theory

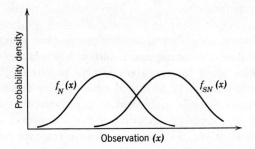

Figure 2.   The probability density functions of noise and signal plus plus noise.

as having a single dimension. Although this answer is quite acceptable when concerned only with the visual case, we prefer to advance a different answer, one that is applicable also to audition experiments, where, for example, the signal may be a segment of a sinusoid presented in a background of white noise.

So let us assume that the response of the sensory system does have several dimensions, and proceed to represent it as a point in an m-dimensional space. Call this point y. For every such point in this space there is some probability density that it resulted from noise alone, $f_N(y)$, and, similarly, some probability density that it was due to signal plus noise, $f_{SN}(y)$. Therefore, there exists a likelikhood ratio for each point in the space, $\lambda(y) = f_{SN}(y)/f_N(y)$, expressing the likelihood that the point y arose from SN relative to the likelihood that it arose from N. Since any point in the space, i.e., any sensory datum, may be thus represented as a real, nonzero number, these points may be considered to lie along a single axis. We may then, if we choose, identify the observation x with $\lambda(y)$; the decision axis becomes likelihood ratio.

Having established that we may identify the observation x with $\lambda(y)$, let us note that we may equally well identify x with any monotonic transformation of $\lambda(y)$. It can be shown that we lose nothing by distorting the linear continuum as long as order is maintained. As a matter of fact we may gain if, in particular, we identify x with some transformation of $\lambda(y)$ that results in Gaussian density functions on x. We have assumed the existence of such a transformation in the representation of the density functions, $f_{SN}(x)$ and $f_N(x)$, in Figure 2. We shall see shortly that the assumption of normality simplifies the problem greatly. We shall also see that this assumption is subject to experimental test. A further assumption incorporated into the picture of Figure 2, one made quite tentatively, is that the two density functions are of equal variance. This is equivalent to the assumption that the SN function is a simple translation of the N function, or that adding a signal to the noise merely adds a constant to the N function. The results of a test of this assumption are also described below.

To summarize the last few paragraphs, we have assumed that an observation may be characterized by a value of likelihood ratio, $\lambda(y)$, i.e., the likelihood that the response of the sensory system y arose from SN relative to the likelihood that it arose from N. This permits us to view the observations as lying along a single axis. We then assumed the existence of a particular transformation of $\lambda(y)$ such that on the resulting variable, x, the density functions are normal. We regard the observer as basing his decisions on the variable x.

Definition of the Criterion

If the representation depicted in Figure 2 is realistic, then the problem posed for an observer attempting to detect signals in noise is indeed similar to the one faced by the player of our dice game. On the basis of an observation, one that varies only in magnitude, he must decide between two alternative hypotheses. He must decide from which hypothesis the observation resulted; he must state that the observation is a member of the one distribution or the other. As did the player of the dice game, the observer must establish a policy which defines the circumstances under which the observation will be regarded as resulting from each of the two possible events. He establishes a criterion, a cutoff x_c on the continuum of observations, to which he can relate any given observation x_i. If he finds for the ith observation, x_i, that $x_i > x_c$, he says "yes"; if $x_i < x_c$, he says "no." Since the observer is assumed to be capable of locating a criterion at any point along the continuum of observations, it is of interest to examine the various factors that, according to the theory, will influence his choice of a particular criterion. To do so requires some additional notation.

In the language of statistical decision theory the observer chooses a subset of all of the observations, namely the Critical Region A, such that an observation in this subset leads him to accept the Hypothesis SN, to say that a signal was present. All other observations are in the complementary Subset B; these lead to rejection of the Hypothesis SN, or, equivalently, since the two hypotheses are mutually exclusive and exhaustive, to the acceptance of the Hypothesis N. The Critical Region A, with reference to Figure 2, consists of the values of x to the right of some criterion value x_c.

As in the case of the dice game, a decision will have one of four outcomes: the observer may say "yes" or "no" and may in either case be *correct* or *incorrect*. The decision outcome, in other words, may be a *hit* ($SN \cdot A$, the joint occurrence of the Hypothesis SN and an observation in the Region A), a *miss* ($SN \cdot B$), a *correct rejection* ($N \cdot B$), or a *false alarm* ($N \cdot A$). If the a priori probability of signal occurrence and the parameters of the distributions of Figure 2 are fixed, the choice of a criterion value x_c completely determines the probability of each of these outcomes.

Clearly, the four probabilities are interdependent. For example, an increase in the probability of a hit, $p(SN \cdot A)$, can be achieved only by accepting an increase in the probability of a false alarm, $p(N \cdot A)$, and decreases in the other probabilities, $p(SN \cdot B)$ and $p(N \cdot B)$. Thus a given criterion yields a particular balance among the probabilities of the four possible outcomes; conversely, the balance desired by an observer in any instance will determine the optimal location of his criterion. Now the observer may desire the balance that maximizes the expected value of a decision in a situation where the four possible outcomes of a decision have individual values, as did the player of the dice game. In this case, the location of the best criterion is determined by the same parameters that determined it in the dice game. The observer, however, may desire a balance that maximizes some other quantity— i.e., a balance that is optimum according to some other definition of optimum—in which case a different criterion will be appropriate. He may, for example, want to maximize $p(SN \cdot A)$ while satisfying a restriction on $p(N \cdot A)$, as we typically do when as experimenters we assume an .05 or .01 level of confidence. Alternatively, he may want to maximize the number of correct decisions. Again, he may prefer a criterion that will maximize the reduction in uncertainty in the Shannon sense.

In statistical decision theory, and in the theory of signal detectability, the optimal criterion under each of these definitions of optimum is specified in terms of the likelihood ratio. That is to say, it can be shown that, if we define the observation in terms of the likelihood ratio, $\lambda(x) = f_{SN}(x)/f_N(x)$, then the optimal criterion can always be specified by some value β of $\lambda(x)$. In other words, the Critical Region A that corresponds to the criterion contains all observations with likelihood ratio greater than or equal to β, and none of those with likelihood ratio less than β.

We shall illustrate this manner of specifying the optimal criterion for just one of the definitions of optimum proposed above, namely, the maximization of the total expected value of a decision in a situation where the four possible outcomes of a decision have individual values associated with them. This is the definition of optimum that we assumed in the dice game. For this purpose we shall need the concept of *conditional probability* as opposed to the *probability of joint occurrence* introduced above. It should be stated that conditional probabilities will have a place in our discussion beyond their use in this illustration; the ones we shall introduce are, as a matter of fact, the fundamental quantities in evaluating the observer's performance.

There are two conditional probabilities of principal interest. These are the conditional probabilities of the observer saying "yes": $p_{SN}(A)$, the probability of a Yes decision *conditional upon*, or *given*, the occurrence of a signal, and $p_N(A)$, the probability of a Yes decision given the occurrence of noise alone. These two are sufficient, for the other two are simply their complements: $p_{SN}(B) = 1 - p_{SN}(A)$ and $p_N(B) = 1 - p_N(A)$. The conditional and joint probabilities are related as follows:

$$p_{SN}(A) = \frac{p(SN \cdot A)}{p(SN)}$$

$$p_N(A) = \frac{p(N \cdot A)}{p(N)}$$

(1)

where: $p(SN)$ is the a priori probability of signal occurrence and $p(N) = 1 - p(SN)$ is the a priori probability of occurrence of noise alone.

Equation (1) makes apparent the convenience of using conditional rather than joint probabilities—conditional probabilities are independent of the a priori probability of occurrence of the signal and of noise alone. With reference to Figure 2, we may define $p_{SN}(A)$, or the conditional probability of a hit, as the integral of $f_{SN}(x)$ over the Critical Region A, and $p_N(A)$, the conditional probability of a false alarm, as the integral of $f_N(x)$ over A. That is, $p_N(A)$ and $p_{SN}(A)$ represent, respectively, the areas under the two curves of Figure 2 to the right of some criterion value of x.

To pursue our illustration of how an optimal criterion may be specified by a critical value of likelihood ratio β, let us note that the expected value of a decision (denoted EV) is defined in statistical decision theory as the sum, over the potential outcomes of a decision, of the products of probability of outcome and the desirability of outcome. Thus, using the notation V for *positive* individual values and K for costs or *negative* individual values, we have the following equation:

$$EV = V_{SN \cdot A} p(SN \cdot A) \\ + V_{N \cdot B} p(N \cdot B) \\ - K_{SN \cdot B} p(SN \cdot B) \\ - K_{N \cdot A} p(N \cdot A) \qquad (2)$$

Now if a priori and conditional probabilities are substituted for the joint probabilities in Equation 2 following Equation 1, for example, $p(SN)p_{SN}(A)$ for $p(SN \cdot A)$, then collecting terms yields the result that maximizing EV is equivalent to maximizing:

$$p_{SN}(A) - \beta p_N(A) \qquad (3)$$

where

$$\beta = \frac{p(N)}{p(SN)} \cdot \frac{(V_{N \cdot B} + K_{N \cdot A})}{(V_{SN \cdot A} + K_{SN \cdot B})} \qquad (4)$$

It can be shown that this value of β is equal to the value of likelihood ratio, $\lambda(x)$, that corresponds to the optimal criterion. From Equation 3 it may be seen that the value β simply weights the hits and false alarms, and from Equation 4 we see that β is determined by the a priori probabilities of occurrence of signal and of noise alone and by the values associated with the individual decision outcomes. It should be noted that Equation 3 applies to all definitions of optimum. Equation 4 shows the determinants of β in only the special case of the expected-value definition of optimum.

Return for a moment to Figure 1, keeping in mind the result that β is a critical value of $\lambda(x) = f_{SN}(x)/f_N(x)$. It should be clear that the optimal cut-off x_c along the x axis is at the point on this axis where the ratio of the ordinate value of $f_{SN}(x)$ to the ordinate value of $f_N(x)$ is a certain number, namely β. In the symmetrical case, where the two a priori probabilities are equal and the four individual values are equal, $\beta = 1$ and the optimal value of x_c is the point where $f_{SN}(x) = f_N(x)$, where the two curves cross. If the four values are equal but $p(SN) = \frac{5}{6}$ and $p(N) = \frac{1}{6}$, another case described in connection with the dice game, then $\beta = \frac{1}{5}$ and the optimal value of x_c is shifted a certain distance to the left. This shift may be seen intuitively to be in the proper direction—a higher value of $p(SN)$ should lead to a greater willingness to accept the Hypothesis SN, i.e., a more lenient cut-off. To consider one more example from the dice game, if $p(SN) = p(N) = 0.5$, if $V_{N \cdot B}$ and $K_{N \cdot A}$ are set at 5 dollars and $V_{SN \cdot A}$ and $K_{SN \cdot B}$ are equal to 1 dollar, then $\beta = 5$ and the optimal value of x_c shifts a certain distance to the right. Again intuitively, if it is more important to be correct when the Hypothesis N is true, a high, or strict, criterion should be adopted.

In any case, β specifies the optimal weighting of hits relative to false alarms: x_c should always be located at the point on the x axis corresponding to β. As we pointed out in discussing the dice game, just where this value of x_c will be with reference to the x axis depends not only upon the a priori probabilities and the values but also upon the overlap of the two density functions, in short, upon the signal strength. We shall define a measure of signal strength within the next few pages. For now, it is important to note that for any detection goal to which the observer may subscribe, and for any set of parameters that may characterize a detection situation (such as a priori probabilities and values associated with decision outcomes), the optimal criterion may be specified in terms of a single number, β, a critical value of likelihood ratio.

Receiver-Operating-Characteristic

Whatever criterion the observer actually uses, even if it is not one of the optimal criteria, can also be described by a single number, by some value of likelihood ratio. Let us proceed to a consideration of how the observer's performance may be evaluated with respect to the location of his criterion, and, at the same time we shall see how his performance may be evaluated with respect to his sensory capabilities.

As we have noted, the fundamental quantities in the evaluation of performance are $p_N(A)$ and $p_{SN}(A)$, these quantities representing, respectively, the areas under the two curves of Figure 2 to the right of some criterion value of x. If we set up a graph of $p_{SN}(A)$ versus $p_N(A)$ and trace on it the curve resulting as we move the decision criterion along the decision axis of Figure 2, we sketch one of the arcs shown in Figure 3. Ignore, for a moment, all but one of these arcs. If the decision criterion is set way at the left in Figure 2, we obtain a point in the upper right-hand corner of Figure 3: both $p_{SN}(A)$ and $p_N(A)$ are unity. If the criterion is set at the right end of the decision axis in Figure 2, the point at the other extreme of Figure 3, $p_{SN}(A) = p_N(A) = 0$, is obtained. In between these extremes lie the criterion values of more practical interest. It should be noted that the exact form of the curve shown in Figure 3 is not the only form which might result, but it is the form which will result if the observer chooses a criterion in terms of likelihood ratio, and the probability density functions are normal and of equal variance.

This curve is a form of the *operating characteristic* as it is known in statistics; in the context of the detection problem, it is usually referred to as the *receiver-operating-characteristic*, or ROC, curve. The optimal "operating level" may be seen from Equation 3 to be at the point of the ROC curve were its slope is β. That is, the expression $p_{SN}(A) - \beta p_N(A)$ defines a utility line of slope β, and the point of tangency of this line to the ROC

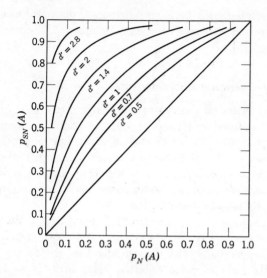

Figure 3. The receiver-operating-characteristic curves. (These curves show $p_{SN}(A)$ versus $p_N(A)$ with d' as the parameter. They are based on the assumptions that the probability density functions, $f_N(x)$ and $f_{SN}(x)$, are normal and of equal variance.

curve is the optimal operating level. Thus the theory specifies the appropriate hit probability and false alarm probability for any definition of optimum and any set of parameters characterizing the detection situation.

It is now apparent how the observer's choice of a criterion in a given experiment may be indexed. The proportions obtained in an experiment are used as estimates of the probabilities, $p_N(A)$ and $p_{SN}(A)$; thus, the observer's behavior yields a point on an ROC curve. The slope of the curve at this point corresponds to the value of likelihood ratio at which he has located his criterion. Thus we work backward from the ROC curve to infer the criterion that is employed by the observer.

There is, of course, a family of ROC curves, as shown in Figure 3, a given curve corresponding to a given separation between the means of the density functions $f_N(x)$ and $f_{SN}(x)$. The parameter of these curves has been called d', where d' is defined as the difference between the means of the two density functions expressed in terms of their standard deviation, i.e.:

$$d' = \frac{M_{f_{SN}(x)} - M_{f_N(x)}}{\sigma_{f_N(x)}} \tag{5}$$

Since the separation between the means of the two density functions is a function of a signal amplitude, d' is an index of the detectability of a given signal for a given observer.

Recalling our assumptions that the density functions $f_N(x)$ and $f_{SN}(x)$ are normal and of equal variance, we may see from Equation (5) that the quantity denoted d' is simply the familiar normal deviate, or x/σ measure. From the pair of values $p_N(A)$ and $p_{SN}(A)$ that are obtained experimentally, one may proceed to a published table of areas under the normal curve to determine a value of d'. A simpler computational procedure is achieved by plotting the points $[p_N(A), p_{SN}(A)]$ on graph paper having a probability scale and a normal deviate scale on both axes.

We see now that the four-fold table of the responses that are made to a particular stimulus may be treated as having two independent parameters—the experiment yields measures of two independent aspects of the observer's performance. The variable d' is a measure of the observer's sensory capabilities, or of the effective signal strength. This may be thought of as the object of interest in classical psychophysics. The criterion β that is employed by the observer, which determines the $p_N(A)$ and $p_{SN}(A)$ for some fixed d', reflects the effect of variables which have been variously called the set, attitude, or motives of the observer. It is the ability to distinguish between these two aspects of detection performance that comprises one of the main advantages of the theory proposed here. We have noted that these two aspects of behavior are confounded in an experiment in which the dependent variable is the intensity of the signal that is required for a threshold response.

The introduction of statistical decision theory into psychophysics stimulated renewed efforts to settle some of the ancient mysteries of the sensory threshold, efforts that are continuing vigorously into the 1960's. We have already drawn several examples of statistical reasoning from the study of sensory and perceptual processes, however, so we must turn our attention now to other topics.

The statistical flavor of psychological theories extended also into learning theory. Here, as in so many instances, it was once more Thurstone who showed the way.

We have already seen one example of Thurstone's thinking about the learning function in Chapter 4. That earlier (1919) paper was purely empirical and made no use of probability theory to derive the proposed equation. In the following selection—the opening pages of his second attempt in 1930—he introduces probabilities immediately and uses them to derive a rational equation for learning. The earlier paper left the definition of "attainment" more or less flexible; the later paper defines attainment as "the probability that an act will be counted as successful." That use of probability was a small change psychologically, but it was enormously important mathematically.

* * *

Louis Leon Thurstone

The Learning Function

In order to make it possible to write a rational equation for the learning function it is necessary to make some assumptions which

L. L. Thurstone, The learning function. *J. gen. Psychol.*, 1930, 3, 469–493. Pp. 469–478 reprinted by permission of The Journal Press.

are certain to oversimplify the complex phenomena of learning. But oversimplification is the very nature of scientific law. There is probably no law in any science which is not easily violated by introducing any of the practical irrelevancies in which the phenomena are actually experienced. So it is with the law of falling bodies which is violated if you drop them in the air. Even if we know that our assumptions will ultimately be replaced by a scheme of things much more comprehensive it may still serve the purposes of more modest generalization to describe the phenomena of learning quantitatively by an equation that fits more or less with current doctrine and which has a few parameters with physical interpretation consistent with current doctrine.

The two principal variables in learning are (a) practice, and (b) attainment. Attainment is, of course, an increasing function of practice. Practice may be measured either in terms of repetition or in terms of time devoted to it, and effort is assumed to be constant. Repetitions may be counted as successful acts only, or they may include both successes and failures. Perhaps the most serious assumption in current learning theory is that learning consists in a lot of separable acts and that some of them are right and others are wrong. In the present analysis we shall also make that assumption, namely, that learning consists in a series of separable acts, that some of these are counted as successful and that others are counted as errors. Each act whether right or wrong will be counted as a unit of practice.

Attainment can also be expressed in various ways, but we shall adopt here as a measure of attainment the probability that an act will be counted as successful. This measure of attainment is proportional to and consequently for our purposes synonymous with the number of successful acts per unit time. We now have a part of our schema. The animal performs a series of acts toward a certain goal, and with repeated attempts the proportion of successes increases. At the start the probability of a success is low. With repeated attempts this possibility rises toward unity. But we shall make a reservation about the act. In the early stages of learning the subject tries as hard perhaps as in the later perfected stages, but he does not produce as many overtly countable acts. We shall assume that the acts initiated in his attempts to succeed are at least as numerous then as later but that the incipient acts are lost as failures even before they reach sufficiently tangible form to be counted overtly as attempts or as complete acts. We assume, in other words, that the number of acts initiated per unit time is the same for the novice as for the advanced learner provided that effort remain constant. Some of these initiated acts are lost in confusion and tension without ever reaching overt form. Others which do reach overt form are counted as failures. Some reach overt completion and are counted as successes. Our assumption here is that the rate at which acts are initiated is directly proportional to effort, which is assumed to be constant.

At any one moment of time all the acts which the learner is at all likely to initiate in his effort toward a goal may then be arbitrarily divided into two categories, those that lead to success and those that lead either to overt or implicit error. Our classifications so far may be summarized as follows:

$s =$ total number of acts which the learner is likely to initiate and which would be credited as successes.

$e =$ total number of acts which the learner is likely to initiate and which would lead to error or failure or loss of time.

$p =$ probability that the act initiated at any moment of time will lead to successful completion.

$q =$ probability that the act initiated at any moment of time will lead to error or loss of time.

Then, clearly,

$$p = \frac{s}{s + e} \qquad (1)$$

$$q = \frac{e}{s + e} \qquad (2)$$

and
$$ps + pe = s \qquad (3)$$

The object of the learner is, of course, to reduce the errors e and to raise the proportion p. We make here no assumption whatever about the mechanism by which errors become eliminated. The fact is, of course, that they disappear. We say that a subject is superior if he profits by his mistakes so that errors are not repeated over and over again. The good learner is one who never repeats an error, and the perfect learner is the hypothetical animal that beats the game by anticipating the erroneous outcome of an intiated act so that he never makes an overt error. If one subject makes an error twice, on the average, before it is eliminated and if another subject in the same situation makes an error three times, on the average, before it is eliminated, then the first subject will evidently make faster progress. He profits more quickly from his mistakes. Both subjects will sooner or later eliminate all errors so that the value of p approaches unity.

Analytically this looks very much like an urn problem. Let all the probable or plausible acts of a learner be represented by white and black balls in an urn. He is drawing them out, for the present, one at a time, and he draws them out at a uniform rate. At any moment there is a certain probability p that the ball which he draws will be white and a certain probability q that it will be black. If it turns out to be black, then there is the probability k that it will be eliminated from the urn and the probability $(1 - k)$ that the black ball will be returned to the urn.

$p =$ probability that he will draw a white ball (success).

$q = (1 - p) =$ probability that he will draw a black ball (error).

$kq =$ probability that he will draw a black ball and that it will be eliminated (thrown out of the urn).

$q(1 - k) =$ probability that he will draw a black ball and that this error will be repeated in future attempts. (He throws the ball back in the urn again.)

For a subject who makes each mistake twice before eliminating it the constant $k = .5$ because, on the average, he will return as many black balls to the urn as he throws out of it. For another subject who makes each mistake four times before it disappears the constant $k = .25$. This means that when a black ball is drawn for the fourth time the learner withdraws it from the urn instead of returning it to the urn. Of course, we need not insist that all errors are repeated exactly the same number of times. We are dealing only with the average number of times that a learner repeats an error before eliminating it.

But whenever an error is eliminated it is obvious that the total number of possible errors e is reduced by one. Further if the probability that a particular draw will give a black ball and that it will be eliminated is kq, then this is also the average number of black balls by which e is reduced *per draw*. This enables us to write the differential equation

$$\frac{de}{dt} = -kq \tag{4}$$

By (2) we have

$$\frac{de}{dt} = \frac{-ke}{s+e} \tag{5}$$

This equation describes the rate at which the subject is eliminating his errors in terms of the probability k that he will eliminate a committed mistake.

It is interesting to see what common-sense interpretation can be given to different values of k. Suppose that k were zero for some subject. Then he could never progress because, when he makes a mistake, the probability is zero that he will ever eliminate it. Suppose that k were unity for some other subject. That would mean that, on the average, he eliminates every mistake he makes. He never repeats his errors. But now suppose that k were greater than unity. That has a very interesting interpretation. It means that when this subject makes one mistake he not only eliminates that error but also some more errors that he has not yet made. That is the very essence of rational learning. It looks as though we might have a gradation from trial-and-error learning to rational learning represented by the numerical value of k in our differential equation (5).

But so far we have not mentioned the possibility that a successful act has some effect favoring its recurrence. We shall assume not only that overtly committed errors decrease their probability of recurrence but also that overtly successful acts increase their probability of recurrence. We can write a differential equation for successes, corresponding to equation (5) and it takes the form

$$\frac{ds}{dt} = +kp \tag{6}$$

which by (1) becomes

$$\frac{ds}{dt} = \frac{ks}{s+e} \tag{7}$$

Here we have used the same constant k as in (5). We probably are not doing much violence to the truth if we assume that the extent to which a subject profits by his errors is about the same as the extent to which he profits by his successes. At any rate we shall adopt this approximation.

We are treating the total number of *plausible* errors e as a decreasing quantity, and we are treating the total number of *plausible* successes as though it were in effect an increasing quantity. This does not mean that the total number of *possible* successful acts is actually increased. If one act has been repeatedly successful we may simply represent it in the urn by several *duplicate* white balls. This carries the urn analogy by which the probability of repeating that act is increased.

The differential equations (5) and (7) enable us to find a simple relation between the total number of plausible errors e and the equivalent or effective number of successes s which the learner has at his disposal at any particular moment of practice. Dividing (7) by (5) we have

$$\frac{ds}{de} = -\frac{s}{e} \tag{8}$$

and consequently

$$\int \frac{ds}{s} + \int \frac{de}{e} = 0 \tag{9}$$

so that

$$\log s + \log e = \log m \tag{10}$$

where m is a constant. This may be written more simply

$$se = m \tag{11}$$

In other words, the product of the total number of errors and the *effective* number of successes in the learner's repertoire is a constant. The physical meaning of this constant m is evidently related to the complexity of the learning task. When the learning process is intrinsically complex for the subject the product se is large. When this product is small, the task is correspondingly simple. The constant k is an attribute of the individual learner while the constant m is primarily an attribute of the learning problem or task.

We want to know the relation between practice time t and attainment p. From (3) we may write the following differential equation.

$$p\frac{ds}{dt} + s\frac{dp}{dt} + p\frac{de}{dt} + e\frac{dp}{dt} = \frac{ds}{dt} \qquad (12)$$

Substituting (5) and (7) in (12) we have

$$\frac{pks}{s+e} + s\frac{dp}{dt} - \frac{pke}{s+e} + e\frac{dp}{dt} = \frac{ks}{s+e} \qquad (13)$$

and collecting terms it becomes

$$(s+e)^2\frac{dp}{dt} = k\,(pe + s - ps) \qquad (14)$$

The relation between p and t is then

$$\int\frac{(s+e)^2 dp}{s - ps + pe} = k\int dt \qquad (15)$$

In order to perform the integration, the variables s and e may be stated first in terms of the individual learning constants k and m and the desired variables p and t. This can be done as follows. From (3) we have

$$e = \frac{s - ps}{p} \qquad (16)$$

and from (11) we have

$$e = \frac{m}{s} \qquad (17)$$

Solving (16) and (17) simultaneously for s and e, we get

$$s = \sqrt{\frac{mp}{1-p}} \qquad (18)$$

and

$$e = \sqrt{\frac{m(1-p)}{p}} \qquad (19)$$

The numerator of (15) contains the factor $(s + e)^2$ which is evaluated in terms of (18) and (19) as follows.

$$(s + e) = \frac{\sqrt{mp}}{\sqrt{1 - p}} + \frac{\sqrt{m(1 - p)}}{\sqrt{p}} \tag{20}$$

which simplifies so that

$$(s + e)^2 = \frac{m}{p\,(1 - p)} \tag{21}$$

The denominator of (15) can also be evaluated in terms of the individual learning constants k and m and the desired variables p and t as follows.

$$s - ps + pe = \frac{\sqrt{mp}}{\sqrt{1 - p}} - \frac{p\sqrt{mp}}{\sqrt{1 - p}} + \frac{p\sqrt{m(1 - p)}}{\sqrt{p}} \tag{22}$$

which simplifies so that

$$s - ps + pe = 2\sqrt{mp\,(1 - p)} \tag{23}$$

Equation (15) may be rewritten in more convenient form by substituting (21) and (23). After simplifying, it takes the form

$$\int \frac{dp}{p^{\frac{3}{2}}(1 - p)^{\frac{3}{2}}} = \frac{2k}{\sqrt{m}} \int dt \tag{24}$$

Here we have a relation between the two variables p and t of the learning curve and the two constants k and m.

In order to facilitate integration, make the substitution $p = \sin^2\phi$. The limits of p and $\sin^2\phi$ are the same. Then (24) becomes

$$\int \frac{d\phi}{\sin^2\phi \cos^2\phi} = \frac{k}{\sqrt{m}} \int dt \tag{25}$$

$$= \int \csc^2\phi \sec^2\phi \, d\phi = \int (1 + \cot^2\phi)\,(1 + \tan^2\phi)\,d\phi$$

$$= \int (2 + \tan^2\phi + \cot^2\phi)\,d\phi$$

$$= \tan\phi - \cot\phi + C = \frac{kt}{\sqrt{m}} \tag{26}$$

But from the substitution it follows that

$$\tan \phi = \sqrt{\frac{p}{1-p}}$$

and

$$\cot \phi = \sqrt{\frac{1-p}{p}}$$

and hence (24) becomes

$$\frac{2p-1}{\sqrt{p-p^2}} = \frac{kt}{\sqrt{m}} + z \qquad (27)$$

in which z is a constant of integration. This is the desired learning curve equation.

* * *

Thurstone's statistical theory of learning was developed further by his students—first by Gulliksen in 1934,* then by Gulliksen and Wolfle in 1938.† This was, of course, only one of several places where Thurstone taught his colleagues the power of probability and statistics.

By 1950, therefore, psychologists were ready to entertain some reasonably complex statistical theories. Almost simultaneously R. R. Bush and F. Mosteller at Harvard University and W. K. Estes at Indiana University began to propose statistical theories of learning that were far more deeply probabilistic in nature than the earlier work by Thurstone, Gulliksen, and Wolfle. Whereas the first statistical theories tried merely to account for the average learning curve, the newer theories tried to account for all the statistical properties of the experimental data—for variability, for runs of failures or successes, for trials required to reach a criterion, and so on.

The first publication of this newer work was an article by Estes in 1950. The following passage formed the opening section of that article.

* H. Gulliksen, A rational equation of the learning curve based on Thorndike's law of effect. *J. gen. Psychol.*, 1934, **11**, 305–434.

† H. Gulliksen and D. L. Wolfle, A theory of learning and transfer. *Psychometrika*, 1938, **3**, 127–149.

William Kaye Estes

A Statistical Theory of Learning

Improved experimental techniques for the study of conditioning and simple discrimination learning enable the present day investigator to obtain data which are sufficiently orderly and reproducible to support exact quantitative predictions of behavior. Analogy with other sciences suggests that full utilization of these techniques in the analysis of learning processes will depend to some extent upon a comparable refinement of theoretical concepts and methods. The necessary interplay between theory and experiment has been hindered, however, by the fact that none of the many current theories of learning commands general agreement among researchers. It seems likely that progress toward a common frame of reference will be slow so long as most theories are built around verbally defined hypothetical constructs which are not susceptible to unequivocal verification. While awaiting resolution of the many apparent disparities among competing theories, it may be advantageous to systematize well established empirical relationships at a peripheral, statistical level of analysis. The possibility of agreement on a theoretical framework, at least in certain intensively studied areas, may be maximized by defining concepts in terms of experimentally manipulable variables, and developing the consequences of assumptions by strict mathematical reasoning.

This essay will introduce a series of studies developing a statistical theory of elementary learning processes. From the definitions and assumptions which appear necessary for this kind of

W. K. Estes, Toward a statistical theory of learning. *Psychol. Rev.*, 1950, 57, 94–107. Pp. 94–98 reprinted by permission of the author and the American Psychological Association.

formulation, we shall attempt to derive relations among commonly used measures of behavior and quantitative expressions describing various simple learning phenomena.

Preliminary Considerations

Since propositions concerning psychological events are verifiable only to the extent that they are reducible to predictions of behavior under specified environmental conditions, it appears likely that greatest economy and consistency in theoretical structure will result from the statement of all fundamental laws in the form

$$R = f(S),$$

where R and S represent behavioral and environmental variables respectively. Response-inferred laws, as for example those of differential psychology, should be derivable from relationships of this form. The reasoning underlying this position has been developed . . . by Spence. Although developed within this general framework, the present formulation departs to some extent from traditional definitions of S and R variables.

Many apparent differences among contemporary learning theories seem to be due in part to an oversimplified defintion of stimulus and response. The view of stimulus and response as elementary, reproducible units has always had considerable appeal because of its simplicity. This simplicity is deceptive, however, since it entails the postulation of various hypothetical processes to account for observed variability in behavior. In the present formulation, we shall follow the alternative approach of including the notion of variability in the definitions of stimulus and response, and investigating the theoretical consequences of these definitions.

It will also be necessary to modify the traditional practice of stating laws of learning in terms of relations between isolated stimuli and responses. Attempts at a quantitative description of learning and extinction of operant behavior have led the writer to believe that a self-consistent theory based upon the classical S-R model may be difficult, if not impossible, to extend over any very wide range of learning phenomena without the continual addition of ad hoc hypotheses to handle every new situation. A recurrent difficulty might be described as follows. In most formulations of simple learning, the organism is said originally to "do nothing" in the presence of some stimulus; during learning, the organism comes to make some predesignated response in the presence of the stimulus; then during extinction, the response gradually gives way to a state of "not responding" again. But this type of formulation does not define a closed or conservative system in any sense. In order to derive properties of conditioning and extinction from the same set of general laws, it is necessary to assign specific properties to the state of not responding which is the alternative to occurrence of the designated response. One solution is to assign properties as needed by special hypotheses, as has been done, for example, in the Pavlovian conception of inhibition. In the interest of simplicity of theoretical structure, we shall avoid this procedure so far as possible.

The role of competing reactions has been emphasized by some writers, but usually neglected in formal theorizing. The point of view to be developed here will adopt as a standard conceptual model a closed system of behavioral and environmental variables. In any specific behavior-system, the environmental component may include either the entire population of stimuli available in the situation or some specified portion of that population. The behavioral component will consist in mutually exclusive classes of responses, defined in terms of objective criteria; these classes will be exhaustive in the sense that they will include all behaviors which may be evoked by that stimulus situation. Given the initial probabilities of the various responses available to an organism in a given situation, we shall expect the laws of the theory to enable predictions of changes in those probabilities as a function of changes in values of independent variables.

Definitions and Assumptions

R-variables. It will be assumed that any movement or sequence of movements may be analyzed out of an organism's repertory of behavior and treated as a "response," various properties of which can be treated as dependent variables subject to all the laws of the theory. (Hereafter we shall abbreviate the word response as R, with appropriate subscripts where necessary.) In order to avoid a common source of confusion, it will be necessary to make a clear distinction between the terms R-class and R-occurrence.

The term R-class will always refer to a class of behaviors which produce environmental effects within a specified range of values. This definition is not without objection but has the advantage of following the actual practice of most experimenters. It may be possible eventually to coordinate R-classes defined in terms of environmental effects with R-classes defined in terms of effector activities.

By R-occurrence we shall mean a particular, unrepeatable behavioral event. All occurrences which meet the defining criteria of an R-class are counted as instances of that class, and as such are experimentally interchangeable. In fact, various instances of an R-class are ordinarily indistinguishable in the record of an experiment even though they may actually vary with respect to properties which are not picked up by the recording mechanism.

Indices of tendency to respond, e.g., probability as defined below, always refer to R-classes.

These distinctions may be clarified by an illustration. In the Skinner-type conditioning apparatus, bar-pressing is usually treated as an R-class. Any movement of the organism which results in sufficient depression of the bar to actuate the recording mechanism is counted as an instance of the class. The R-class may be subdivided into finer classes by the same kind of criteria. We could, if desired, treat depression of a bar by the rat's right forepaw and depression of the bar by the left forepaw as instances of two different classes provided that we have a recording mechanism which will be affected differently by the two kinds of movements and mediate different relations to stimulus input (as for example the presentation of discriminative stimuli or reinforcing stimuli). If probability is increased by reinforcement, then reinforcement of a right-forepaw-bar-depression will increase the probability that instances of that subclass will occur, and will also increase the probability that instances of the broader class, bar-pressing, will occur.

S-variables. For analytic purposes it is assumed that all behavior is conditional upon appropriate stimulation. It is not implied, however, that responses can be predicted only when eliciting stimuli can be identified. According to the present point of view, laws of learning enable predictions of changes in probability of response as a function of time under given environmental conditions.

A stimulus, or stimulating situation, will be regarded as a finite population of relatively small, independent, environmental events, of which only a sample is effective at any given time. In the following sections we shall designate the total number of elements associated with a given source of stimulation as S (with appropriate subscripts where more than one source of stimulation must be considered in an experiment), and the number of elements effective at any given time as s. It is assumed that when experimental conditions involve the repeated stimulation of an organism by the "same stimulus," that is by successive samples of elements from an S-population, each sample may be treated as an independent random sample from S. It is to be expected that sample size will fluctuate somewhat from one moment to the next, in which case s will be treated as the average number of elements per sample over a given period.

In applying the theory, any portion of the environment to which the organism is exposed under uniform conditions may be considered an S-population. The number of different S's said to be present in a situation will depend upon the number of independent experimental operations, and the degree of specificity with which predictions of behavior are to be made. If the experimenter attempts to hold the stimulating situation constant during the course of an experiment, then the entire situation will be treated as a single S. If in a conditioning experiment, a light and shock are to be independently manipulated as the CS and US, then each of these sources of stimulation will be treated as a separate S-population, and so on.

It should be emphasized that the division of environment and behavior into elements is merely an analytic device adopted to enable the application of the finite-frequency theory of probability to behavioral phenomena. In applying the theory to learning experiments we shall expect to evaluate the ratio s/S for any specific situation from experimental evidence, but for the present at least no operational meaning can be given to a numerical value for either S or s taken separately.

Probability of Response. Probability will be operationally defined as the average frequency of occurrence of instances of an R-class relative to the maximum possible frequency, under a specified set of experimental conditions, over a period of time during which the conditions remain constant. In accordance with customary usage the term probability, although defined as a relative frequency, will also be used to express the likelihood that a response will occur at a given time.

Conditional Relation. This relation may obtain between an R-class and any number of the elements in an S-population, and has the following implications.

(a) If a set of x elements from an S are conditioned to (i,e., have the conditional relation to) some R-class, R_1, at a given time, the probability that the next response to occur will be an instance of R_1 is x/S.

(b) If at a given time in an S-population, x_1 elements are conditioned to some R-class, R_1, and x_2 elements are conditioned to another class, R_2, then x_1 and x_2 have no common elements.

(c) If all behaviors which may be evoked from an organism in a given situation have been categorized into mutually exclusive classes, then the probabilities attaching to the various classes must sum to unity at all times. We consider the organism to be always "doing something." If any arbitrarily defined class of activities may be selected as the dependent variable of a given experiment, it follows that the activity of the organism at any time must be considered as subject to the same laws as the class under consideration. Any increase in probability of one R-class during learning will, then, necessarily involve the reduction in probability of other classes; similarly, while the probability of one R decreases during extinction, the probabilities of others must increase. In other words, learning and unlearning will be considered as transfers of probability relations between R-classes.

Conditioning. It is assumed that on each occurrence of a response, R_1, all new elements (i.e., elements not already conditioned to R_1) in the momentarily effective sample of stimulus elements, s, become conditioned to R_1.

An important implication of these definitions is that the conditioning of a stimulus element to one R automatically involves the breaking of any pre-existing conditional relations with other R's.

Motivation. Experimental operations which in the usual terminology are said to produce motives (e.g., food-deprivation) may affect either the composition of an S or the magnitude of the s/S ratio. Detailed discussion of these relations is beyond the scope of the present paper. In all derivations presented here we shall assume motivating conditions constant throughout an experiment.

Reinforcement. This term will be applied to any experimental condition which ensures that successive occurrences of a given R will each be contiguous with a new random sample of elements from some specified S-population. Various ways of realizing this definition experimentally will be discussed in the following sections.

Simple Conditioning: Reinforcement by Controlled Elicitation

Let us consider first the simplest type of conditioning experiment. The system to be described consists of a subpopulation of stimulus elements, S_c, which may be manipulated independently of the remainder of the situation, S, and a class, R, of behaviors defined by certain measurable properties. By means of a controlled original stimulus, that is, one which has initially a high probability of evoking R, it is ensured that an instance of R will occur on every trial contiguously with the sample of stimulus elements which is present. In the familiar buzz-shock conditioning experiment, for example, S_c would represent the population of stimulus elements emanating from the sound source and R would include all movements of a limb meeting certain specifications of direction and amplitude; typically, the R to be conditioned is a flexion response which may be evoked on each training trial by administration of an electric shock.

Designating the mean number of elements from S_c effective on any one trial as s_c, and the number of elements from S_c which are conditioned to R at any time as x, the expected number of new elements conditioned on any trial will be

$$\Delta x = s_c \frac{(S_c - x)}{S_c}. \tag{1}$$

If the change in x per trial is relatively small, and the process is assumed continuous, the right hand portion of (1) may be taken as the average rate of change of x with respect to number of trials, T, at any moment, giving

$$\frac{dx}{dT} = s_c \frac{(S_c - x)}{S_c}. \tag{2}$$

This differential equation may be integrated to yield

$$x = S_c - (S_c - x_0)e^{-qT}, \tag{3}$$

where x_0 is the initial value of x, and q represents the ratio s_c/S_c. Thus x will increase from its initial value to approach the limiting value, S_c, in a negatively accelerated curve. A method of evaluating x in these equations from empirical measures of response latency, or reaction time, will be developed in a later section.

If the remainder of the situation has been experimentally neutralized, the probability of R in the presence of a sample from S_c will be given by the ratio x/S_c. Representing this ratio by the single letter p, and making appropriate substitutions in (3), we have the following expression for probability of R as a function of the number of reinforced trials.

$$p = 1 - (1 - p_0)e^{-qT}. \tag{3'}$$

Since we have not assumed any special properties for the original (or unconditioned) stimulus other than that of regularly evoking the response to be conditioned, it is to be expected that the equations developed in this section will describe the accumulation of conditional relations in other situations than classical conditioning, provided that other experimental operations function to ensure that the response to be learned will occur in the presence of every sample drawn from the S-population.

* * *

There was good communication between the several workers who were developing these new statistical ideas about learning. By 1955, when Bush and Mosteller published a book on the subject, they were able to draw on a rapidly expanding technical literature that included several detailed analyses of experimental data.

The following passage, which is the final section of the book by Bush and Mosteller, does not develop any of the equations from this new branch of mathematical psychology. It is selected instead because it conveys so clearly what they hoped to accomplish with this kind of approach.

* * *

Robert Ray Bush and Frederick Mosteller

The Value of Stochastic Models

We have often been asked to explain the sense in which our general model, or one of our specific models, represents anything more than curve-fitting. Furthermore, we have been asked to explain the sense in which the parameters of the model are psy-

R. R. Bush and F. Mosteller, *Stochastic models for learning.* New York: Wiley, 1955, pp. 333–336. Reprinted by permission of the authors and the publisher.

chologically meaningful. Unfortunately such a discussion could come only after applications had been provided. An explanation can best go forward if we think of an idealized situation in which the model is correct in every particular. People seriously asking about these issues understand perfectly well that, in the end, the question of goodness-of-fit will arise, but they are puzzled about the status of the model even if it consistently fits real data very closely. Therefore we set aside the goodness-of-fit question for the moment. Part of the trouble arises from the fact that if a sequence of rather similar experiments, say rote-learning studies, is planned, our model does not predict in advance the various parameters that will be found. Once this is understood, the original questions arise with still more force.

Suppose a learning experiment, involving 1000 subjects for 300 trials each, has recorded either a success or a failure for each subject on each trial. These data are turned over to a clerk for summary analysis. There are now literally thousands of independent questions that can be asked about these data without ever getting down to the level of the single cell (outcome for a particular subject on a particular trial). To make the point clear we shall list a few of the more usual questions and a few of the more esoteric ones. For our purpose it does not matter whether or not a psychologist would be interested in the entire range of such questions. The point is that each can be asked of the data and an answer could be obtained. Examples are:

1. What is the overall percentage of successes?

2. What are the trial-by-trial success percentages?

3. What is the best-fitting cubic curve that can be drawn through the trial-by-trial percentages?

4. What is the mean trial number on which the last failure occurred? (How about the median instead of the mean?)

5. What is the mean trial number on which the first success occurred? (The second, the third, . . . ?)

6. What is the average number of runs of successes? failures?

7. What percentage of subjects had at least twenty successes in a row?

8. What percentage of the subjects had failures on the third,

fourth, ninth trials and successes on the eighteenth and twentieth? (This question can be varied thousands of ways.)

9. What is the correlation between numbers of successes in the
first twenty and last twenty trials?

10. What is the variance of the subjects' total scores?

Even this small group of questions makes clear the rich variety
of possible summary questions that can be asked of this simple
data sheet. A complete summary could clearly take hundreds of
pages. The clerk working over these data would just have to
compute a new number in response to each question. There would
be no necessary relation between the answers to the different
questions. Knowing answers to one hundred questions would not
help appreciably in answering the next hundred.

The clerk may find it convenient and useful to employ classical
methods of curve-fitting in preparing to answer these questions.
For example, in question 5 above, he might compute the mean
trial of the nth success for each n in the data, and then fit one of
the common curves (linear, quadratic, logarithmic, or exponential function) to those means. When asked about the mean trial
number for the third success, he might report the fitted answer
rather than the one computed from the raw data. This answer
might be preferable because local fluctuations are smoothed out
by the fitted function. The curve itself may be of interest because
it summarizes the trend of the observed means. However, when
the clerk is asked question 9, for example, he must return to the
data, and if he chooses can do some additional curve fitting for
correlation coefficients. Hence, for each class of questions a new
curve could be fitted. Many classes of questions are possible,
however, and therefore many numerical functions would be required to summarize all the information in the data.

A different level of analysis can be accomplished with a model.
Suppose our model fitted closely the results of experiments like
the one described. Then after a few questions had been asked and
answered (say questions 1, 5, 6), we would obtain a few numbers,
say three (we will regard these as parameters). With these three
numbers we would be able to retire from the data and be prepared to answer question for question with the clerk. Our an-

swers would not agree perfectly with the clerk's responses, but they would be generally close. Thus on the basis of three numbers we are prepared, in principle, to answer all the questions the original data sheet can answer provided that the questions do not get down to the level of a single cell. ("In principle," means it might take us a long time, but with computing machines we could do it.) This is saying a great deal. Furthermore, if we are given the three numbers we can work out in advance the answers to the questions, just in case someone ever comes across an experiment that has these three parameters. In addition, we would be glad to turn the rules for finding the three numbers over to someone else, and tell him how to generate the various answers so that when an experiment is done he could see for himself just how the generated answers agree with the results of the experiment. Thus for three numbers derived from the data we plan to be able to answer a wealth of questions. If these three numbers plus the model can answer every possible question above the level of the single cell, it is hard to see what more succinct way there is to summarize the data (unless another model can do it with fewer parameters).

Now what about the psychological meaningfulness of the three parameters? In almost any situation like the one we describe, if there are three numbers that will do all this heavy labor, there will be many other sets of three numbers derivable from the first three that can also be used to achieve the same end. Some of these sets of three numbers can be given familiar names and descriptions more easily than others. Furthermore some sets of parameters that appear strange initially seem, after maturer reflection and experience, more suitable than others. And, again, which set is more suitable sometimes depends on the specific nature of the question. In elementary mathematics we are used to having both rectangular and polar coordinates available (two of the many possible kinds), and we seldom, if ever, see a discussion as to which is more meaningful, though there is plenty of evidence that some problems that are easy in one set become vicious when discussed in the other. In the course of our own work we have gradually turned from the view that quantities like p_0, a_i, and b_i are the natural parameters to the view that p_0, λ_i, and α_i are easier to work with and lead more smoothly to generalizations. Yet each set has its own simple meaning, and one easy to explain and use. Thus preference for equivalent basic sets of parameters may be partly determined by individual taste, but more strongly determined by the services rendered by the particular sets.

The description of our model in an idealized situation is not unlike the situation with Kepler's laws for heavenly bodies. After working with a large set of numbers, he stated a few simple laws that explain (describe) a great deal of what had been measured. On the other hand, if a new heavenly body were to appear, the laws tell us very little that is absolutely quantitative about the motion. But given in addition to the laws a few accurate measurements for the particular body, its course both before and after the observations could be described in specific details. There is another similarity too; the chemical composition of the body, its temperature, color, and other properties that would interest an observer were not included in the laws. Again, for our model there are many protocol features and quantitative measurements of deep importance to a psychologist that not only are not handled but that also we see no hope of handling.

Reluctantly, we rouse ourselves a little from this delightful dream world in which our model reproduces psychological data perfectly. Suppose that when we compare the clerk's detailed computations with the answers generated by the basic three numbers that there are indeed hundreds of pages of close agreement, but that there seems to be a class of questions which the most motherly comparison finds wanting. The usual procedure is to try to find what special conditions have given rise to such error. Indeed, reasoning from such a discrepancy in Kepler's laws, a new planet was found. The model suggested both where not to look further, and also where investigation was needed. Sometimes such discrepancies lead to reformulations of the model, sometimes to interesting discoveries. But in any case a model that predicts a great many things nearly correctly will almost certainly serve as a temporary baseline until a more comprehensive model appears. Nor is it always true that an outmoded model is always discarded; its use may merely be restricted to a narrower sphere.

The feature of a baseline provided by a model may be viewed

in another important way. It changes considerably our practical view of data. In much of psychology the search is for statistically significant differences, and the aim is to show, or at least find out, whether different conditions lead to different results. Big differences are usually a source of great satisfaction. With a quantitative model the emphasis is usually in the reverse direction. We look for close agreement with the model, and regard large differences with dissatisfaction as owing to a lack of understanding. The lack may, of course, stem from the inadequacy or inappropriateness of the model; it might also stem from inadequacies of the design and execution of the experiment, but more hopefully it may stem from a principle soon to be discovered.

Lest some reader has entered this discussion *in medias res*, we remind him that we have not had a fit of arrogance, nor do we have delusions of grandeur; we are merely explaining the value of our type of model under the most favorable conditions imaginable.

* * *

If we accept this as a general statement of aims and objectives for this branch of mathematical psychology, then we must agree that the statistical theory of learning provides a reasonably good model of the data obtained from learning experiments—especially from learning experiments conducted with animals. But is a model of learning data necessarily the same thing as a model of the learning process? On that question there is still room for argument. How well the data that we collect (and try to understand with our models) represent the process we hope to study raises questions that run well beyond the proper bounds of any mathematical discussion.

In historical perspective it is obvious that statistical reasoning has exerted a steadily increasing influence on mathematical theories in psychology. Beginning with the simple notion of errors of measurement, statistical tools were first generalized by Galton and his followers to describe and relate individual differences. Then during the 1930's statistical reasoning was imported into psychophysics and the theory of psychological scales, and was used to describe performances in a learning situation. Following World War II there was a rapid advance in the depth and sophistication of these applications, stimulated by the interrelated development of the theory of information, the theory of games, the theory of detection, and the theory of stochastic process generally. These advances indicated a growing awareness that performance is an unpredictable thing, that choices and decisions are an ineradicable feature of intelligent behavior, and that the data we gather from psychological experiments are inescapably statistical in character. Given these basic facts of the theoretical psychologist's life, statistical theories in psychology would seem to have come to stay.

6

Structural Applications

Any use of mathematics in science or technology rests on an analogy: something about the way the symbols are related must resemble something about the relations among the observed phenomena. What matters is not the symbols or the objects themselves, but the pattern of interrelations among them. The "something" that is analogous between the two is generally called their *structure*. The task of an applied mathematician is to construct (or borrow) a system of symbols and rules whose structure is isomorphic with the structure that the empirical scientist discovers in his data and his experience.

Since every mathematical theory or model has some structural aspects, therefore, the title of this chapter may be misleading. We have already mentioned several structural applications of mathematics. In game theory, for example, coalitions among players are structural in exactly the sense we shall be concerned with here. In statistical communication theory the source-channel-receiver structure that is imposed on the sets of events that can occur is essential to the theory; it plays much the same role as the stimulus-organism-response-reinforcement structure assumed in learning theory. Analyses of response sequences sometimes presume a kind of structure called a "Markov chain" —there is a finite number of discrete and different states the system can get into, and events are generated as the system moves with given transitional probabilities over a highly structured network of paths between the various states. Some theorists—Rashevsky, for example—like to base their psychological arguments on the structural properties of neural networks. And so on and on.

Such structures may be more or less elaborate, more or less important to the theory, but they are always there. Even the simplest measurement procedures make structural assumptions about the ordinal relations among the things measured. Consequently, the structural application of mathematics is not really a new topic that we are introducing for the first time in this chapter. The excuse for the title, however, is that in this chapter we will consider examples where the structural side of the model is its main source of interest; where any measure defined over the structure plays a secondary role, or is ignored entirely.

Just as functional psychology and functional mathematics are sometimes confused, so are structural psychology and structural mathematics. In particular, Gestalt psychologists have always been preoccupied with structural aspects of psychological processes and have even made some attempts to describe them formally: Wolfgang Köhler once wrote a rather mathematical book on physical Gestalten, and we have already had a glimpse of Kurt Lewin's mathematics. In recent years, however, most psychologists working in the Gestalt tradition have made relatively little use of mathematics. Yet so closely are structure and Gestalt associated in the minds of American psychologists that any attempt to consider structure is apt to be classified automatically as a contribution to *Gestalttheorie*. No such doctrinaire implications should attach to the present discussion of mathematical structures. In the sense intended here, an association theory can have just as much structure as any Gestalt theory.*

Often there are two distinct levels of structure involved in a psychological theory. First, the experimental subject remembers or constructs (often tactily) some kind of model to guide his be-

---

* A psychological theory of structure that was inspired by statistical communication theory and that differs in several important respects from the traditional Gestalt theory has been presented by W. R. Garner, *Uncertainty and structure as psychological concepts*. New York: Wiley, 1962.

havior in the experimental situation, then, second, the psychologist constructs his model of what the subject has done. If the scientific model incorporates and makes explicit the folk model, then the status of the folk model can become somewhat confusing. Apparently anthropologists have worried about this complication more than psychologists have;* the different levels of model building become strikingly obvious when, for example, one considers the scientific description of primitive religions or legal codes. From a psychologist's point of view, grammar, logic, and mathematics are highly evolved, normative forms of folk models (social practices) that must somehow be included as part of any comprehensive psychological theories of talking and reasoning. As the problem of constructing a formal model of a person using a formal model begins to receive more attention from psychologists, however, the importance of keeping the two levels distinct should become increasingly apparent. One task for the theorist is to make explicit the model that a subject is using; another is to construct a model that accounts for why and how he tries to use it. Thus the completed theory may contain two very different kinds of structure.

The simplest kinds of structures for us to verbalize and work with are spatial in character. It is not surprising, therefore, that there are many examples of the use of n-dimensional space to describe quite diverse psychological phenomena.

Probably the oldest example of a spatial structure in a psychological theory is the one used to describe color mixing. As early as 1704 Isaac Newton suggested that there was a circular structure underlying his laws of color mixture. His scheme has been frequently revised and occasionally improved by Thomas Young, Hermann von Helmholtz, J. Clerk Maxwell, Hermann Grassmann, Wilhelm Wundt, and many others,† down to the present day. Their various circles, triangles, and cones are all attempts to create an abstract space in which every point represents a different color and where the result of mixing two colors

---

* C. Levi-Strauss, Social structure. In A. L. Kroeber (Ed.), *Anthropology today*. Chicago: University of Chicago Press, 1953, pp. 524–553.

† E. G. Boring, *Sensation and perception in the history of experimental psychology*. New York: Appleton-Century-Crofts, 1942.

is given by computing their "center of gravity" in the space. (There is, moreover, a folk model implicit in the color names of the language that a person happens to speak, and care must be exercised to keep these folk categories from contaminating the scientific model. This folk model will probably not affect the outcome of most color-mixing experiments, but it can have considerable effect on what a person remembers or the way he describes the color to someone else.)

Efforts have also been made to represent feelings and emotions in a spatial structure. Wilhelm Wundt believed that every feeling could be assigned to a separate point in a three-dimensional space whose coordinates were excitement, strain, and pleasure. More recently, Harold Schlosberg* has found that facial expressions can all be arranged in a circular structure whose two dimensions are pleasantness-unpleasantness and attention-rejection. And Charles Osgood† has reported that connotative meanings (attitudes) can be arranged in a three-dimensional space of evaluation, potency, and activity.

These are all structural models. They make use of familiar, Euclidean space—the same kind of space in which we imagine ourselves to live and move about. These are the easiest structures for us to grasp intuitively, and when such a model will fit the facts, we are able to bring to bear all the beautiful machinery of classical mathematics to formulate and solve our problems.

By far the most general and ambitious attempt to exploit Euclidean space as a source of models for psychological phenomena is *factor analysis*. When it was originally discovered by Charles E. Spearman, however, the spatial aspects were not at all apparent. Spearman was searching for a general structure underlying the matrix of correlation coefficients that he had computed between various psychological measures. The fact that Spearman's insight was essentially spatial did not become apparent for more than a quarter of a century.

Spearman's discovery was published first in 1904 as part of a

---

* H. Schlosberg, The description of facial expression in terms of two dimensions. *J. exp. Psychol.*, 1952, **44**, 229–236.

† C. E. Osgood, G. J. Suci, and P. H. Tannenbaum, *The measurement of meaning*. Urbana: University of Illinois Press, 1957.

study on the measurement of intelligence. He tested groups of English children for their acuity in discriminating lights, weights, and sounds, and he estimated their intelligence by how well they did in school, by the amount of "common sense" they demonstrated, and so on. (The Binet-Simon tests of children's intelligence were not available until 1905.) He then correlated all these different measures with each other, two at a time, until he had constructed a matrix of correlation coefficients. Each coefficient indicated how well a child's score on measure p could be predicted from a knowledge of his score on measure q.

As he studied his matrix of correlations, Spearman made a curious observation. He noticed that if he took any two measures, their correlations with all the other measures tended to be in a constant ratio to each other. If the two measures are, say, p and q, then the ratio of r_{px} (the correlation of p and any other measure x) to r_{qx} was always the same for all the other measures. In short, if x, y, z represent the other measures,

$$\frac{r_{px}}{r_{qx}} = \frac{r_{py}}{r_{qy}} = \frac{r_{pz}}{r_{qz}} = \cdots, \tag{1}$$

or, as he later came to describe it, all the *tetrad differences* were zero:

$$r_{px}r_{qy} - r_{py}r_{qx} = 0. \tag{2}$$

In 1904, however, Spearman represented his insight as an attempt to get rid of irrelevant errors of measurement that were attenuating his estimate of the true correlation. If we rewrite the tetrad difference equation as follows for the special case when $x = p$ and $y = q$:

$$r_{pp}r_{qq} - r_{pq}r_{qp} = 0,$$

and recall that $r_{pq} = r_{qp}$, it is a simple matter to rearrange the terms to get

$$\frac{r_{pq}}{\sqrt{r_{pp}r_{qq}}} = 1. \tag{3}$$

The coefficients r_{pp} and r_{qq} indicate the reliability of the measures p and q; they indicate how well repeated measurements would correlate with themselves. Presumably r_{pp} and r_{qq} would both be 1.0, except that random errors operate to attenuate the correlations. These random errors in the measuring instruments place an

upper limit on the degree of correlation we can expect to find between p and q. By using estimates of r_{pp} and r_{qq}, therefore,
Spearman thought he could get at the "true" correlation between
p and q, unattenuated by irrelevant errors or defects in the
measuring instruments. But when he did this—as the following
passage indicates—he found that the "true" correlation was almost always $+1.0$. That is to say, he found that Equation (3)
was (approximately) true for his data. When he thought about
this remarkable result—that the "true" correlations among all
his measures of intelligence was $+1.0$ when irrelevant errors of
measurement were eliminated—he decided that it could only
mean that all his measures had measured one and the same
thing, general intelligence.

The following selection is the provocative heart of Spearman's
1904 paper.

* * *

Charles Edward Spearman

"General Intelligence"

Correspondence between General Discrimination and General Intelligence

Up to now, we have only discussed the correspondence of the
various Intelligences with the various sensory activities, Hearing, Sight, Touch, etc. Such isolated facts are interesting enough,
but quite otherwise important is the relation of *any common and
essential element in the Intelligences to any common and essential element in the Sensory Functions*. For brevity, we will term
these common elements "General Intelligence" and "General

C. Spearman, "General intelligence," objectively determined and measured. *Amer. J.
Psychol.*, 1904, 15, 201–292. Pp. 268–274 quoted.

Discrimination," but always with the reservations made in the first section of this chapter.

Curiously, this more general correspondence can in the present case be settled with much greater precision than was possible for the specific relations. This is due to our now having adequate data wherewith to measure the errors of observation, seeing that all the experimentally obtained gradings of specific Discrimination constitute so many one-sided independent attempts to grade the General Discrimination; the amount of observational error will be quantitatively revealed in the correlations between one grading and another.

The Village School.   Here our calculation is as follows. The average of the nine correlations between the Intelligences and the Discriminations comes, as we have seen, to 0.38;[1] the two kinds of intellective gradings correlate with one another by an average of 0.55, and the three gradings in Discrimination do so by 0.25.[2] Therefore by the theoretical formula the true correlation between General Intelligence and General Discrimination comes to

$$\frac{0.38}{\sqrt{0.55 \times 0.25}} = 1.01.$$

Checking this by the second or empirical method, we find that on taking an amalgamation of the three intellective gradings with an amalgamation of the three gradings in Discrimination, the correlation rises to 0.66. Therefore the true correlation between General Intelligence and General Discrimination comes in this way to

$$\frac{\sqrt{3} \times 0.66 - 0.38}{\sqrt{3} - 1} = 1.04$$

This again may be further checked by taking our amalgamation two instead of three lists at a time; in this way we get nine different correlations which present an average of 0.55, so that our

---

[1] These correlations are here taken as actual measurements, and therefore are obviously required raw, not corrected; the correction then issues from their joint product according to the formula.

[2] This value is precisely the same as that found for adults.

required result now becomes 0.96.[3] Therefore an average again gives us as nearly as possible 1.00.

Thus we arrive at the remarkable result that the *common and essential element in the Intelligences wholly coincides with the common and essential element in the Sensory Functions.*

The High Class School. Here, also, the children were tested in the three senses, but unfortunately, as we have seen, the results for Light and Weight are not seriously usable,[4] so that we no longer have sufficient material for constructing a "General" Discrimination.

This default, however, has been made good by what appears to be a very happy substitute. Our main correlations have dealt with reagents all undergoing musical instruction, and I have kindly been furnished with a complete order of their relative abilities in this department. Musical talent has always been recognized as being not so much an intellective as a sensory function; whole nations appear almost devoid of it, without therefore showing themselves any less intelligent; lunatic asylums, on the contrary, often contain a surprising share of the faculty. We will, then, take this as our second sensory function, will note whether it presents any community with Discrimination of Pitch, and if so will compare this common element with that obtaining between the intellective functions. As regards the first point, it may be noted that hitherto very conflicting opinions have been stoutly maintained; the great majority of writers have held Musical Talent and Pitch Discrimination to be very intimately connected and even go so far as to directly term the discriminative power "musical sensitiveness"; while a few, but including perhaps the ablest judges, flatly deny any such correspondence whatever. The actual facts would at first sight seem to lie wholly on the side of the former tenet, seeing that the correlation works out to the substantial amount of 0.40 (or about 0.63, when corrected for errors). Next, these two auditory functions correlate with the Intelligences by 0.57 and 0.55 respectively, and the lat-

---

[3]
$$\frac{\sqrt{2} \times 0.55 - 0.38}{\sqrt{2} - 1} = 0.96$$

[4] As far as they go, they indicate results entirely similar to those above.

ter correlate with one another to the amount of 0.71. Thus the relation between the element common to the two former and that common to the four latter will be given by

$$\frac{0.56}{\sqrt{0.40 \times 0.71}} = 1.04$$

We can now check the result by the empirical formula; for we find that the amalgamated order derived from the two sensory faculties correlates with the amalgamated order derived from the four Intelligences by 0.72; so that the required correlation comes to

$$\frac{\sqrt[4]{8} \times 0.72 - 0.56}{\sqrt[4]{8} - 1} = 0.96$$

Taking as usual the mean,[5] we again reach a final correlation of precisely 1.00, and therefore once more must conclude that the element common to the sensory activities also wholly coincides with that common to the intelligences.

Before passing, it may be remarked that thus after all those were virtually in the right who maintained Musicality and Pitch Discrimination to have no correspondence with one another; for though a correspondence really does exist, yet it is not to the smallest degree of the specific character contemplated by those who talk of "musical sensitivity." It must here also be noted that this surprising intellectuality of musical talent by no means annihilates the many well-evidenced phenomena seeming to indicate the contrary; one fact cannot destroy another, and any apparent conflict merely proves our imperfect acquaintance with their true nature.

Practical Verification of the Argument. The conclusion above arrived at is so important and the method of argument is so new, that I have endeavored to reproduce analogous circumstances artificially, so that any one may easily test any portion of the reasoning.

The main argument was repeated as follows. A target was

[5] If this small difference of value between the theoretical and empirical results be minutely investigated, it can be clearly proved to be solely attributable to mere chance, as indeed might well be expected from its small dimensions.

constructed of a great many horizontal bands, numbered from top to bottom. Then a man shot successively at a particular series of numbers in a particular order; clearly, the better the shot, the less numerical difference between any number hit and that aimed at; now, just as the measurement of any object is quite appropriately termed a "shot" at its real value, so, conversely, we may perfectly well consider the series of numbers actually hit in the light of a series of measurements of the numbers aimed at. When the same man again fired at the same series, he thereby obtained a new and independent[6] series of measurements of the same set of objects. Next, a woman had the same number of shots at some set of numbers in a similar manner. If, then, our above reasoning and formulae are correct, it should be possible, by observing the numbers hit and working out their correlations, to ascertain the exact resemblance between the series aimed at by the man and woman respectively. In actual fact, the sets of numbers hit by the man turned out to correlate with those hit by the woman to the extent of 0.52; but it was noted that the man's sets correlated with one another to 0.74, and the woman's sets with one another to 0.36; hence the true correspondence between the set aimed at by the man and that aimed at by the woman was not the raw 0.52, but

$$\frac{0.52}{\sqrt{0.74 \times 0.36}} = 1.00,$$

that is to say, the two persons had fired at exactly the same series of bands, which was really the case. I repeated this experiment, testing three times by the first or theoretical formula and four times by the empirical one; by both methods the average came to just upon 1.00, with a mean variation above and below of precisely similar dimensions to those in our instances of Discrimination and Intelligence. Thus the experimental justification of our method of argumentation was as complete as could well be desired.

Conclusion.   On the whole, then, we reach the profoundly important conclusion that *there really exists a something that we may provisionally term "General Sensory Discrimination" and*

[6] Provided, of course, that there be no appreciable constant error.

similarly a "General Intelligence," and further that the functional correspondence between these two is not appreciably less than absolute.

Besides its intrinsic value, such a general theorem has the enormous advantage over the specific results of the last section of being independent of any particular conditions; it has nothing to do with the procedure selected for testing Discrimination and Intelligence, nor even with the accuracy of its execution, nor indeed even with the homogeneousness of the experimental subjects; if correct, the proof should be reproducible in all times, places, and manners—on the sole condition of adequate methodics.

Universal Unity of the Intellective Function

In view of this community being discovered between such diverse functions as in-school Cleverness, out-of-school Common Sense, Sensory Discrimination, and Musical Talent, we need scarcely be astonished to continually come upon it no less paramount in other forms of intellectual activity. Always in the

present experiments, approximately, $\dfrac{r_{pq}}{\sqrt{r_{pp} \cdot r_{qq}}} = 1.$[7]

I have actually tested this relation in twelve pairs of such groups taken at random, and found the average value to be precisely 1.00 for the first two decimal places with a mean deviation of only 0.05. All examination, therefore, in the different sensory, school, or other specific intellectual faculties, may be regarded as so many independently obtained estimates of the one great common Intellective Function.

Though the range of this central Function appears so universal, and that of the specific functions so vanishingly minute, the lat-

---

[7] Where r_{pq} = the mean of the correlations between the members of the one group p with the members of the other group q,

r_{pp} = the mean of the inter-correlations of the members of the group p among themselves,

and r_{qq} = the same as regards group q.

ter must not be supposed to be altogether non-existent. We can always come upon them eventually, if we sufficiently narrow our field of view and consider branches of activity closely enough resembling one another. When, for instance, in this same preparatory school we take on the one side Latin translation with Latin grammar and on the other side French prose with French dictation, then our formula gives us a new result; for the two Latin studies correlate with the French ones by an average of 0.59, while the former correlate together by 0.66 and the latter by 0.71; so that the element common to the Latin correlates with the element common to the French by

$$\frac{0.59}{\sqrt{0.66 \times 0.71}} = 0.86 \text{ only.}$$

That is to say, the two common elements by no means coincide completely this time, but only to the extent of 0.86^2 or 74%;[8] so that in the remaining 26%, each pair must possess a community purely specific and unshared by the other pair.[9]

We therefore bring our general theorem to the following form. *Whenever branches of intellectual activity are at all dissimilar, then their correlations with one another appear wholly due to their being all variously saturated with some common fundamental Function (or group of Functions).* This law of the Universal Unity of the Intellective Function is both theoretically and practically so momentous, that it must acquire a much vaster corroborative basis before we can accept it even as a general principle and apart from its inevitable eventual corrections and limitations. Discussion of the *subjective* nature of this great central Function has been excluded from the scope of the present work. But clearly, if it be mental at all, it must inevitably become one of the foundation pillars of any psychological system claiming to accord with actual fact—and the majority of prevalent theories may have a difficulty in reckoning with it.

[8] The influence of an element is measured by the *square* of its correlational value.
[9] Of course this specific community is further resolvable into natural talent and favoring circumstances of which factors the latter may often be paramount.

234 Mathematics and Psychology

Of its objective relations, the principal is its unique universality, seeing that it reappears always the same in all the divers forms of intellectual activity tested; whereas the specific factor seems in every instance new and wholly different from that in all the others. As regards amount, next, there seems to be an immense diversity; already in the present examples, the central factor varies from less than $\frac{1}{5}$ to over fifteen times the size of the accompanying specific one. But all cases appear equally susceptible of positive and accurate measurement; thus we are becoming able to give a precise arithmetical limitation to the famous assertion that "at the bottom, the Great Man is ever the same kind of thing."

. . .

Spearman soon discovered that he could not really explain *all* the correlations among mental tests by a single faculty, function, or factor called "general intelligence." He was, of course, strongly impressed by the fact that nearly all mental tests are positively correlated, so he would never abandon his conception of a general factor *g*. But he did admit that it was necessary to assume several specific factors in addition to the main general factor. His method was to explain as much of a correlational structure as he could by a general factor, and then use specific factors to explain what was left (the "residual" correlations) after the general factor had been subtracted out.

Spearman's view of intelligence contrasted sharply with the view popular in America at that time. In the United States there had been a long tradition of regarding the various intellectual functions as quite separate and independent.

An intermediate position between Spearman's general factor and the American doctrine of discrete abilities soon became popular among other British psychologists. Cyril Burt, influenced by William McDougall, suggested that there was a hierarchical structure to the various factors. After the general factor is removed, he said, the residual correlations are mostly within two main groups: the verbal-numerical-educational tests on the one hand and the practical-mechanical-spatial-physical tests on the other. These group factors in turn were supposed to break up into further divisions, until eventually the specific factors—one specific to each test—are reached at the bottom of the hierarchy.

A hierarchy is, of course, one kind of structure, but a relatively simple kind. The notion that factor analysis should yield a spatial structure, however, was not made explicit until 1931, when L. L. Thurstone introduced "multiple-factor analysis." Instead of Spearman's one general factor, or a general factor plus several group factors (possibly in hierarchical relation), Thurstone reaffirmed the traditional American faith in several separate and coordinate factors. Each factor, in Thurstone's formulation, was thought to be a separate coordinate (axis, dimension) of a spatial framework in which the tests could be located.

As Thurstone phrased the mathematical problem, factor analysis was a method to find the rank of a correlation matrix. Spearman's matrix, where the columns of correlations maintained a constant ratio to each other, were simply matrices of unit rank, and so could be represented by a single factor. A matrix of rank two required two factors, a matrix of rank three required three, and so on. When the problem was viewed in this perspective, Thurstone saw no reason to call one factor more general than any other.

The fundamental equation of Thurstone's multiple-factor analysis rests on the assumption, expressed in Equation (1) in the following passage, that the test score a person makes is a linear function of the amounts he has of each of the primary factors required by the test. That is, one person can score well on a test because he is high on factor F_1, whereas another person scores high on the same test because of another factor F_2; for that test, therefore, the factors F_1 and F_2 can be substituted for one another according to the fundamental linear equation. This is a very strong and, in the opinion of some psychologists, a somewhat unrealistic view of the primary mental abilities.

The following passage, taken from the opening pages of Thurstones' 1931 article, formulates the factor problem in very general terms. The actual procedures that Thurstone used to solve the problem have been deleted—our space is limited and, moreover, a better presentation of Thurstone's views on these technical problems can be found in his book, *Multiple-Factor Analysis*, published in 1947.

*   *   *

Louis Leon Thurstone

Multiple-Factor Analysis

The two-factor problem of Spearman consists in the analysis of a table of intercorrelations for the discovery of some general factor that is common to all of the variables in the table. Spearman differentiates three types of factors, namely, a general factor which is common to all of the variables, group factors which are common to some of the variables but not to all of them, and specific factors that are peculiar to single variables alone. In practice, the Spearman two-factor methods meet with the difficulty that group factors are frequently encountered. The two-factor methods are not applicable to situations that involve group factors except in indirect ways. This is a serious limitation on Spearman's technique since many important psychological problems involve a complex of variables that are known from the nature of the problem to contain group factors. The present multiple factor methods in no way contradict the Spearman two-factor methods which are very ingenious and powerful in the situations to which they apply. The present multiple factor method may be thought of as supplementary to the Spearman two-factor method in that we do not have any restrictions as to the number of general factors or the number of group factors.

It is the purpose of this paper to describe a more generally applicable method of factor analysis which has no restrictions as regards group factors and which does not restrict the number

L. L. Thurstone, Multiple factor analysis. *Psychol. Rev.*, 1931, 38, 406–427. Pp. 406–414 reprinted by permission of the American Psychological Association.

of general factors that are operative in producing the intercorrelations. Our first question concerns the number of general,
independent, and uncorrelated factors that are operative in producing a given table of intercorrelations for any number of variables. In our terminology general factors will include what Spearman calls general and group factors. This question can be answered by methods that will here be described and which are
applicable to any table of intercorrelations. We may consider
three examples to illustrate the nature of this first problem. If
we have a table of intercorrelations for a battery of motor tests
it is of considerable psychological interest to know how many independent motor abilities it is necessary to postulate in order to
account for the whole table of intercorrelations. If this turns out
to be three, then our next task would be to hunt about for the
nature of these three motor abilities. If we have a table of intercorrelations of the interests of eighteen professions it would be of
considerable importance to know how many independent interest
factors it is necessary to postulate in order to account for the
whole table of intercorrelations. This refers to the tables published by E. K. Strong. We have applied our methods to his data
and we have found that his table of intercorrelations can be ac-
counted for by postulating four general interest factors which
turn out to be (1) interest in science, (2) interest in language,
(3) interest in people, and (4) interest in business. Again, Professor Moore[1] has prepared a table of intercorrelations of 48
psychotic symptoms on the basis of his work with about four
hundred patients with various psychoses. A general factor analysis of the type here discussed would enable us to know how many
general factors or mental disease entities it is necessary to postulate in order to account for the whole table of correlations of
psychotic symptoms. If this should turn out to be five, for example, then we should be justified to look for five fundamentally
different psychoses.

Our next problem is to assign a weight or loading of each of
the general factors to each of the variables. For example, in the

[1] T. V. Moore, The empirical determination of certain syndromes and underlying praecox and manic depressive psychoses. *Amer. J. Psychiat.*, 1930,
9, 719–738.

table of interest-correlations above referred to we should assign four loadings, one for each of the four general factors, to each of the eighteen professions. It then turns out that Engineering, for example, has a high loading of interest in science, a rather low loading of interest in language. The profession of law has just the reverse loadings, namely low for science and high for language. The ministry is loaded high for interest in people and in language but low for science. Finally, we should want to be able to assign to each individual subject a quantitative rating in the form of a standard score for each of the general factors or abilities that have been isolated.

Let there be n factors. In this explanation n will be assumed to be three. It can be any number.

Let there be N individuals in a group, all of whom have taken w tests.

Let a, b, c, d, etc., represent the tests.

Let the three factors be represented by numerals 1, 2, 3.

S_a = standard score of one individual in test a.
S_b = standard score of one individual in test b.
S_c = standard score of one individual in test c.

$S_a = \dfrac{X_a - m_a}{\sigma_a}$ = the usual definition of a standard score.

The standard score S_a of an individual in test a depends on (1) his rating in each of the three abilities or factors 1, 2, 3, and (2) the weight or loading of each of these abilities in test a. For example, if test a calls for much of ability No. 1 and very little of abilities 2 and 3, and if one subject has a low rating in ability No. 1 and average or high ratings on the other two abilities, then this subject may be expected to do poorly on test a. The loadings of the three general factors in each test and for each subject may be represented by the following notation.

Let
x_1 = standard score of an individual in ability No. 1.
x_2 = standard score of an individual in ability No. 2.
x_3 = standard score of an individual in ability No. 3.
and let
a_1 = loading of ability No. 1 in test a,
a^2 = loading of ability No. 2 in test a,
a^3 = loading of ability No. 3 in test a.

Then we shall assume that the standard score of each individual subject is a sum of the products of his standard score in each ability and the loading of the ability in each test. This assumption leads to the following fundamental equations.

$$S_a = a_1 x_1 + a_2 x_2 + a_3 x_3 \tag{1}$$

and

$$S_b = b_1 x_1 + b_2 x_2 + b_3 x_3.$$

Strictly speaking, we should add to each of these two expressions a term to account for those additional general factors, beyond three, which are here ignored, and also a term to account for the specific factor, peculiar to the particular test. However, our object is to ascertain how many general and independent factors it is necessary to postulate in order to account for a whole table of intercorrelations and we shall therefore intentionally ignore these additional specific factors as well as those minor group factors which may not appreciably affect the correlations.

We want to express the correlation between tests a and b in terms of the standard scores in the three abilities and the loadings of the three abilities in each of the two tests. For this purpose we shall need the product $S_a S_b$. Then

$$S_a S_b = a_1 b_1 x_1^2 + a_2 b_2 x_2^2 + a_3 b_3 x_3^2 + \text{cross products}.$$

The correlation r_{ab} can be expressed simply as

$$r_{ab} = \frac{\Sigma S_a \cdot S_b}{N},$$

because S_a and S_b are both standard scores so that the standard deviations of the given scores are all unity. Then

$$\frac{\Sigma S_a S_b}{N} = a_1 b_1 \frac{\Sigma x_1^2}{N} + a_2 b_2 \frac{\Sigma x_2^2}{N} + a_3 b_3 \frac{\Sigma x_3^2}{N},$$

in which the cross products vanish because x_1, x_2, x_3 are uncorrelated. But

$$\frac{\Sigma x_1^2}{N} = \frac{\Sigma x_2^2}{N} = \frac{\Sigma x_3^2}{N} = 1,$$

since x_1, x_2, x_3 are all standard scores in the three abilities. Therefore

$$r_{ab} = a_1 b_1 + a_2 b_2 + a_3 b_3. \tag{2}$$

This is one of the fundamental equations. Here the correlation between two tests is expressed in terms of the loadings of the three abilities in the two tests. By analogy we may write equation (2) for any pair of tests, as

and so on.
$$r_{ac} = a_1 c_1 + a_2 c_2 + a_3 c_3$$

Another fundamental equation can be derived as follows:

Squaring,
$$S_a = a_1 x_1 + a_2 x_2 + a_3 x_3.$$

$$(S_a)^2 = a_1{}^2 x_1{}^2 + a_2{}^2 x_2{}^2 + a_3{}^2 x_3{}^2 + \text{cross products.}$$

Summing and dividing by N

$$\frac{\Sigma S_a{}^2}{N} = a_1{}^2 \frac{\Sigma x_1{}^2}{N} + a_2{}^2 \frac{\Sigma x_2{}^2}{N} + a_3{}^2 \frac{\Sigma x_3{}^2}{N}.$$

The cross products vanish because x_1, x_2, x_3 are uncorrelated by definition. But

and
$$\frac{\Sigma x_1{}^2}{N} = \sigma_1{}^2 = 1$$

Hence
$$\frac{\Sigma S_a{}^2}{N} = 1 \text{ by definition.}$$

$$a_1{}^2 + a_2{}^2 + a_3{}^2 = 1, \tag{3}$$

and similarly by analogy for every other test, as

$$b_1{}^2 + b_2{}^2 + b_3{}^2 = 1.$$

Equations (3) come about because x_1, x_2, x_3 and S_a, S_b are standard scores.

Still another fundamental equation that we shall need can be derived as follows:

$$\begin{aligned}
r_{aa} &= a_1{}^2 + a_2{}^2 + a_3{}^2 = 1. \\
r_{ab} &= a_1 b_1 + a_2 b_2 + a_3 b_3 \\
r_{ac} &= a_1 c_1 + a_2 c_2 + a_3 c_3 \\
r_{ad} &= a_1 d_1 + a_2 d_2 + a_3 d_3
\end{aligned}$$

. . . .

$$\Sigma r_{ak} = a_1 \Sigma k_1 + a_2 \Sigma k_2 + a_3 \Sigma k_3 \tag{4}$$

In the summation equation $\Sigma k_1 =$ sum of all loadings of the first factor in all of the tests of the set. The notation k refers to each of the tests in succession, i.e., k takes values from 1 to w when there are w tests in the series. But this summation equation may be written for each one of the tests as follows

$$\Sigma r_{ak} = a_1 \Sigma k_1 + a_2 \Sigma k_2 + a_3 \Sigma k_3$$
$$\Sigma r_{bk} = b_1 \Sigma k_1 + b_2 \Sigma k_2 + b_3 \Sigma k_3$$
$$\Sigma r_{ck} = c_1 \Sigma k_1 + c_2 \Sigma k_2 + c_3 \Sigma k_3$$

$$\cdot \quad \cdot \quad \cdot \quad \cdot \quad \cdot \quad \cdot$$

$$\overline{\Sigma r_{kk} = (\Sigma k_1)^2 + (\Sigma k_2)^2 + (\Sigma k_3)^2} \qquad (5)$$

in which

$\Sigma r_{kk} =$ sum of all intertest correlations in the whole table. Since the full table is symmetrical it follows that each intertest correlation enters twice in this sum. Also, the full table of intercorrelations includes the correlation of each test with itself and this is here regarded as unity.

$\Sigma k_1 =$ sum of all loadings of factor No. 1 in all tests.

$\Sigma k_2 =$ sum of all loadings of factor No. 2 in all tests.

$\Sigma k_3 =$ sum of all loadings of factor No. 3 in all tests.

Note that equation (3) is the equation of a sphere and that a_1, a_2, a_3 are the three coordinates of a point on the surface of the sphere. The space order of the sphere is equal to the number of postulated general factors. If five factors were postulated we should have a five-dimensional sphere, and so on.

Also note that each test is here really a point on the surface of a sphere. Hence, if there are three factors essentially operative in producing the intercorrelations, then it should be possible to locate each test as a point on the surface of a ball.

Note also that each correlation is the cosine of the central angle subtended by the two points a and b. Hence, if three factors are operative, then each test would be represented by a point on the surface of the ball, and the points would be so allocated that the cosine of each central angle is equal to the intercorrelation between the respective pair of tests. This will be shown in more detail later.

Our problem is to ascertain the coordinates a_1, a_2, a_3 for test a, the coordinates b_1, b_2, b_3 for test b, and so on for each of the w

tests in the whole series. Then, if our determinations are correct, it should be possible to calculate the correlation coefficients by equations (2). These calculated coefficients should agree with the observed correlations within reasonable experimental error.

If we had all of the tests allocated to as many points on the surface of a ball we could not determine the coordinates for any of these points without first deciding where our coordinate axes are to be drawn. The location of these axes is arbitrary and not at all given by the intercorrelations because the latter are merely the cosines of the angular separations between all pairs of points on the surface of the ball.

One simple plan would be to draw the axis OX through one of the tests which might be more or less arbitrarily chosen, such as a. Then if this x-axis represents the first factor, it follows of course that the xyz coordinates of point a are $(+1, 0, 0)$ and hence that

$$a_1 = +1, \ a_2 = 0, \ a_3 = 0.$$

The y-axis must of course be at right angles to the x-axis but it could be drawn through the origin in any direction in the plane at right angles to the x-axis.

We might now revolve the sphere around the x-axis until any arbitrarily selected second test b lies in the xy-plane. Then it is clear that the z-coordinate of point b must be zero so that b_3 in equation (3) vanishes. Therefore equation (3) becomes

$$b_1{}^2 + b_2{}^2 = 1$$

and

$$a_1 = 1.$$

The correlation between a and b is

$$r_{ab} = a_1 b_1 + a_2 b_2 + a_3 b_3,$$

but since $a_1 = 1, a_2 = 0, a_3 = 0, b_3 = 0$, this reduces to

$$r_{ab} = b_1.$$

But

$$b_1 = \cos \phi$$

and hence the correlation between tests a and b is the cosine of the central angle between them. Since the sphere can be revolved

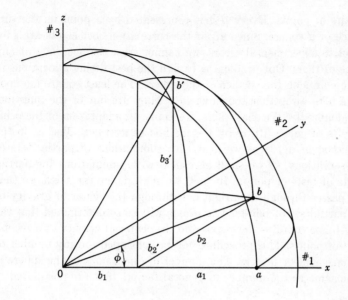

Figure 1. This diagram shows the relation between the correlation coefficient and the central angle between the two tests or points. Let two points which represent any two tests be designated a and b'. Let the x-axis, representing the first general factor, pass through the point a. Then its coordinates are $(1, 0, 0)$. Therefore $a_1 = 1$ while a_2 and a_3 are both zero. Revolve the sphere about the x-axis so that the point b' is in the horizonal xy-plane at b. Then the z-coordinate of the point b is evidently zero whole $b_1^2 + b_2^2 = 1$. Let the angle aob be designated ϕ. Then, clearly, $\cos \phi = b_1$ since the radius of the sphere is unity. The correlation between a and b can be written as follows:

$$r_{ab} = a_1b_1 + a_2b_2 + a_3b_3$$

Since a_2 and a_3 are both zero, the second and third terms vanish and since $a_1 = 1$, it follows that $r_{ab} = b_1$. The angle aob is equal to the angle aob'. Hence the correlation coefficient is equal to the cosine of the central angle between the points that represent the two tests.

in a similar manner for any pair of tests we see that the correlation coefficient for any pair of tests is the cosine of the central angle between them. This is true for any number of factors that may be postulated and hence for any space order.

Our problem can now be restated as follows. We have a table of intercorrelations which are cosines of central angles between pairs of points. Every test is represented by a point on the surface of a sphere. Since all of the correlation coefficients are subject to experimental errors, we cannot trust the accuracy of any one of them. Our problem is to find the best fitting allocations of the points on the surface of the sphere. The least square methods are here altogether too unwieldy. They are out of the question, undoubtedly. We shall therefore apply an adaptation of the principles of curve fitting by the method of averages. Just as in the method of averages we deal with summations of partial sets of observations, so we shall here deal with summations for partial sets of tests or points. In fact, we shall define the x-axis so that it passes through the origin and through the center of gravity of a partial set of points. The y-axis will be so determined that the xy-plane contains the x-axis and the center of gravity of a second set of points. This procedure can be continued for any number of dimensions or factors. The number of dimensions of the sphere is the same as the number of general factors that are postulated.

* * *

The correlations among the several pairs of tests defines a configuration of test vectors without a reference frame. If the first axis of the reference frame is passed through the center of gravity of all the test vectors, the loadings of all the tests on that axis are maximized and the residuals are minimized. (If the residuals are considered negligible at this point, we have Spearman's special case of a single factor.) The second axis is then passed through the center of gravity of the residuals, and so the process of factoring continues. In this way a reference frame is provided for the test vectors.

There is nothing inviolate about this particular reference frame, however. It is perfectly possible to rotate the reference frame into any desired position without changing the structure of test vectors in that space. Thus, once the rank of a correlation matrix is determined and the factors (axes) are extracted, there still remains the problem of rotating the axes until the reference frame seems to make some kind of psychological sense. In general, one would like to rotate the reference frame until each factor had as many loadings near ± 1 or near 0 as possible. Thurstone's prescription for establishing the proper reference frame was to search for what he called a "simple structure," but it was not obvious that the result would be unique or that the factors defining the simple structure would necessarily be psychologically meaningful. Debate about the best solution of the rotation problem is both hot and technical, so we will not pursue it further here.

Although factor analysis originated in the study of intellectual abilities, the mathematical techniques are completely general and can be applied whenever one has a matrix of correlations between many pairs of variables. It has been used, therefore, to give spatial representations for a great variety of psychological structures.

There are, however, other kinds of nonspatial mathematical structures that psychologists have also considered.

By way of contrast, and as an example of a psychological theory that involves a nonspatial structure, we can point to the work of the Swiss psychologist, Jean Piaget. Piaget has searched for some way to represent the *operations* that a person can perform. Instead of adopting a spatial structure that assumes some linear combination of a person's various abilities, Piaget has turned to the more abstract structures of modern mathematics—to the structures of logic, set theory, lattice theory, and so on. In the example below we find him arguing that group theory represents a fundamental structure implicit in the formal thought processes of children.

Piaget's mathematics do not seem to lead on to anything beyond the basic analogies that he describes, and for that reason some American psychologists have ignored or dismissed his use of mathematics as purely discursive. We have included him here, however, because he seems to provide an example of a psychologist who is, at least implicitly, aware of the two levels of structure we mentioned above. At one level there is the experimental subject, struggling to understand a situation in terms of a sort of lay version of group theory, and at the second level there is

Piaget himself trying to explain how this folk model evolves in the mind of the child. It is not apparent that Piaget has succeeded in this double undertaking—certainly he has not succeeded as a formalist in providing an elegant descriptive model—but he has pointed in a direction that others will sooner or later be trying to travel.

The following short passage was taken from a book written jointly with Bärbel Inhelder. A number of physical phenomena and simple experiments were presented to children whose ages ranged from about 4 to 12 years; the children were encouraged to describe and explain what was going on. Piaget attempted to characterize the children's understanding (their "operational schemata") in terms of structures borrowed from modern mathematics, and then tried to weave all these structures together into a genetic narrative of the growth of logical thinking. The following passage introduces the discussion of the problem of two communicating vessels, which is then used to illustrate the development of a four-group (INRC) in the children's thinking.

* * *

Bärbel Inhelder and Jean Piaget

Communicating Vessels

In the problem of the conservation of motion, we encountered the simplest form of the operational schemata relating to group structure, for the construction of this notion by the adolescent rests directly on formal reversibility by inversion. In the equilib-

B. Inhelder and J. Piaget, The growth of logical thinking from childhood to adolescence, transl. by A. Parsons and S. Milgram. New York: Basic Books, 1958, pp. 133–135. Reprinted by permission of the publishers. Original French edition: De la Logique de L'Enfant à la Logique de L'Adolescent. Paris: Presses Universitaires de France, 1955.

rium problems, of which the problem of communicating vessels gives us a first example, we come to a more complex variety of schema resting on group structure. In every equilibrium the two possible forms of reversibility operate simultaneously: *inversion*, which corresponds to the additions or eliminations effected in the parts of the system which come into equilibrium, and *reciprocity*, which corresponds to the symmetries or compensations between these parts (thus to actions which are both equivalent as regards their respective products and oriented in opposite directions). But, inversions and reciprocities also form a group between themselves.

In order to illustrate our point and, more particularly, in order to understand more clearly in what way the operational schema corresponding to the notion of equilibrium is at the center of the mechanisms of formal thought, we have to remind ourselves that beyond the operations themselves in the strict sense of the term (or "operators")—i.e., the operations of propositional logic, such as disjunction $(p \vee q)$, implication $(p \supset q)$, etc.—there are more general transformations which transform particular operators into others. Thus an operator such as $p \vee q$ can be transformed by inversion or negation into $\bar{p}.\bar{q}$, a transformation that we may designate by N, so that $\mathrm{N}(p \vee q) = \bar{p}.\bar{q}$. But $(p \vee q)$ can also be transformed by reciprocity R, so that $\mathrm{R}(p \vee q) = \bar{p} \vee \bar{q} = p/q$. Again $(p \vee q)$ can be transformed, by correlativity C (i.e., by permuting the $\vee$ and the .), so that $\mathrm{C}(p \vee q) = p.q$. Finally, the operator $(p \vee q)$ may be transformed into itself by identical transformation I, so that $\mathrm{I}(p \vee q) = (p \vee q)$. Thus, one can see that I, N, R, and C form a commutative group of four transformations among themselves, for the correlative C is the inverse N of the reciprocal R, so that $\mathrm{C} = \mathrm{NR}$ (and $\mathrm{C} = \mathrm{RN}$ as well). Likewise, we have $\mathrm{R} = \mathrm{CN}$ (or NC) and $\mathrm{N} = \mathrm{CR}$ (or RC). Finally, we have $\mathrm{I} = \mathrm{RCN}$ (or CRN, etc.).

This group is of psychological importance because it actually corresponds to certain fundamental structures of thought at the formal level, for inversion N expresses negation, reciprocity R expresses symmetry (equivalent transformations oriented in opposite directions), and correlativity is symmetric with negation. This explains why the notion of equilibrium, which at a very early age gives rise to certain rough intuitions (balance, etc.) is not really understood before the formal level, when the subject can both distinguish and coordinate inversions, reciprocities, and correlativities (*inversions:* for example, increase or diminish a force in one of the parts of the system; *reciprocities:* compensate for a force by an equivalent force, thus assuring symmetry between the parts; *correlativities:* reciprocity in negation).

Although they may be relatively simple in certain concrete cases, these transformations actually require thinking and statements of a very abstract sort in most problems involving action and reaction, for here the difficulty is to grasp that X is at the same time equal to Y and acting in the opposite direction from it. In such cases, the instruments necessary for thinking go beyond propositional logic to include its fundamental group I N R C. This is what we shall see in the following chapter in reference to the problem of the equilibrium between the pressure of a piston and the resistance of liquids; but at this time take note of the same question as it relates to the preliminary problem of the equilibrium of communicating vessels.

In the case of communicating vessels, *reciprocity* serves to express the compensatory actions between separate vessels; transformations by *inversion* express the rise and fall of the water level. (Changes in water level are brought about not by adding or taking away water but by raising and lowering the receptacles.)

*   *   *

Our next example of a structural application of mathematics is drawn from psycholinguistics. Here again the structures invoked are essentially nonspatial in character.

Beginning in 1948 with the work of Claude Shannon on communication theory, there has been a growing interest in describing the statistical structure underlying our spoken and written messages; some mention of this development was made in the preceding chapter. Parallel with this growth of statistical communication theory, however, there has also been an intensive effort to establish a formal basis for descriptive linguistics. Both of these developments have profoundly modified the psychologist's conception of linguistic behavior.

One must be sensitive to the dual level of psycholinguistic structures. At one level—the level at which linguists naturally work—the problem is to characterize explicitly what a person knows tacitly about the structure of his language. At another level—where psychologists become involved—the theoretical problem is to describe an automaton that incorporates this linguistic knowledge in some form but is psychologically limited in various ways in its attempts to perform the operations that it knows are linguistically appropriate.

As we have already mentioned, during the 1930's G. K. Zipf stirred up considerable interest in various statistical regularities that he uncovered in his analyses of word frequencies. Twenty years later the mathematician Benoit Mandelbrot* was able to demonstrate that Zipf's laws were attributable to random processes and implied no deep linguistic or psychological consequences. Meanwhile, however, Shannon's statistical communication theory had come prominently to the attention of American psychologists, and the much more sophisticated statistical theory of Markov chains was seriously proposed as a model for the human talker. A Markov chain has a structural aspect (the network of paths between states of the system) and a statistical aspect (the conditional probabilities, given that the system is now in state i, that it will go next to state j). At first many theorists thought that this mathematical structure was sufficiently general to accommodate any particular grammar that might be required for a natural language. The fact that Markovian structures are not adequate for all the things a grammar must allow us to do was first proved by the linguist and logician Noam Chomsky. Chomsky's argument is not statistical in character, but rests entirely on certain familiar structural properties of natural language that are not available in Markov chains.

* B. Mandelbrot, On recurrent noise limiting coding. In E. Weber (Ed.), *Symposium on information networks* (Proceedings, 1954). Brooklyn: Polytechnic Institute of Brooklyn, 1955, pp. 205–221. See also G. A. Miller, Some effects of intermittent silence. *Am. J. Psychol.*, 1957, **70**, 311–313.

The following passage by Chomsky is an excerpt from a book published in 1957.

* * *

Noam Chomsky

An Elementary Linguistic Theory

1 Assuming the set of grammatical sentences of English to be given, we now ask what sort of device can produce this set (equivalently, what sort of theory gives an adequate account of the structure of this set of utterances). We can think of each sentence of this set as a sequence of phonemes of finite length. A language is an enormously involved system, and it is quite obvious that any attempt to present directly the set of grammatical phoneme sequences would lead to a grammar so complex that it would be practically useless. For this reason (among others), linguistic description proceeds in terms of a system of "levels of representations." Instead of stating the phonemic structure of sentences directly, the linguist sets up such "higher level" elements as morphemes, and states separately the morphemic structure of sentences and the phonemic structure of morphemes. It can easily be seen that the joint description of these two levels will be much simpler than a direct description of the phonemic structure of sentences.

Let us now consider various ways of describing the morphemic structure of sentences. We ask what sort of grammar is necessary to generate all the sequences of morphemes (or words) that constitute grammatical English sentences, and only these.

One requirement that a grammar must certainly meet is that it be finite. Hence the grammar cannot simply be a list of all mor-

N. Chomsky, *Syntactic structures.* The Hague: Mouton, 1957, pp. 18–25. Reprinted by permission of the author and the publisher.

pheme (or word) sequences, since there are infinitely many of these. A familiar communication theoretic model for language suggests a way out of this difficulty. Suppose that we have a machine that can be in any one of a finite number of different internal states, and suppose that this machine switches from one state to another by producing a certain symbol (let us say, an English word). One of these states is an *initial state;* another is a *final state.* Suppose that the machine begins in the initial state, runs through a sequence of states (producing a word with each transition), and ends in the final state. Then we call the sequence of words that has been produced a "sentence." Each such machine thus defines a certain language; namely, the set of sentences that can be produced in this way. Any language that can be produced by a machine of this sort we call a *finite state language;* and we can call the machine itself a *finite state grammar.* A finite state grammar can be represented graphically in the form of a "state diagram."[1] For example, the grammar that produces just the two sentences "the man comes" and "the men come" can be represented by the following state diagram:

(1)

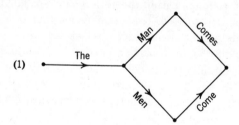

We can extend this grammar to produce an infinite number of sentences by adding closed loops. Thus the finite state grammar of the subpart of English containing the above sentences in addition to "the old man comes," "the old old man comes," . . ., "the old men come," "the old old men come," . . ., can be represented by the following state diagram:

[1] C. E. Shannon and W. Weaver, *The mathematical theory of communication* (Urbana, 1949), pp. 15f.

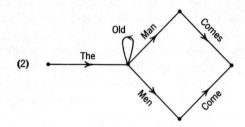

(2)

Given a state diagram, we produce a sentence by tracing a path from the initial point on the left to the final point on the right, always proceeding in the direction of the arrows. Having reached a certain point in the diagram, we can proceed along any path leading from this point, whether or not this path has been traversed before in constructing the sentence in question. Each node in such a diagram thus corresponds to a state of the machine. We can allow transition from one state to another in several ways, and we can have any number of closed loops of any length. The machines that produce languages in this manner are known mathematically as "finite state Markov processes." To complete this elementary communication theoretic model for language, we assign a probability to each transition from state to state. We can then calculate the "uncertainty" associated with each state and we can define the "information content" of the language as the average uncertainty, weighted by the probability of being in the associated states. Since we are studying grammatical, not statistical structure of language here, this generalization does not concern us.

This conception of language is an extremely powerful and general one. If we can adopt it, we can view the speaker as being essentially a machine of the type considered. In producing a sentence, the speaker begins in the initial state, produces the first word of the sentence, thereby switching into a second state which limits the choice of the second word, etc. Each state through which he passes represents the grammatical restrictions that limit the choice of the next word at this point in the utterance.

In view of the generality of this conception of language, and its utility in such related disciplines as communication theory, it is important to inquire into the consequences of adopting this point of view in the syntactic study of some languages such as English or a formalized system of mathematics. Any attempt to construct a finite state grammar for English runs into serious difficulties and complications at the very outset, as the reader can easily convince himself. However, it is unnecessary to attempt to show this by example, in view of the following more general remark about English:

(3) English is not a finite state language.

That is, it is *impossible,* not just difficult, to construct a device of the type described above (a diagram such as (1) or (2)) which will produce all and only the grammatical sentences of English. To demonstrate (3) it is necessary to define the syntactic properties of English more precisely. We shall proceed to describe certain syntactic properties of English which indidate that, under any reasonable delimitation of the set of sentences of the language, (3) can be regarded as a theorem concerning English. To go back to the question asked in the second paragraph [above], (3) asserts that it is not possible to state the morphemic structure of sentences directly by means of some such device as a state diagram, and that the Markov process conception of language outlined above cannot be accepted, at least for the purposes of grammar.

2 A language is defined by giving its "alphabet" (i.e., the finite set of symbols out of which its sentences are constructed) and its grammatical sentences. Before investigating English directly, let us consider several languages whose alphabets contain just the letters $a, b,$ and whose sentences are as defined in (4i–iii):

(4) (i) *ab, aabb, aaabbb, ...,* and in general, all sentences consisting of n occurrences of a followed by n occurrences of b and only these;

(ii) *aa, bb, abba, baab, aaaa, bbbb, aabbaa, abbbba, ...,* and in general, all sentences consisting of a string X followed by the "mirror image" of X (i.e., X in reverse), and only these;

(iii) *aa, bb, abab, baba, aaaa, bbbb, aabaab, abbabb,...,*
and in general, all sentences consisting of a string X of
a's and *b*'s followed by the identical string X, and only
these.

We can easily show that each of these three languages is not a
finite state language. Similarly, languages such as (4) where the
a's and *b*'s in question are not consecutive, but are embedded in
other strings, will fail to be finite state languages under quite
general conditions.[2]

But it is clear that there are subparts of English with the basic
form of (4i) and (4ii). Let $S_1, S_2, S_3, \ldots$ be declarative sentences
in English. Then we can have such English sentences as:

(5) (i) If S_1, then S_2.
     (ii) Either S_3, or S_4.
     (iii) The man who said that S_5, is arriving today.

In (5i), we cannot have "or" in place of "then"; in (5ii), we cannot have "then" in place of "or"; in (5iii), we cannot have "are"
instead of "is." In each of these cases there is a dependency between words on opposite sides of the comma (i.e., "if"–"then,"
"either"–"or," "man"–"is"). But between the interdependent
words, in each case, we can insert a declarative sentence $S_1, S_3,$
S_5, and this declarative sentence may in fact be one of (5i–iii).
Thus if in (5i) we take S_1 as (5ii) and S_3 as (5iii), we will have
the sentence:

(6) if, either (5iii), or S_4, then S_2,

and S^5 in (5iii) may again be one of the sentences of (5). It is clear,
then, that in English we can find a sentence $a + S_1 + b$, where
there is a dependency between a and b, and we can select as S_1
another sentence of the form $c + S_2 + d$, where there is a de-

---

[2] See my "Three models for the description of language," *I.R.E. Transactions on Information Theory,* Vol. IT-2, Proceedings of the symposium on
information theory, Sept., 1956, for a statement of such conditions and a
proof of (3). Notice in particular that the set of well-formed formulas of
any formalized system of mathematics or logic will fail to constitute a
finite state language, because of paired parentheses or equivalent restrictions.

pendency between c and d, then select as S_2 another sentence of this form, etc. The set of sentences that is constructed in this way (and we see from (5) that there are several possibilities available for such construction—(5) comes nowhere near exhausting these possibilities) will have all of the mirror image properties of (4ii) which exclude (4ii) from the set of finite state languages. Thus we can find various kinds of nonfinite state models within English. This is a rough indication of the lines along which a rigorous proof of (3) can be given, on the assumption that such sentences as (5) and (6) belong to English, while sentences that contradict the cited dependencies of (5) (e.g., "either S_1, then S_2," etc.) do not belong to English. Note that many of the sentences of the form (6), etc., will be quite strange and unusual (they can often be made less strange by replacing "if" by "whenever," "on the assumption that," "if it is the case that," etc., without changing the substance of our remarks). But they are all grammatical sentences, formed by processes of sentence construction so simple and elementary that even the most rudimentary English grammar would contain them. They can be understood, and we can even state quite simply the conditions under which they can be true. It is difficult to conceive of any possible motivation for excluding them from the set of grammatical English sentences. Hence it seems quite clear that no theory of linguistic structure based exclusively on Markov process models and the like, will be able to explain or account for the ability of a speaker of English to produce and understand new utterances, while he rejects other new sequences as not belonging to the language.

3 We might arbitrarily decree that such processes of sentence formation in English as those we are discussing cannot be carried out more than n times, for some fixed n. This would of course make English a finite state language, as, for example, would a limitation of English sentences to length of less than a million words. Such arbitrary limitations serve no useful purpose, however. The point is that there are processes of sentence formation that finite state grammars are intrinsically not equipped to handle. If these processes have no finite limit, we can prove the literal inapplicability of this elementary theory. If the processes have a limit, then the construction of a finite state grammar will not be literally out of the question, since it will be possible to list the sentences, and a list is essentially a trivial finite state grammar. But this grammar will be so complex that it will be of little use or interest. In general, the assumption that languages are infinite is made in order to simplify the description of these languages. If a grammar does not have recursive devices (closed loops, as in (2), in the finite state grammar) it will be prohibitively complex. If it does have recursive devices of some sort, it will produce infinitely many sentences.

In short, the approach to the analysis of grammaticalness suggested here in terms of a finite state Markov process that produces sentences from left to right, appears to lead to a dead end. . . . If a grammar of this type produces all English sentences, it will produce many non-sentences as well. If it produces only English sentences, we can be sure that there will be an infinite number of true sentences, false sentences, reasonable questions, etc., which it simply will not produce.

The conception of grammar which has just been rejected represents in a way the minimal linguistic theory that merits serious consideration. A finite state grammar is the simplest type of grammar which, with a finite amount of apparatus, can generate an infinite number of sentences. We have seen that such a limited linguistic theory is not adequate; we are forced to search for some more powerful type of grammar and some more "abstract" form of linguistic theory. The notion of "linguistic level of representation" put forth at the outset of this section must be modified and elaborated. At least one linguistic level *cannot* have this simple structure. That is, on some level, it will not be the case that each sentence is represented simply as a finite sequence of elements of some sort, generated from left to right by some simple device. Alternatively, we must give up the hope of finding a *finite* set of levels, ordered from high to low, so constructed that we can generate all utterances by stating the permitted sequences of highest level elements, the constituency of each highest level element in terms of elements of the second level, etc., finally stating the phonemic constituency of elements of the next-to-lowest level. . . . We proposed that levels be established in this way in order to *simplify* the description of the set of grammatical phoneme sequences. If a language can be described in an elementary, left-to-right manner in terms of a single level (i.e., if it is a finite state language) then this description may indeed be simplified by construction of such higher levels; but to generate nonfinite state languages such as English we need fundamentally different methods, and a more general concept of "linguistic level."

* * *

The fact that English grammar permits sentences to be embedded inside sentences means that it must be able to deal with parenthetical structures: (), (()), ((())),.... . These are, of course, just the sentences in Chomsky's language (4i). Since no limit is imposed by the grammar on the number of left parentheses, and since each different number of left parentheses implies a different state of the assumed Markovian system (so that it can remember how many right parentheses are required to complete the string grammatically), it follows that the number of states must be denumerably infinite. But this is absurd, because a grammar with an infinite number of rules cannot be learned in a finite childhood or stored in a finite nervous system. An infinitely long grammar is, in fact, no improvement over an exhaustive list of all grammatical sentences, so the whole purpose of a grammar is vitiated. The only reasonable conclusion is that languages should not be characterized by structures having a finite number of states with specific transitions among them.

It is a metaphysical axiom which most scientists would be reluctant to abandon that all living organisms, man included, are finite-state devices. The number of different states is vast but, like the universe itself, not without limit. Chomsky showed that grammar incorporates rules (just as do logic and mathematics) that no finite-state device, man included, can follow without error under all conditions. At this point a distinction between the structure of language and the structure of a finite device that uses language was no longer a mere convenience; it had become a logical necessity. Somehow, the psychological theory must include, yet remain distinct from, the grammatical rules that a language user knows.

We have now discussed the structure of colors, of intelligence, of reasoning, of language. To round out our somewhat heterogeneous collection, consider next a study of social structure.

The following selection represents a sociometric study of a housing project for married graduate students at the Massachusetts Institute of Technology. Westgate was part of this housing project; it was organized into separate courts, named Tolman, Howe, Williams, and so on. The social psychologists who conducted the study—Leon Festinger, Stanley Schachter, and Kurt Back—asked the residents of each house to name their friends; on the basis of the choices it was possible to construct a network of friendships that represented something about the social structures of the separate courts.

In the following passage, published in 1950, Festinger, Schachter, and Back described a mathematical method for analyzing these group structures.

*   *   *

Leon Festinger, Stanley Schachter, and Kurt Back

Patterns of Group Structure

In the study of groups by means of sociometric data much attention has been given to the exact pattern of connections among individuals. The need to describe and analyze the patterning of these connections has been apparent. It is not only important to know how many friendships exist in a group and what proportion of them are mutual friendships, but it is also important to

L. Festinger, S. Schachter, and K. Back, *Social pressures in informal groups.* New York: Harper, 1950. Copyright 1950 by Harper & Row. Pp. 132–147 reprinted by permission of the publishers.

know who a particular person's friends are, what his relations are with the friends of his friends, and what tendencies to sub-group or clique formation exist. We need to know how many paths of influence exist among members of a group, who can influence whom, over how much of a group a person's influence extends, and what is the nature of the indirect influence chains that may exist. If an item of information enters a group it is not only important to know how many people will eventually hear about it but also to know exactly who will hear it and from whom and how far removed from the original source it will be by the time a specific person hears about it.

Without an adequate representational technique of handling such data the analysis of the exact patterns of interconnections among members of a group is virtually impossible unless the group is very small. As the size of the group increases, the complexity of the pattern generally makes it difficult to comprehend by mere inspection. The result has been the relative neglect of this kind of analysis. Investigators have, by and large, contented themselves with analyzing sociometric patterns in such terms as the number of choices people receive, the kind of people who get most choices, the proportion of the choices inside the group, and other such summary measures which serve to relate the sociometric choices to other variables.

The major portion of this chapter will be devoted to the development of a method of treating sociometric choices which makes it possible to analyze more complex interrelationships. By the use of some of the standard and relatively simple manipulations of matrix algebra we are able to analyze such things as subgroup formations, cliques, and indirect chains of influence from one person to another. The application of this analysis technique to the sociometric data from the Westgate courts yields some important insights into their structure.

Previous Methods of Analysis

Initial attempts at the analysis and description of the exact patterning of interconnections in a group took the form of drawing complicated diagrams where the connections were represented by lines, with arrows on them, between individuals. Such diagrams might, for example, be drawn for the patterns of interconnections within Tolman Court and within Howe Court, as shown in Figure 1a and b. Some things become readily apparent from an inspection of and comparison between these "socio-

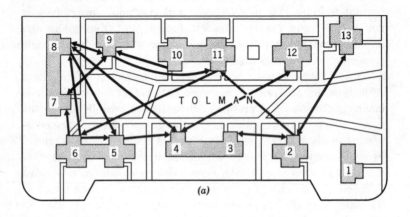

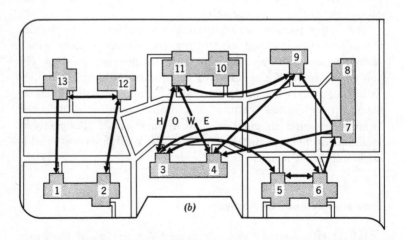

Figure 1. Pattern of sociometric connections in (a) Tolman Court and (b) Howe Court.

grams." Both courts seem very similar. In each court there are
seven or eight people who give several choices among each other
and four other people who are relatively or completely separated
from the larger sugbroup of seven or eight. Also, in each court
there are one or two complete isolates who neither give nor receive any choices within the court. It is extremely difficult to determine more than this from inspection of these diagrams.

It is understandable that such a diagram would become unwieldy if the number of members increased or if the number of
choices made by each member increased to any appreciable degree. There are no operating rules for such diagrams. One merely
arranges them by trial and error so as to make the diagram
look as simple as possible and then one further examines it with
the hope that he will be alert enough to see what is to be seen.
The differences between these two courts, which we shall later
clearly show to exist, are difficult to perceive in these diagrams.
Indeed, we were not aware of them until the sociometric patterns
were subjected to a more systematic and rigorous form of
analysis. . . .

The Method of Matrix Multiplication

When the sociometric pattern is presented in a matrix form,
an analysis of some aspects of the structure of the group can be
performed by the relatively simple means of squaring and cubing
this matrix.[1] Let us follow through these operations to see how
they are performed and what type of information they will yield.
In Figure 2a are shown, side by side, the original matrices for
Tolman and Howe Courts. Figure 2b shows the squares of these
two matrices and Figure 2c shows the matrices cubed. The
squared matrix is readily obtained in the following way: to obtain the number which goes into the cell designated by column
c and row r of the squared matrix, we multiply each cell in
column c of the original matrix by the corresponding cell of row

[1] The application of matrix multiplication to the analysis of sociometric
patterns was developed together with Mr. Albert Perry and Mr. Duncan
Luce of the Massachusetts Institute of Technology.

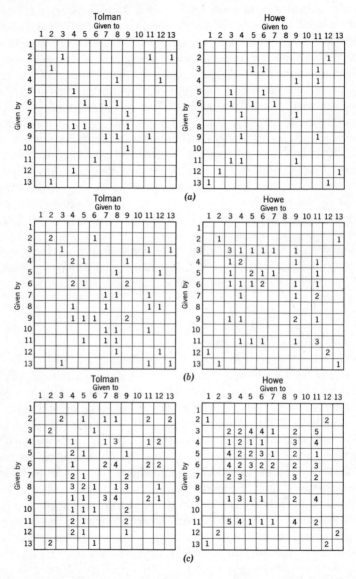

Figure 2. (a) Matrices of sociometric patterns for Tolman and Howe courts. (b) Squared matrices. (c) Cubed matrices.

r and then add these products up. The cells in any row which "correspond" with the cells of any column are easy to determine. For example, the corresponding cells of the third row and the fourth column are such that if person 3 chooses someone who in turn chooses person 4, this will cause a 1 to appear in the squared matrix cell designated by row 3, column 4. The general equation for this multiplication might be written as follows:

$$A^2{}_{rc} = A_{1c}A_{r1} + A_{2c}A_{r2} + A_{3c}A_{r3} + \cdots + A_{nc}A_{rn}$$

In this equation $A^2{}_{rc}$ refers to the number in the cell of the squared matrix in the r row of the c column; $A_{1c}A_{r1}$ refers to the product of the number in the cell in the first row of the c column and the number in the r row of the first column of the unsquared matrix, and so on.

This procedure is carried out through a short cut. The products of the corresponding cells of a row and a column will yield numbers other than zero only if a 1 appears in both cells which are being considered. Thus, a two-step connection where individual 2 chooses individual 11, and 11 chooses individual 6 (as is the case in the matrix of Tolman Court) will contribute a number in the row 2, column 6 cell of the squared matrix. Thus, to obtain the numbers which, for example, go in row 8 of the squared Tolman matrix, we observe that row 8 in the original matrix has 1's in columns 4, 5, and 9. We then look down each column of the original matrix successively looking only for numbers in the corresponding rows 4, 5, and 9. Column 1 has nothing in either 4, 5, or 9 row, nor do columns 2 and 3. Column 4 has a 1 in row 5 and so we write a 1 in the fourth column of the eighth row of the squared matrix. If a column of the original matrix contained 1's in two or all three of these rows a 2 or 3, respectively, would be written in the appropriate position of the squared matrix.

Each figure in this matrix represents the number of two-step connections that exist between the specified two members of the group. Thus the one in the eleventh column of the third row of the squared Tolman Court matrix in Figure 2b indicates that there is one two-step connection from number 3 to number 11. Looking at the original matrix we can easily locate this connection. Number 3 chooses number 2 and individual number 2 chooses number 11. It is clear, of course, that this relationship need not be symmetrical, just as the one-step connections need not be symmetrical. Here for example, there is not any two-step connection from number 11 to number 3.

The numbers that appear in the diagonal of this squared matrix have a special meaning. They indicate the number of two-step connections that exist from a person back to himself, or, in other words, they indicate the number of mutual sociometric choices in which this person was involved. Thus, the number 2 in the fourth row of the fourth column of the squared Howe Court matrix indicates that individual number 4 had two mutual choices. Looking back at the original unsquared matrix we readily see that these mutual choices were with individuals numbers 9 and 11. It is immediately clear in comparing the two courts that while about the same number of people in each court were involved in mutual choices, the number of such mutual choices were considerably greater in Howe Court than in Tolman Court.

The meaning of these two-step connections between different people is quite important. For example, if the original sociometric choice indicates influence from Mr. A to Mr. B, the squared matrix would indicate the extent of indirect influence which Mr. A has and exactly which other people he influences indirectly. If the original sociometric data indicated channels of communication for information, the squared matrix would tell us, for example, that an item of information starting with number 8 in Tolman Court would be heard by numbers 4, 7, 11, and 12 in two steps, and if started with number 12 in Howe Court would be heard in two steps only by number 1. In Tolman Court, individual number 8 could communicate to number 4, 5, and 9 and from these people the information would spread to the others. In Howe Court, individual number 12 could communicate to numbers 2 and 13 but the information would not travel far. Number 2 could communicate to no one except back to number 12. Number 13 could communicate back to number 12 and also to number 1. Individual number 1 would thus be the only one to have heard it in two steps. It is interesting to note that this would be the end of the circulation of this item of information in Howe

Court since individual number 1 has no connections with anyone other than 13, his original informant.

While most people in these courts had more indirect two-step connections than direct one-step connections, there were some who did not. Thus, number 2 in Tolman Court had three one-step connections with other people but only one two-step connection with anyone else. Thus, while communications or influences (assuming the connections imply communication or influence) would tend to spread farther and farther if started with most people; if started with someone like number 2 in Tolman Court, it would probably taper off quickly and not spread far at all.

The cube of the matrix shown in Figure 2c, which gives information on three-step connections, is obtained by multiplying the original matrix by the squared matrix in the same way that the original matrix was multiplied by itself. The formula for obtaining the values of the cells of the cubed matrix would be written similarly as:

$$A^3{}_{rc} = A_{1c}A^2{}_{r2} + A_{2c}A^2{}_{r2} + A_{3c}A^2{}_{r3} + \cdots + A_{nc}A^2{}_{rn}$$

The actual calculation is again performed rather simply. To obtain the numbers which appear in the seventh row of the cubed matrix of Howe Court, for example, we note that in the original matrix there are 1's in the fourth and ninth columns of the seventh row. We then look at each column of the squared matrix to see if there are any numbers in the fourth and ninth rows. Column 1 has zero; column 2 has zero; column 3 has a 1 in the fourth and a 1 in the ninth row and consequently a 2 appears in the cubed matrix; column 4 has a 2 in row four and a 1 in row nine and consequently a 3 appears in the appropriate cell of the cubed matrix, and so on.

The meaning of the figures in this cubed matrix is similar to their meaning in the squared matrix. They indicate the number of three-step connections that exist between any two people. The numbers in the diagonal of the matrix now indicate the number of three-step connections from a person back to himself. The implications of these numbers in the diagonal of the cubed matrix will be elaborated on shortly.

It is apparent that these matrices may also be raised to higher powers to obtain the four-step or five-step or even more indirect connections among the members of a group. If we are concerned with a question such as how many people will hear a given item of information in three or fewer steps if it is started with any particular person, the answer may be obtained by adding together the original, the squared, and the cubed matrices. We can obtain information such as who influences the greatest number of people in less than a specified number of steps, which people are influenced by the greatest number of people and which individuals are only subject to the influence of a few, which people in the group are most indirectly connected to each other and how indirect this connection is, or what proportion of the possible connections among the various people actually exists. Being able to handle conveniently and efficiently these aspects of group structure and patterning of connections should make it feasible to study their effects on such processes as communication, influence, social pressures, and many others.

The Determination of Cliques

The manipulation of matrices by means of raising them to the third power can, with complete accuracy, determine the existence of cliques of various sizes and with various degrees of "cliquishness." Let us begin by defining an extreme instance of clique formation within a group and then see how we may determine whether or not such cliques exist in any given structure. We shall define this extreme type of clique as three or more individuals all of whom choose each other mutually. In other words, direct one-step symmetrical connections exist between every possible pair of members of such a clique. Clearly, in order to determine the existence of such a clique we would concern ourselves with the symmetrical submatrix consisting only of mutual choices and not with the complete matrix of connections. If we raise such a symmetrical submatrix to the third power we will obtain all the three-step connections that exist between any two people which involve only mutual choices. What would then be the meaning of a three-step connection from a member back to himself which involves only symmetrical choices—that is, what will be the meaning of the numbers which appear in the main diagonal of this cubed symmetrical submatrix? Numbers will appear in the main diagonal of this cubed matrix if and only if there exists a clique, as defined above, within the group. If such a clique does exist then numbers will appear in those positions on the diagonal which correspond to those persons who are members of the clique. If only one clique exists in the group or if more than one clique exists but they contain different members, then the number which appears in the diagonal for a particular individual will bear a given relationship to the number of people in the clique. If the clique is composed of n members, the number appearing in the diagonal for each of the members will be equal to $(n-1)(n-2)$. We may thus immediately determine from this cubed matrix whether or not cliques exist, who belongs to these cliques if they exist, and how many members each clique has.

Let us examine the cubed symmetrical submatrices for Tolman and Howe courts which are presented in Figure 3. In Tolman Court it is immediately clear there were no cliques at all, since there are no numbers occurring in the main diagonal. In other words, in Tolman Court there was no subgroup as tightly knit as the requirements of our definition imply. In Howe Court, on the contrary, we observe that six people have numbers in the main diagonal and that all of these numbers are 2's. Since the number 2 occurring in the main diagonal of this matrix indicates the existence of a clique of three people we may immediately conclude that in Howe Court there were two nonoverlapping cliques of three people each. We may separate the two cliques very quickly with reference to the original matrix. There we may observe that number 4 chose number 9 and number 11. We consequently know that 4, 9, and 11 comprise one clique and that 3, 5, and 6 comprise the other. Since indirect three-step connections exist in the matrix between the two cliques, we may also conclude that there was at least one mutual choice made between them. Since the greatest number of indirect connections exist between number 3 and number 11, it is highly likely that this is the direct connection. Looking at the original matrix we indeed find a mutual choice between number 3 and number 11. It is clear

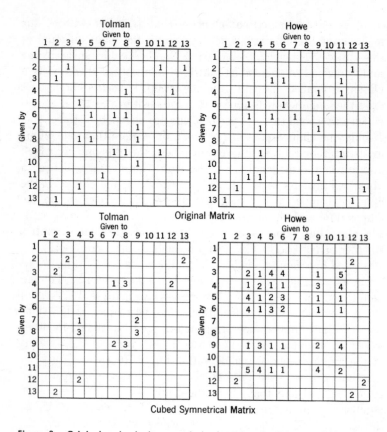

Figure 3. Original and cubed symmetrical submatrices for Tolman and Howe courts.

that these two courts differed markedly with respect to cliques although we found them to be similar in many other respects.

It is also possible to distinguish subgroups which are not extreme cliques. These subgroups may be defined on the basis of mutual choices or on the basis of the complete matrix. We shall give some examples of such more moderate subgroup formations. If we look at the cubed symmetrical submatrix of Tolman Court we see that numbers 3, 2, and 13 are linked together. Here direct choices between numbers 3 and 13 are completely lacking. If we look at the cube of the complete matrix of Tolman Court we find that three, and only three people have 1's in the main diagonal. These three, numbers 4, 5, and 8, are consequently tied together in a circle. Anyone can get back to himself in three steps via the other two. One can, however, only go around this circle in one direction. The best criteria for distinguishing subgroups of less than the extreme degree must still be determined but it is clear that once defined, they may be relatively easily found by means of matrix multiplication.

*   *   *

A more advanced exposition of the matrix algebra involved in this sociometric analysis can be found in articles by Luce and Perry.*

The finite-state devices that Chomsky mentioned and the sociometric networks that Festinger, Schachter, and Back analyzed take us squarely into the heart of a branch of mathematics known generally as the *theory of graphs*. Neural nets, chemical notation, electrical circuits, sociometric diagrams, topological simplexes, administrative charts, genealogical trees, finite-state diagrams, communication nets, flow charts—all these are different names for what, in the abstract, is simply a topological graph. Graph theory represents the study of structure in a pure form. If the frequency with which behavioral scientists talk about structure is any guide, then many more applications will probably be found for graph theory as it becomes more widely known.

* R. D. Luce and A. D. Perry, A method of matrix analysis of group structure. *Psychometrika*, 1949, **14**, 96–116. R. D. Luce, Connectivity and generalized cliques in sociometric group structure. *Psychometrika*, 1950, **15**, 169–190.

7

Quasimathematical Psychology

An entire new technology emerged very rapidly in the years following World War II. It was an information technology and its most authentic symbol soon became the large, high-speed computer. By performing immensely intricate feats of information processing at rates that stagger the imagination, by controlling complicated industrial operations accurately and automatically, these machines opened a new chapter in the history of the industrial revolution. Whereas the steam engine magnified men's muscles, the computer magnified their brains; the latter could scarcely be less consequential than the former. The scientific and social implications of this technological explosion reached far and deep. They were dramatically forecast as early as 1948 by the mathematician Norbert Wiener in his widely read book on *Cybernetics,* a book that tried to outline a whole new area of scientific and technological endeavor that was then opening up.

Like everyone else, psychologists were intrigued and impressed by these marvelous new machines. A comparison of human and machine intelligence was invigorating to the psychological imagination. Soon some psychologists learned to speak the formal languages that were used to describe and direct the machines; it was inevitable that they would try to use those languages to describe the behavior of living organisms, too. In a remarkably short time, therefore, a variety of fresh psychological hypotheses and models had been proposed, and experimenters were furiously at work testing their new psychomechanistic analogies.

Theories that rely on a structural isomorphism between the behavior of organisms and the behavior of machines should probably not be counted as instances of mathematical psychology—certainly not as we have used that term in the preceding chapters. But computer models are usually conceived and tested in much the same spirit as are mathematical models. And often, because mathematically trained psychologists were among the first to learn how to use the new machines, the same people have worked on both kinds of models. Thus, in both intent and history, the relation of computer models to mathematical models is close enough to justify our calling them "quasimathematical" and including here two examples. One example involves an analogue computer, the other, a digital computer. Both are somewhat recent for inclusion here, but in a field that grows as rapidly as this one, ideas turn quickly into history.

The first example invites us to contemplate an analogy between a man and a servomechanism. This comparison assumed special importance during World War II when psychologists were called on to select and train men who could keep guns or various other kinds of gear aimed at fast-moving targets.

A servo is a system in which some function of the output is fed back for comparison with the input, and the difference between them is then used to control the system. If the feedback is negative, so that it can cancel the input, the servo will act to reduce the difference between the input and the output to zero. When a man aims a gun at a target, he can be said to function as a servo system: he matches his perceptual input (the target position) with his motor output (the position of the gun) and tries to reduce the difference to zero. With a small gun and a stationary target, a man can learn to perform this task with great accuracy. When the target is moving at high speeds and the gun is large and heavy, however, he must have help to predict the target's future position, and he must have help to move the gun. In these more difficult situations, therefore, a human operator becomes just one more link in a complicated system of computers and motors.

For very practical reasons the engineers who designed these systems tried to use the same kind of equations and parameters to describe the human operator as they were using to describe all the other components. The engineers, of course, hoped to develop automatic tracking devices that would eventually replace the sluggish and inaccurate operator. But before they could replace him, they had to specify explicitly the function he performed as a null device. It was their method of specification that seemed so novel and interesting; the psychologists involved quickly picked up some clever new ways to describe behavior. Following the war several articles appeared in psychological and other technical journals almost simultaneously reporting the thought and effort that different research teams had invested in the tracking problem.

The following selection by Kenneth J. W. Craik illustrates the kind of theorizing that resulted from this interaction of engineers and psychologists. "The human operator," says Craik, "behaves basically as an intermittent correction servo." The same differential equations that describe intermittent servos could, if we took him seriously, describe human operators. In fact, however, Craik did not explicitly use the mathematical tools that his postulate put at his disposal, although he might have, and other psychologists have frequently done so. Craik preferred instead to consider actual electrical devices that would literally *simulate* the operator's behavior. (Note incidentally that simulation was not the goal of the engineer; he hoped to invent servos that would do far better than any human operator could. It was the psychologist who saw in simulation a new technique for formulating his theories of behavior.)

This selection is the first of two papers prepared by Craik shortly before his premature death by accident in 1945. They were probably intended as preliminary drafts for discussion and might have been considerably revised had he lived to do it. But in view of the lively interest in these problems that developed following the war, and of the original way in which Craik handled them, it was decided to publish the papers posthumously in spite of their tentative character.

Kenneth James Williams Craik

Theory of the Human Operator in Control Systems

The Operator as an Engineering System

1 *The human operator behaves basically as an intermittent correction servo.* The evidence for this is the periodic or "wavy" nature of the time-record of tracking errors, showing a spectrum with a predominant frequency of about 0.5 sec. with a smaller cluster of frequencies from 0.25 to 1 sec. This periodicity might be attributed to a sensory threshold or "dead zone," such that misalinements smaller than a certain value evoke no corrective movement; but there is evidence against this. First, the display-magnification is usually such that the misalinements occurring during steady tracking exceed the known threshold (i.e. visual acuity). Secondly, if the rate of the course, or the magnification of the display for a given course, is increased by a certain factor, the periodicity of the corrections is little, if at all, affected; whereas if their periodicity were determined by the time taken for the misalinements to reach a certain "threshold" value this alteration should shorten the periodicity of the corrections in the same ratio.

Consistently with the above principle, we find that the mean error in tracking any given variable-direction course is nearly proportional to the rate of the course, over a wide range of speeds. We should account for this by saying that the faster the course the greater the misalinements that occur in each period between two corrections, in strict proportion.

K. J. W. Craik, Theory of the human operator in control systems: I. The operator as an engineering system. *Brit. J. Psychol.,* 1947, 38, Part 2, 56–61. Reprinted by permission of the *British Journal of Psychology.*

2 *The intermittent corrections consist of "ballistic" movements.*
For example, they have a predetermined time-pattern and are
"triggered off" as a whole. This behaviour may be contrasted
with that of an intermittent correction servo in which, for instance, a follow-up motor is intermittently switched into a circuit
in which it runs until it has reduced the misalinement to zero,
and this action reduces the input to it to zero so that the motor
stops. In the human operator, on the other hand, at a particular
instant (i.e. about 0.3 sec. after the end of the preceding corrective movement), a corrective movement having a predetermined
time-course (usually occupying about 0.2 sec.) is triggered off.
The evidence for this is based on studies of reaction time, i.e. on
the internal time-lag of the operator, due to the time taken by
the sense-organ to respond, for the nerve-impulses to traverse the
central nervous system, for the appropriate response to be "selected" and for the nerve impulses reaching it to traverse the
motor nerves. This lag is about 0.2–0.3 sec. Thus, if a human
operator's limb movement amplitude, or velocity, or acceleration,
were determined continuously by the misalinement, continued
oscillations of approximately 0.5 sec. period, and of whatever
amplitude they commenced at, would inevitably result. This
tendency could be overcome if a misalinement triggered off a
ballistic movement of fairly correct amplitude (say $\pm 10\%$); the
eye would then detect the residual misalinement, which may be
composed of two parts—the error in the first ballistic movement,
and any movement of the target which has occurred in the mean-
time. In the absence of the latter (e.g. in aiming at a stationary
target) the second corrective movement may again be accurate
to $\pm 10\%$ of its own value so that the misalinement is reduced
to 1% of its original value.

Direct evidence bearing on this ballistic behaviour can be obtained in various ways. First it is easy to present a misalinement
to an operator, and then screen his eyes just before he makes his
corrective movement. A movement accurate to within about 10%
will result, if he has previously learned the "feel" of the control.
If he operated like a follower motor, intermittently switched in,
such obscuration of the misalinement would be equivalent to
cutting the input connexions, and the motor would not of course
make any further corrective movement.

Physiologists might make a further hypothesis to avoid the "ballistic" theory. They might say that the visual misalinement, once it has been detected by the eye, becomes translated into a "limb-movement-misalinement" (i.e. a kinaesthetic misalinement) which acts as the continuous input to the limb until our kinaesthetic (i.e. joint and muscle senses) register "correct position," or no misalinement. We certainly do possess such a sense, but it is less easy to abolish it experimentally and to see what happens in its absence, than in the case of vision. Patients with *tabes dorsalis* have considerable loss of kinaesthetic sensation, but it is difficult to know how complete this loss is in any particular case.

In any case, the same general argument as before—that a continuous series of oscillations of the initial amplitude would occur if elimination of kinaesthetic misalinement were the sole determinants of movements, owing to the inevitable reaction-time lag —seems to apply. Further, it is possible to show that considerable precision of movement is maintained even when the movements are made so rapidly that they are completed before the kinaesthetic stimulus corresponding to their first approximation to the right position could have "gone the round" of the central nervous system and controlled the subsequent output-movement; unless indeed reaction-times to kinaesthetic stimuli were vastly shorter than to any other kind. It is, however, possible to show experimentally that kinaesthetic reaction times are very little shorter than auditory, for instance. Thus, we may ask the operator to move a lever against a stiff spring, so as to make a rapid movement to correct a misalinement, and then to return to his starting point. After he has learned the "feel" of the control (i.e. its gear ratio and spring tension) and is making fairly accurate movements, we suddenly alter the spring tension, so that he over- or under-shoots. A record of this on a fast-moving drum shows that about 0.15 sec. elapses after he begins his movement, until he is able to begin a readjustment of it, to meet the modification of resistance.

Similarly, it is possible to show that in playing musical instruments, typewriting, sending morse, etc., complicated patterns of movement are executed at a rate which would be impossible if they were continuously governed by the value of the misalinement, with the inevitable reaction-time lag. Apparently they must be individually performed, triggered off ballistically, and the sensory feed-back must take the form of a delayed modification of the amplitude of subsequent movements. Sensory control, in other words, alters the "internal gear ratio" or amplification of the operator with a time lag and determines whether subsequent corrective movements will be made; it does not govern the amplitude of each individual movement while it is being made. We could make a servo, using existing engineering principles, which would show the features of intermittent, ballistic correction. But this last point—the fact that the sensory misalinement alters not merely the amplitude of the response but the *relation* between the input, or misalinement and the output, or response—introduces a further complication, the nearest approach to which, in engineering, seems to be "floating plus proportional control." Even this involves a quantitative alteration of the amplification of the system by the residual misalinement, whereas something more complex still seems to be occurring—a very wide alteration in the functional relationship between input and output.

For instance, if the operator is using a positional control, his successive ballistic corrective movements should be linearly proportional to the misalinements; but if he is using a velocity control they would have to be linearly proportional to the *derivatives* of the misalinements. Roughly speaking, we might call this *qualitative* modification or output on a basis of some response to the difference between instantaneous input and output at the previous instant, or "qualitative feed-back."

A further complication is introduced by the operator's ability to "anticipate" movements of the target, or alterations in misalinement. For instance, with a positional control, the errors in tracking a moving target are usually less than we should predict on the above theory of intermittent ballistic corrections. The operator goes on turning the handle steadily, or even accelerating it; his record, after some practice, becomes much smoother than it was initially; and if he finds that he is still lagging behind the target (as if the above theory is correct he is bound to do) he can put in an extra forward movement. Here we have several processes.

3 *There are some counteracting processes tending to make controls seem continuous.* First, there is one akin to momentum, or inertia. If the operator has been turning the handle, in a series of discrete movements, for some seconds, he will tend to convert this into as steady a rotation as he is capable of, and to continue doing so although the misalinement may be zero, i.e. he has zero input to produce this output! (This can be shown experimentally by suddenly stopping the target, when the operator will overshoot for the period of one reaction time, until the serious misalinement which results stops his steady output from continuing.) It is for this reason that in Section 1 it was stated that the human operator is *basically* an intermittent correction servo; he has in addition this mechanism for going on doing whatever is giving a satisfactory result, or zero misalinement rather like a heavy flywheel, and having the same valuable smoothing effect.

What are the essential features of this process, and can we conceive any mechanisms which will accomplish it? When the operator continues to turn the handle at the same speed, independently of whether there is any input or not, he is, in humanistic terms, assuming that he is justified in doing so, in order to compensate for his reaction time lag. Since he is always subject to this lag, in attempting to keep up with the present he is always in fact being a prophet and extrapolating from past data! It is really no different from the further kind of anticipation which enables him to extrapolate into the physical future. Now all scientific prediction consists in discovering, in data of the distant past and of the immediate past which we incorrectly call the present, laws or formulae which apply also to the future, so that if we act in accordance with those laws our behaviour will be appropriate to that future when it becomes the present. Thus the essential feature of extrapolation and anticipation is, again in humanistic terms, that the operator should detect the *constants* in what he is doing. Thus, he may move a handwheel in a series of jerks, so that its *position* changes from moment to moment, but he may realize after a few seconds that he is turning it at a *steady rate*, i.e. its *angular velocity* is constant; and having discovered this he may try whether it will not pay him to go on doing so; usually it will. He may, however, find that its rate is changing—the target has angular acceleration. He may, in theory, at any rate, be able to feel this acceleration which he is having to put into the hand-wheel, and if he happens to find that it is constant, or nearly so, and is able to put out a constant acceleration of this value in turning the wheel, again he may achieve better following.

Now let us look at the same thing from a mechanical point of view. There are many devices—such as speedometers and accelerometers—which do the differentiations involved in recording velocities and accelerations; and the problem would be how, for instance, to couple a number of such devices to a telephone selector-switch operating motor, so that if the output of the motor over a few seconds of intermittent corrective action showed a constant reading on the speedometer, or even on the accelerometer, the motor would be caused to go on putting out this speed or acceleration, irrespective of whether there was any input or not, unless or until such behaviour gave rise to a large misalinement. If that happened the extrapolating system would be overridden and intermittent corrections would begin again, until a new value for a constant was found. The solution would seem to be to provide the motor with positive feed-back of such a kind that it continued to go on doing whatever it was doing at the moment—running steadily or accelerating uniformly. Such a system would need considerable smoothing and stabilization, otherwise any slight disturbance, such as a slight acceleration, would very rapidly be cumulative, and the machine would reach its maximum speed; but if the feed-back were delayed and smoothed, the system could be sufficiently stable and would not "wander" too badly. This system would of course be combined with negative feed-back of the ordinary kind (viz. actuation by the difference between input and output quantities), so that if the positive feed-back led to overestimation of the velocity, or if the target started to decelerate, the motor would overshoot and this would introduce a positional misalinement, which would reverse the direction of mechanical control. This would alter the average value, for the last time-interval, to the positive feed-back system, which would therefore cease from perpetuating this velocity but would, when it had time to steady down, start putting in a new one.

4 *Electrical models could fairly exactly simulate the human operator's behaviour in tracking.* In general terms, the extraction of the inputs for the positive feed-back network consists of successive differentiations, while the extrapolations on the basis of them consist of successive integrations. Let us consider in more detail some circuits by which this might be accomplished. Suppose the motor drives a generator across whose output terminals is a capacity in series with a high resistance, constituting a differentiating circuit with a time-lag or averaging effect, owing to the time-constant of the system. Then the generator voltage is proportional to the speed of the motor and the voltage across the resistance of the differentiating system is proportional to its acceleration; if necessary, higher derivatives can be obtained in the same way. The lag in the first differentiation can be obtained by putting a resistance and capacity in series across the generator output and taking the voltage off the capacity. The output voltage from this smoothing system is taken to the input of the amplifier supplying the motor fields, and should cause the motor to continue running at the mean speed at which it has been manually rotated for a sufficient time to cause the voltage delayed and smoothed across the generator to reach a steady value. The speed of running will of course wander slowly in time if the system also has ordinary velodyne negative feed-back for velocity control. If the manually applied speed was an accelerating one, the system will maintain a mean steady speed if it is supplied with one differentiating stage only (i.e. the generator with its delaying system). But if there is a second differentiating system, with a longer time-constant, it will register a manually imposed change of velocity over several periods of operation of the first differentiating system, i.e. an acceleration, and if this is integrated by a resistance-capacity circuit and applied to the amplifier serving the fields, a uniform acceleration will occur.

Of course, it is not necessary for the original speeds to be put in manually; with a velodyne fitted up as a servo auto-following system in which the task of the velodyne is to make a slider keep on the centre of a potentiometer, for instance, which is moved by an external agency, the mechanical control will commence by ordinary positional following being actuated by the misalinements. Further, though this alone would lead to a lag behind a uniformly moving target, once it has started to run at a constant velocity, the remaining misalinement will still be operative, if arranged to be in series with the positive feed-back voltage, so as to cause the shaft to step on and make up for the lag. This system would have many of the same characteristics as a velodyne with phase advance produced by delayed negative feed-back— i.e. a condenser across the generator output.

It should be possible to make a velodyne simulate the "intermittent ballistic correction" process considered in principles (1) and (2). Thus, the error-voltage representing the misalinement could be connected periodically by a rotating contact to a condenser which is charged. This condenser would then be switched on to the amplifier input and would result in a "ballistic" rotation of the output shaft through an angle proportional to the charge on the condenser.

Little is known of possible physiological mechanisms for accomplishing this kind of thing. There is evidence (e.g. from sensory adaptation and accommodation of nerve) of differentiating systems, at least of the first order, which may serve to measure rates of change of stimulation, though our knowledge extends only to stimulus *intensity* and not to more complex stimuli such as misalinements in space. Even here, it is possible to suggest hypothetical spatial differentiating systems which are not physiologically inconceivable. The other aspect—the integration, resulting from positive feed-back—would seem to require "autorhythmic" nervous centres which continue to discharge once they have been forced to do so, and in a way which follows the original forcing stimulus. The beating of the isolated frog's heart and the spontaneous oscillatory potentials in the excised frog's brain and in the intact cortex of man (both Berger rhythms and the abnormal rhythms of epilepsy) are suggestive in this respect, for they are evidence of self-maintaining neural oscillators. Lorente de No's and Ranson's concept of the "closed neurone circuit" would serve the same purpose. What has to be considered is clearly a form of positive feed-back and the main difficulty in all the cases just mentioned would seem to be that what is required is continuous feed-back of excitation in the form of nerve-impulses following after the neurones have recovered from their refractory phase, whereas slow potential oscillations probably imply discharges of some other kind than trains of nerve impulses.

We should also consider long-lasting changes of stimulus-response relationship (i.e. learning) which, in an electrical model, would probably require to be imitated by some autoselective switching device rather than regarded as time-constants of a resistance-capacity system. Another type of control demands the establishing of complex response-patterns which are "triggered off" as a whole by the stimulus. Instances are the action of word-habits in typewriting, or of blocks of stimuli in transmitting morse, or of associated movement groups in knitting. These seem to require some "sequencing" switchgear, of the type used in the Relay Automatic telephone system, and make us think of the physiologists' "chain reflexes" and of rhythmic reflexes such as walking and breathing.

*   *   *

Craik's general notion of intermittent operation—either perceptual or response intermittency—has been a popular one and has led to considerable discussion and experimentation. This work forms an important part of that branch of psychotechnology generally referred to as "human engineering."*

It would be misleading, however, to suggest that servos were the first machines to attract the attention of psychologists. As early as 1931, for example, Clark Hull reported mechanical and electrochemical models that illustrated some of the phenomena of conditioning,† and he was certainly not the first to dabble in

* An excellent survey of this work through 1955 has been prepared by J. C. R. Licklider, Quasi-linear operator models in the study of manual tracking. In R. D. Luce (Ed.), *Developments in mathematical psychology.* Glencoe, Ill.: The Free Press, 1960, pp. 167–279.

† H. D. Baernstein and C. L. Hull, A mechanical model of the conditioned reflex. *J. gen. Psychol.*, 1931, **5**, 99–106. R. G. Kreuger and C. L. Hull, An electrochemical parallel to the conditioned reflex. *J. gen. Psychol.*, 1931, **5**, 262–269.

this concrete form of model building. But prior to the emergence of the modern computing machine these psychomechanistic parallels were necessarily simple and small in scale. As the computers began to grow in size and complexity, the psychological models could grow correspondingly.

A servo can be used as a null instrument to solve simultaneous equations, and as such it plays an important role in various special-purpose, analogue computers. As the computer art developed, however, the digital machines proved faster, more accurate, and more adaptable to a wide range of problems. Consequently, the more recent attempts to use computers for simulation have been oriented around the digital machines.

A digital machine accepts input data and a program of instructions as to what operations it should perform on the data. When it is used as a computer, the instructions are mathematical operations (addition, multiplication, testing for equality, and so on) plus rules for retrieving data from the memory, for storing the results in the memory, and others. When the machine is used as a simulator, however, little numerical computation is usually involved. Special programming techniques are used to create various non-numerical operations; exactly what the operations are is a crucial feature of the theory that the psychologist holds about the behavior he is trying to simulate.

In principle, any set of operations that people perform on their sensory input can—if they can be precisely described in logical terms—be performed by a computer. The theoretical possibility of using the machines to perform various non-numerical, presumably psychological operations was recognized and widely discussed for many years before anyone actually tried to do it. A. M. Turing, Warren McCulloch, Norbert Wiener, John von Neumann, W. Ross Ashby, Claude Shannon, D. M. MacKay, and many others discussed these possibilities with great wisdom and imagination. They described machines (or ways of programming machines) that would recognize perceptual patterns; play chess; hold general conversations; derive theorems in logic and mathematics; organize, store, and retrieve information in a library; translate from one language to another; transcribe from dictation; compose and arrange musical scores; form concepts and profit in various ways from experience; and so on and on.

Very little was actually done to implement these schemes, however, until the latter half of the 1950's. By then computers were large enough and programming techniques were advanced enough to support a serious attack on the problem of artificial intelligence in general and on the simulation of human intelligence in particular. One of the first persons to actually program a digital computer—the Edsac (Electronics Delay Storage Automatic Calculator) at Cambridge, England—to simulate a psychological phenomenon was A. G. Oettinger. Because the computers of 1952 were relatively small, Oettinger had to keep the size of his simulation within strict bounds. But in spite of its simplicity, most of the important ideas are represented here. Oettinger used two different examples. One was a "response-learning programme" that operated at a level roughly corresponding to that of conditional reflexes; the other is described in the following excerpt.

*   *   *

Anthony Gervin Oettinger

Programming the Edsac to Go Shopping

Since a computing machine like the Edsac is equipped with an information store, it is trivial to programme it to absorb information from the outside world and to reproduce this information verbatim when required. For example, to make the Edsac first "memorize" the English alphabet and then "recite" it, by printing it on the teleprinter, only a series of I [input] and O [output] orders and an input tape holding the alphabet in coded form

A. G. Oettinger, Programming a digital computer to learn. *Phil. Mag.*, 1952, 43, 1243–1263. Pp. 1246–1251 reprinted by permission of the publisher, Taylor and Francis, Ltd.

would be required. More interesting types of learning behaviour can be obtained by giving the machine a programme which provides for the transformation of its own orders in the fashion described above. By the liberal provision of E [branching] orders in the programme the machine is enabled to organize new information meaningfully and to select alternative modes of behaviour on the basis of this organization. Two programmes in which these techniques are applied will now be discussed.

The properties of the shopping programme are summarized in the following illustration. The shopping programme may be imagined to define a small child sent on a shopping tour. If this child were asked by its mother to buy different articles in various shops, it would not know at first where to find these articles, and would hunt for them by going from shop to shop in a random fashion until it came to the desired one. Having found an article once, it would remember in what shop, and would go directly to this shop the next time the same article were requested. In addition, as its curiosity would prompt it to note the whereabouts of articles for which it had not had a specific request, when such a request did come, it would often be able to go directly to the right shop.

Before giving the abstract specification of the shopping programme it is helpful to digress for a moment to define the boundary between the "child machine," defined by the shopping programme, and the outside world. Obviously the simplest definition would be to consider the whole of the Edsac as the machine, and to represent the outside world by a suitably coded input tape. Unfortunately, tape reading is the slowest operation of the Edsac. It is therefore convenient to make a conceptual division of the Edsac into two parts, one to play the role of the experimental subject and designated s-part or s-machine, the remainder to serve as an extension of the outside world. By means of this expedient it becomes possible to conduct experiments at the highest possible machine speed, since less frequent use of the input mechanism need be made.

Provision is made to enter a description of the shops into the part of the Edsac store belonging to the outside world as an $m \times n$ matrix. This matrix has elements a_{ij} such that $a_{ij} = 1$ if shop i has article j, and $a_{ij} = 0$ otherwise. The matrix will be called the stock matrix S. The ith row of S may be regarded as a row vector whose components define the stock of shop i, and will be called a shop vector. The ith shop vector is held in storage location $m + i$, where m is a reference address. Similarly, the jth column has components representing the shops where article j may be found, and it will be called an article vector. The stock matrix shown in Table 1 has eight rows (shops) and seven columns (kinds of articles). A shopping order for article j is given to the s-machine by a row vector (order vector) consisting of zeros everywhere except in column j, where there is a 1. The top line of column 1 (Table 1) shows an order vector for article no. 6. The s-machine proceeds to select a shop number i_k at random, and to form the address $m + i_k$ of the corresponding shop vector. A C [collate, or compare] order $Cm + i_k$, is constructed with this address and, when obeyed, collates the shop vector with the given order vector. After the C order has been obeyed the content of the accumulator is different from 0 if, and only if, shop i_k has article j in stock, that is if $a_{i_n j} = 1$. If this is not the case, another shop number i_l is selected, and so on with i_m, i_n, . . . until either the article is found or all the shops have been scanned. In the first shopping tour of the example given in table 1 the shops were scanned in the order indicated in column 2; column 3 shows that article no. 6 was found in shop no. 8. When an article is unavailable, as is the case with no. 7 in the fifth shopping tour, the s-machine tries all shops—the order of search being indicated in column 2—then prints zero in column 3 to indicate the absence of the article. Once an article has been found, the number of the shop in which it was first discovered is recorded in the appropriate column of the s-memory, as shown in the case of the first shopping tour by the second line of column 1. Before attempting a search for an article the s-machine examines its memory to determine whether or not the location of this article is already known to it. If so, it proceeds directly to the shop where the article was found on the earlier trial. The second shopping tour provides an illustration of this mode of behaviour. When an article j is found in shop i a second collation with the shop vector is made, using an inspection vector, a row with zeros everywhere

TABLE 1. A Typical Stock Matrix and the Corresponding Shopping Tours

Shopping Tours

	1	2	3		
(1)	0000010 0000080	13465728	8		
(2)	0000010 0000080		8		
(3)	0000100 0000480	1234	4		
(4)	0000100 0000480		4		
(5)	0000001 0000480	62413875	0		
(6)	0100000 0550480	45	5		Stock Matrix Articles $\rightarrow$
(7)	0010000 0555480		5		1001000 1010000 0110000
(8)	1000000 1555480	3541	1	Shops $\downarrow$	0000100 0111000 0001000
(9)	0100000 1555480		5		0111100 0000010
(10)	0010000 1555480		5		
(11)	0001000 1555480		5		
(12)	0000100 1555480		4		
(13)	0000010 1555480		8		

except in the two columns adjacent to column j. In this fashion the presence of the articles $j+1$ and $j-1$ in shop i can be detected, and recorded in the memory. In the sixth tour, for example, article no. 3 was found to be in shop no. 5 while shopping for article no. 2. In the seventh tour the request for article no. 3 was met without search, as a result of the discovery made during the sixth tour.

If the s-machine memory were cleared and a new arbitrary $m' \times n'$ ($m' \leqq m$, $n' \leqq n$) matrix S' substituted for the matrix of Table 1, then, proceeding as above, the s-machine would soon discover the location of any article requested. Most observers would hesitate to attribute this ability to intelligent thought on the part of the machine, and in the absence of agreement about the meaning of the word "thought" it is difficult to decide whether or not a machine can be said to think. Turing[1] rightly regards as inappropriate attempts to find the meaning of "thought" by an examination of the common usage of the word. Instead, he suggests that the question "Can Machines Think?" be replaced by a related but less ambiguous one in terms of what he calls the "imitation game." He postulates a game played by a man A, a woman B, and an interrogator C. C knows the man and the woman only by the labels X and Y, and the object of the game is for C to make the correct identification, that is to match X and Y correctly with A and B. A, B, and C are in separate rooms, and communicate only by means of teleprinters. If, when A is replaced by a machine, C is wrong in his identifications as often as when A was a man, the man and the machine become indistinguishable to C. The question "Can Machines Think?" may therefore be replaced by the question "Are there imaginable digital computers which would do well in the imitation game?"

The imitation game can be played with the shopping s-machine taking the part of A, if A and B are both given the same stock matrix, and if the questions are restricted to shopping orders of the form, "In what shop may article j be found?" coded as order vectors. The answer expected from X or Y would be the appropriate shop number, together with a list of the shops that were

[1] A. M. Turing, Computing machinery and intelligence. *Mind*, 1950, **59**, 433–460.

tried, i.e., the data given in column 2 and column 3 of table 1. Under these conditions the interrogator C would find it difficult to make the correct identification. Potentially, of course, the man could answer a far wider range of questions than the machine, but it is clearly possible, within limits, to find that a man thinking and a computing machine obeying a learning programme are behaving identically as far as an observer is concerned. Hence, by Turing's criterion, a denial of a machine's ability to think which hinges on a question of the sort "Yes, this machine certainly gives satisfactory answers to questions of such and such a category, but what can it do if I ask it about something else?" appears to be not so much a denial of machine intelligence as an admission that this intelligence exists, although in a very limited form.

The shopping programme has some severe limitations. The size of the stock matrix has an upper limit and its position in the store is fixed, and the method by which the stock matrix and the s-memory are scanned is explicitly prescribed. Unless a technical fault develops in the machine in the course of operation, the programme does precisely what it was designed to do, and information presented to the machine is interpreted either as a shopping order, in which case the machine proceeds normally, or as nonsense, in which case the machine soon stops. There is, thus, only an extremely small chance that the s-machine could understand and sensibly answer any request other than a shopping order, and an even smaller chance that such a happy accident would be repeated. While the shopping machine appears to learn, it certainly cannot be taught any subject the experimenter chooses.

Several improvements suggest themselves. Some, as the introduction of memory decay or forgetfulness, would give the learning process a greater degree of verisimilitude, that is, a greater resemblance to the mental operations to which we are accustomed. Others would increase the learning capacity of the s-machine. For example, a more general programme could be designed so as to make it possible to teach the s-machine a method of scanning the shop matrix and the s-memory. In the programme described above this scanning method was explicitly prescribed by a fixed sub-programme. The more general programme would allow the s-machine to construct a scanning sub-programme, by trial and error, subject to indications of progress by an external "teacher." The method of trial and error itself would now have to be specified, and hence the set of sub-programmes which could be tried by the s-machine, as well as the order of trial, would essentially be defined implicitly by the initial programme. What would remain for the s-machine to do would be to operate until it obtained explicitly the particular scanning method which met with the approval of the "teacher." Once the scanning method had been learned this machine would proceed as before. If the approved sub-programme were not contained in the trial set there would be no way of teaching the s-machine the corresponding scanning method. An s-machine capable of being taught a scanning method would be capable of competing successfully in a less restricted form of imitation game, a form in which the simpler s-machine would fail; but it is more powerful than the simpler machine only in the sense that its limitations are shifted to a higher level of abstraction. Making it possible to teach the shopping machine the scanning method which it must use in turn to learn the contents of the shops is only one of many imaginable generalizations of the shopping programme. Additional generalizations, and generalizations of these generalizations, could broaden the range of subjects which can be taught to the s-machine, but in every case the method of operation of the machine at the highest level of generalization would have to be prescribed, and the range of operation consequently limited.

*   *   *

It should be noted that the "theory" Oettinger presents is not, strictly speaking, a mathematical theory. But, on the other hand, it is not merely a piece of hardware. The theory is contained implicitly in the program of instructions that he gave to the machine. The modern computer will do anything we tell it to do. Without a program it is, in effect, incomplete; only when it is given a specific program does the machine assume some specific character. Thus it is the program, not the hardware, that determines what kind of machine it will be.

With the continued growth of computers and advances in the art of programming, many other workers have adopted this way of stating and testing their theories. Probably of greatest interest to psychologists was the pioneering work of Newell, Shaw, and Simon,* who developed a programming language specifically designed to facilitate the psychological theorist's task and who used it to simulate problem solving behavior in logic, in chess, in rote learning, and elsewhere.

In spite of the successes that Oettinger, Newell and Simon, and many others have had in research of this kind, there are still many scientists and philosophers who believe there is something more to human thinking than such programs, however complicated, can possibly encompass. Computer specialists are particularly prone to criticize the "thinking machine" view of computers and to point to the awful literalness of the machine as evidence for its basic, ineradicable, inhuman stupidity.

The machine is a perfect slave. It accepts any order, reasonable or absurd, and tries to execute it. A small and irrelevant error in the program of instructions—something a human clerk who understood his job could certainly catch and probably correct—can send the machine spinning merrily through realms of utter nonsense. The machine does not care, for it looks only *at* the symbols; it never looks *through* them to see what they might mean. Such a stupid device, the critics say, can never achieve "real thinking," whatever that may be.

It is possible to dispute this opinion on several grounds, but this is not the place to review these arguments. It should be pointed out, however, that literalness is not unique to computing machines, but is more or less characteristic, although on a more

* A. Newell, J. C. Shaw, and H. A. Simon, Elements of a theory of human problem solving. *Psychol. Rev.,* 1958, **65,** 151–166. For a clear and simple illustration of their techniques for simulating an amateur logician, see A. Newell and H. A. Simon, GPS, a program that simulates human thought. In H. Billings (Ed.), *Lernende Automaten* (Proceedings of conference at Karlsruhe, Germany, April 1961). Munich: Oldenbourg, 1961, pp. 109–124.

sophisticated level, of mathematical models in general.* Once the basic assumptions are stated, any mathematical formulation must take them literally. A scientist may recognize that his assumptions are only approximate, but that recognition is not part of the mathematical model itself. Thus, when a scientist turns himself into a mathematician, he can easily become trapped in much the same way that a machine would be: he proceeds to spin out absurd theorems with great vigor, while the formal glitter of his elegant manipulations seems to blind him to everything that lies outside the scope of his mathematical system.

Because examples of such formal folly are not as rare as we would wish—especially in the social and behavioral sciences—some psychologists have actually become hostile to the whole idea of formulating psychological issues in mathematical terms. Their hostility will probably not deflect the course of history as we have seen it reflected in the preceding pages, but the feeling does exist and a faithful historian should not fail to report it.

By way of reply, however, one can argue that the complete literalness of computing machines and mathematical models is not a flaw, but is an essential source of their power and utility. The real trouble arises from the theorist's proclivity for confusing his model with the reality that his model represents; that affliction is not specific to mathematical theorists, but attacks us all equally. If, however, a theorist will refuse to overlook all the relevant phenomena he cannot explain and will agree to confess to any absurdities that his assumptions imply, then the literalness of mathematics provides him with a powerful way to test his own understanding.

For common sense is not an unmixed blessing. If every idea must first pass the test of ordinary reasonableness and familiarity, then nothing new can ever be created or discovered. Especially in psychology it is tempting to rely on an intuitive understanding of the phenomenon we are explaining, to leave unstated and even unrecognized some of our basic concepts, be-

---

* J. Schwartz, The pernicious influence of mathematics on science. In E. Nagel, P. Suppes, A. Tarski (Eds.), *Logic, methodology and philosophy of science* (Proceedings of 1960 International Congress, Stanford, Calif.) Stanford: Stanford University Press, 1962, pp. 356–360.

cause we know that an intelligent reader will surely provide them for himself out of his tacit store of common sense. When a formal notation, with all its strenuous literalness, can be applied to a problem, it is often possible to discover these missing links and so to redirect our thoughts and theories into more profitable channels.

Mathematics is not a magical wand that can be waved over conceptual difficulties to make them suddenly vanish. It is merely a tool devised for use in thinking and communicating, a tool that can, according to how it is used, create either science or chaos. The historical trend shows clearly that psychologists are using this tool with increasing frequency and skill. Whether or not the science-to-chaos ratio is also increasing, however, is a question best left for the reader to answer for himself.

Name Index

293